BASIC
PROGRAMMING SOLUTIONS
FOR MANUFACTURING

By J. E. Nicks

Published by: Society of Manufacturing Engineers
Marketing Services Department
One SME Drive
P.O. Box 930
Dearborn, Michigan 48121

BASIC
PROGRAMMING SOLUTIONS
FOR MANUFACTURING

Copyright 1982 by the
Society of Manufacturing Engineers
Dearborn, Michigan 48121

First Edition

Second Printing

Library of Congress Catalog Card Number: 81-1201

International Standard Book Number: 0-87263-076-5

This book is dedicated
to Mary, my wife,
whose assistance and encouragement
made this book possible.

ABOUT THE AUTHOR

The author of BASIC Programming Solutions for Manufacturing, Jensen E. Nicks, is currently the Program Director: Manufacturing Engineering. Ferris State College, Big Rapids, Michigan.

His experience in industry spans over 25 years and includes employment with Gardner Denver, the Buechler Corporation, and the Chrysler Corporation. During this time, his responsibilities included Manager of Manufacturing Engineering. Manufacturing Manager, General Superintendent, Superintendent and Chief Industrial Engineer, and General Sales Manager.

His teaching background includes ten years at Ferris State College. In addition, he developed the Manufacturing Engineering curriculum at Ferris.

PREFACE

Any Manufacturing Engineer who has spent hours looking up and working with formulas and working out math problems on a hand-held calculator will find this book useful.

The typical Manufacturing Engineer spends much of his time analyzing and calculating formulas for a given subject. Often, because this work is tedious and time-consuming, the engineer will find short cuts to speed the process. Many times these short cuts translate into a loss of accuracy and the engineer might conclude that a computer should be able to do this work faster and with greater accuracy.

Until recently, there have been several major stumbling blocks for the Manufacturing Engineer to overcome in computer usage. The first stumbling block: someone from data processing had to write the computer programs. To achieve this, the person from data processing had to know as much as the engineer about the subject being programmed. This is not very practical. A second major problem has been reporting relationship. Before the advent of materials requirement planning, most companies with computers found that general accounting and cost accounting were the major functions that consumed most of the computer's time. For years there has been a problem in "having enough programming time" to do other things on the computer, and engineering work on the computer never seemed to assume a very high priority. A third problem was the need for instant answers. When the Manufacturing Engineer needs answers to a problem, the time necessary to write the program, keypunch the cards and run a computer routine is usually too slow. All of this has changed. With the not so quiet microcomputer explosion now occurring, most of the problems that existed in past years have been solved.

The major goal of this book is to demonstrate to Manufacturing Engineers that the microcomputer can provide instant, accurate, well-organized answers to everyday engineering problems at low cost.

This book barely scratches the surface of computer use by the Manufacturing Engineer, but provides an important first step in demonstrating just how easy it is for the Manufacturing Engineer to do his own computer programming.

The format used in this book is first to review briefly the manufacturing problem under consideration, then to present a computer program written in BASIC that addresses the problem under study, and finally to discuss any special features of that program. From a review of the chapter titles, the reader will see a wide range of typical engineering problems have been considered.

The reader can use this book on any one of three levels. First, without any knowledge of computer programming, each program presented can be used, as is, to perform typical engineering work. It is the author's hope, however, that most of the readers or users of this book will not choose this route. Secondly, any of the programs presented in this book can be modified, as necessary, to suit a specific plant application or problem. The knowledge of computer programming to do this is modest.

While this book is not a primer on BASIC programming, the program listing and narrative provided on how the various programs work will help the user understand how the computer does its work. With this knowledge, programs can easily be changed. The third level of use is perhaps the most important of all. Any Manufacturing Engineer or student in a Manufacturing Engineering program in college who has some training programming in BASIC will find the sample programs presented in this book useful in writing his own programs.

Optional lab assignments are provided at the end of each chapter to provide the student engineer with an opportunity to develop his skill in computer programming. To assist in this effort, Chapter One is devoted to a review of the BASIC language.

Several comments should be made about hardware. All of the programs in this book were written and tested on a Radio Shack TRS 80[1], Level II microcomputer. The TRS-80 used has 32K RAM (random access memory) and is disk (5¼″ floppy) operated. A memory listing for each program is shown in the review of that program. Most of the programs in this book require much less than the 32K memory mentioned above. There are, however, three programs that require most of the user memory available.

A hard copy printer is also required to use the programs in this book. The entire system—computer with 32K, disk drive and printer—is less than $3500 at this writing. Just a few short years ago, a computer system with these capabilities would have cost many thousands of dollars more.

One of the goals of this book is to encourage the engineer or engineering manager in industry to purchase a micro-system for use in his department.

As the using engineers write their own programs and gain more confidence in their programming abilities, the world of computer-aided process planning is but a few steps away.

A few words about how programs are written. No attempt has been made in program construction to write "compressed" or memory efficient programs for two reasons. First, those engineers who have limited programming experience with BASIC should find the programs easy to understand. Secondly, memory for the microcomputer is no longer a problem.

J. E. Nicks

[1]*TRS-80 is a trademark of the Radio Shack Division of Tandy Corporation*

ACKNOWLEDGEMENTS

Several companies assisted in the development of this book by permitting the reprinting of previously copyrighted material or by other technical assistance, for which I am grateful. These companies are:

Tandy Corporation/Radio Shack

TRS-80 and TRSDOS are registered trademarks of the Tandy Corporation. The Tandy Corporation authorized, in writing, the reproduction of Tandy Corporation copyrighted material shown on pages 27 and 31.

The Warner & Swasey Company

AC is a registered trademark of the Warner & Swasey Company. The Warner & Swasey Company authorized, in writing, the use of speeds and feeds tables from their copyrighted AC Handbook. This material is shown in the AC computer program in Chapter 10.

The Valeron Corporation

The Valeron Corporation permitted use of speeds and feeds data from their copyrighted Handy Reference Booklet.

Four senior Manufacturing Engineering students, now graduated from Ferris State College, Big Rapids, Michigan, are given special acknowledgement for their assistance in writing two computer programs included in this book.

The "FORGE" program reviewed in Chapter Two was written by:

Edward F. Petee
Mark B. Pulsipher

The "T CHART" program reviewed in Chapter Eleven was written by:

Mark Alder
Michael La Pierre

Finally, I would like to acknowledge the supportive assistance I received from the Ferris State College administrative group.

J. E. Nicks

TABLE OF CONTENTS

CHAPTER 1

A Review
of BASIC

This first chapter is intended to be a review of the BASIC language. This chapter is not written as a primer on BASIC nor is it written on an advanced level. There are many excellent textbooks available that cover the programming language in greater detail than this chapter will. Several of these books are mentioned in the bibliography at the conclusion of this chapter. BASIC is a language that can be self-taught and is much easier to learn than some of the other languages, such as FORTRAN or PASCAL.

If this is your first computer programming effort, then a word of advice. You should purchase several good textbooks on the language. This entire book is written in an applications mode and assumes that the reader has some knowledge of BASIC.

BASIC

BASIC is referred to as a high-level language. Defined, this means that BASIC uses words and symbols to perform various functions by the computer. Also, BASIC is a very easy language to learn. If you have never learned a computer language before, then BASIC is for you. You will be writing programs after several hours of reviewing this first chapter, and with several more hours of experience, your programs will develop into very usable programs for industry.

10 Liners

This chapter includes 10 liners, which are short programs used to illustrate the language. If this is your first experience with a microcomputer, study the examples and then write the suggested lab exercises for practice. Many of the 130 or so BASIC words and symbols are used in this chapter, and each time a new 10 liner is presented with new words, they will be explained in detail.

Demonstration One

Figure 1-1 will outline some of the words, punctuation and symbols to be used in the first demonstration.

Words Used	Math Symbols Used	Punctuation Used
1. REM	1. Multiplication *	1. Quotes " "
2. PRINT	2. Addition +	2. Semicolon ;
3. INPUT	3. Division /	3. Comma ,
4. LET	4. Variable names	
5. END	5. Equal =	
	6. Parentheses ( )	

Figure 1-1. A review of words, math symbols and punctuation

Formulas Used

$$RPM = \frac{SFPM * 12}{D * 3.1416}$$

$$\text{Revolutions required} = \frac{\text{Length of cut} + \text{approach}}{\text{Feed per revolutions}}$$

$$\text{Time} = \text{Revolutions required}/RPM$$

Where:

RPM	= Revolutions per minute
SFPM	= Surface feet per minute
D	= Diameter of the part
Time	= Time in decimal minutes

The above formulas calculate time in decimal minutes for a turning operation.

Review of Words Used

1. REM is a remarks statement that has no affect on the program. A REM statement is used mainly for the programmer or person who might be reviewing the program content. REM statements are not seen by the user when a program is executed and can be used anyplace in the program.

2. PRINT is a statement that prints out a message on the CRT screen. The message can be in the form of instructions or it can be the answer to a problem calculated by the computer.

3. INPUT is a word in BASIC that permits the user to input data into the computer memory while a program is being executed. The INPUT statement interrupts the execution of the computer until the user has typed in the information asked for by the computer.

4. LET is a calculation statement that begins an equation. For example: 30 LET A = B + C LET is optional; this example could also be written 30 A = B + C.

5. END is placed at the conclusion of a program to tell the computer that the program is complete.

Review of Symbols Used

1. The symbols +, *, /, - are all math functions common to a hand-held calculator.

2. Parentheses or brackets ( ) are used to tell the computer what to perform first in the calculation of an equation, and that the rules of algebra apply.

3. The symbol =, just as in algebra, means equal.

4. Variable names must start with an alpha character and can be two characters long. Examples of legal variable names are: A, A1, AA, X, X4, etc. BASIC reads only the first two characters for a variable, therefore, A1A and A1B would be read as A1.

Review of Punctuation

1. Quotes ("") are used after PRINT statements to tell the computer what should be printed.

2. The semicolon (;) has several uses in BASIC. Here it is used to separate the PRINT statement from the variable.

3. The comma (,) has several uses in BASIC. Here it is used to separate more than one input in a single input line.

Additional Comments

1. All programs must have line numbers, or operation numbers, to instruct the computer which sequence comes first, second, etc., when the program is executed.

The following is a demonstration program

```
10 REM      THIS PROGRAM CALCULATES TIME FOR TURNING
            OPERATIONS
20 REM      P = PIE: P = 3.1416
30 PRINT    "THIS PROGRAM CALCULATES TIME IN
            DECIMAL MINUTES"
40 PRINT    "FOR A TYPICAL TURNING OPERATION"
50 PRINT    "INPUT THE DATA ASKED FOR VIA THE KEYBOARD"
60 PRINT    "AND THEN PRESS ENTER"
70 PRINT    "ENTER THE SURFACE FEET PER MINUTE"
80 INPUT S
90 INPUT    "ENTER THE DIAMETER IN INCHES"; D
100 LET R = (S*12)/(D*P)
110 INPUT   "ENTER LENGTH OF CUT AND FEED PER
            REVOLUTIONS AND SEPARATE BY A COMMA";L,F
120 REM     A = APPROACH, RV = REVOLUTIONS REQUIRED, T =
            TIME
130 LET     A = .032
140 LET     RV = (L + A)/F
150 LET     T = RV/R
160 PRINT   "TIME REQUIRED FOR THIS TURNING OPERATION IS"
            ;T
170 PRINT   "THE SFPM IS";S; "AND WORK DIAMETER IS";D
180 PRINT   "THE LENGTH OF CUT IS";L; "AND FEED IS";F
190 END
```

2. The command RUN begins execution. The term command is different from a statement because a command has no arguments.

When this program is executed by typing the command RUN, the CRT screen prints out lines 30 through 80 and should look like the representation below:

THIS PROGRAM CALCULATES TIME IN DECIMAL MINUTES FOR A
TYPICAL TURNING OPERATION.
INPUT THE DATA ASKED FOR VIA THE KEYBOARD AND THEN
PRESS ENTER.
ENTER THE SURFACE FEET PER MINUTE.
?

Line 80 INPUT S generates a question mark and stops program execution until a value is typed in from the keyboard and the ENTER key is pressed. Notice that line 90 includes a printed message in quotes and starts with an INPUT statement. Also note the use of the semicolon in this line which is necessary when an input statement is combined with a printed message.

After the computer calculates line 100 (note the use of parentheses), the computer is again stopped by line 110, which is also an INPUT line. Line 110 combines a printed message in quotes inside the INPUT statement and asks for two variables to be inputted and separated by a comma. The computer will generate two question marks on the screen as a reminder to the user that two inputs are needed.

Line 120 is a REMARK statement that can be placed anywhere in the program. In Line 130, note that A is a fixed or constant variable. Lines 140 and 150 are calculated just the same as Line 100. Lines 160 through 180 are PRINT messages that contain the answer T (Time) and the original data in variable form inputted by the user. The variables T, S, D, L, and F can be placed inside or at the end of the PRINT statement. (Note the use of semicolons.)

Program Comments

Demo Program 1 is a very simple program that can be written any number of different ways. The combination of 14 different words, symbols and punctuation used in this program form a core of words that provides a foundation for programming.

Review

If this is your first programming experience, you should stop at this point and write several "10 liners" to get accustomed to the feel of programming.

You may wish to start by rewriting Demo Program 1 in a logical fashion, using the instructions shown below:
1. REMARK statements.
2. User instructions.
3. All user inputs.
4. All calculations.
5. Print out the answer.

The sequence shown above is a logical sequence for most computer programs. During the execution of a program, the programmer may encounter a SYNTAX error. SYNTAX is a noun meaning grammar, or the way words are put together to form phrases and sentences. In computer jargon, SYNTAX usually means some form of spelling or punctuation error.

Demonstration Two

Figure 1-2 will outline some of the words, symbols and punctuation to be used in the second demonstration.

Words Used	Math Symbols Used	Punctuation Used
1. FOR-NEXT Loops	1. Exponent ↑	1. Comma ,
2. DIM	(up arrow on	2. Subscripted ( )
3. READ	the keyboard)	variables
4. DATA		
5. RESTORE		

Figure 1-2. *A review of words, math, symbols and punctuation used in the second demonstration.*

Formulas Used

$$\text{Drill Feed} = (D/.5)^{.8074} * .007$$

Where:

D = Drill size
Drill Feed = Feed for drill size D
.5 = Constant
.8074 = Constant exponent
.007 = Constant

The above formula calculates drill feed for any size drill, not considering material hardness. This formula could be used for cost estimating where drill feed correctness to several ten thousandths is acceptable.

Review of Words Used

FOR-NEXT Loop. The FOR-NEXT Loop is one of the most powerful programming words in BASIC because it instructs the computer to do something over and over again, also called iteration.

Demo Program

```
10   FOR I = 1 TO 10
20   PRINT "BASIC IS POWERFUL"
30   NEXT I
```

This three-line program tells the computer to print "BASIC IS POWERFUL" ten times.

Line Analysis

```
10   FOR I = 1 TO 10
```

I is arbitrary; line 10 could be written FOR A = 1 TO 10 or FOR Z = 1 TO 10.

```
20   PRINT "BASIC IS POWERFUL"
```

This statement asks the computer to print a message.

> 30   NEXT I

When the program is executed and the computer encounters NEXT I, the computer returns to line 10, remembering how many times it has executed line 10.

There are other valuable variations of the FOR-NEXT Loop.

Example:

> 10   FOR I = 1 TO 10 STEP .1. Unless otherwise told, the computer increments

in steps of 1. If specifically instructed, the computer will increment in any size step, such as .1 (in line 10 above). Elements of the FOR-NEXT Loop can be variables under user control.

Example:

> 10   INPUT "HOW MANY TIMES";N
> 20   INPUT "STEP SIZE?";S
> 30   FOR I = 1 TO N STEP S

And, of course, the computer can count backwards.

Example:

> FOR I = 10 TO 1 STEP -1

DIM or dimension statement. The DIM statement used in BASIC is a statement which allows the programmer to set up an array or matrix. The term used for the array or matrix variables is subscripted variables. A typical dimension statement follows:

> 10   DIM A (20), B(10,10)

Mailboxes

In the DIM statement shown above, memory is set aside for 20 different A inputs subscripted A(1), A(2), A(3), through A(20). These memory positions can be thought of as "mailboxes". For example, the variable A(1) can be assigned 1.215 and A(2) = 1.315, A(4) = 1.415, and so on. The array is generally used with the FOR-NEXT Loop for assignment of the variable and for its retrieval from memory. The program lines shown below will demonstrate this.

> 10   DIM A(10):B=4:   DIM C(10):D=5
> 20   FOR I = 1 TO 10
> 30   LET A(1)=B*I
> 40   NEXT I

After the program has been executed, the mailbox positions and their values in memory would look like *Figure 1-3*

A(1) = 4	A(6) = 24
A(2) = 8	A(7) = 28
A(3) = 12	A(8) = 32
A(4) = 16	A(9) = 36
A(5) = 20	A(10) = 40

Figure 1-3. This figure illustrates the mailbox positions and their values in the computer's memory.

Because these values are in memory, they can be called back later in the program.

Example:

```
50   FOR I = 1 TO 10
60   LET C(I) = A(I)*D
70   PRINT C(I)
80   NEXT I
```

Line 60 retrieves the value of A(1) which is 4 and multiplies it by D, which is 5 and stores it back in memory in another position C(1) with the value of 20. One important note: When a DIM variable is used in a FOR-NEXT Loop, its subscript must be the same as the FOR-NEXT variable.

Examples of a legal and an illegal program follow:

Legal statement:

```
10   FOR I = 1 TO N
20   LET A(I) = B(I)*C(I)
30   NEXT I
```

Illegal statement:

```
10   FOR I = 1 TO N
20   LET A(X) = B(X)*C(Z)
30   NEXT I
```

The next type of DIM statement that should be considered is called multidimensioned.

Example:

```
10   DIM A (2,3)
```

This dimensioned statement produces a matrix whereby the first dimension is the row and the second dimension is the column as shown in *Figure 1-4.*

	Columns		
	1.	2.	3.
1. A(1,1)	A(1,2)	A(1,3)
Rows			
2. A(2,1)	A(2,2)	A(2.3)

Figure 1-4. In this figure, the first dimension is the row and the second dimension is the column.

This matrix or table can be filled with data by INPUT statements or by READ, DATA statements. There are, of course, other ways the table can be filled which we shall see later in this chapter. The input program shown below uses a "nested" FOR-NEXT Loop to fill the matrix.

```
10   DIM A(2,3)
20   FOR J = 1 TO 2
30   FOR K = 1 TO 3
```

```
40    INPUT A(J,K)
50    NEXT K
60    NEXT J
```

Note that in the program above, the K loop is nested inside the J loop. If BASIC can produce a two-dimensioned matrix, how about a three-dimensioned matrix?

Example:

```
10    DIM A(2,3,4)
```

It may be helpful to see this as a file drawer as shown in *Figure 1-5.*

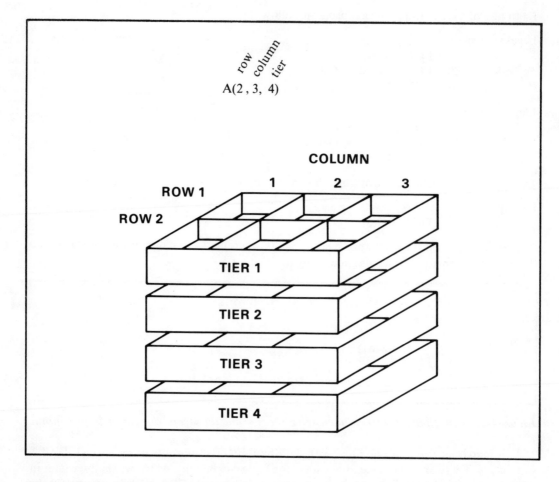

Figure 1-5. *The "File Drawer" Arrangement. Note that the first position in each tier is filled before moving to the next position.*

The program to access the "file drawer" which could be used for inventory control, is shown below:

```
10   DIM A(2,3,4)
20   FOR I = 1 TO 2
30   FOR J = 1 TO 3
40   FOR K = 1 TO 4
50   INPUT A(I,J,K)
60   NEXT K
70   NEXT J
80   NEXT I
```

FOR-NEXT Loops and nested FOR-NEXT Loops can be extremely helpful in handling table type data as information. While BASIC does not contain any MAT or matrix statements, matrix manipulation can be done using the nested FOR-NEXT Loop.

Example:
```
50   LET C(J,K) = A(J,K)*B(J,K)
```

Or, put another way:

C matrix	A matrix	B matrix
C (1,1) C(1,2) =	A(1,1) A(1,2) *	B(1,1) B(1,2)
C(2,1) C(2,2)	A(2,1) A(2,1)	B(2,1) B(2,1)

Properly written, the program will take the contents stored in A(1,1) and multiply them by the contents of B(1,1) and place the result in C(1,1).

READ and DATA. READ and DATA are two words that are used together in a program, and for this reason they will be defined together. DATA can be thought of as constants in a program that represents a way of storing information in the program that may not change. The phrase "may not change" is intended to imply that DATA statements can change by updating them.

Example:
```
10   FOR I = 1 TO 5
20   READ A
30   PRINT A
40   NEXT I
50   DATA 1, 2, 3, 4, 5
```

(Note: The DATA statements are separated by a comma and there are five pieces of data that agree with the five in the FOR-NEXT Loop.)

If the computer runs out of data to read, an ERROR message will appear. Data can also be read into a matrix.

Example:
```
10   DIM A(3,3)
20   FOR J = 1 TO 3
30   FOR K = 1 TO 3
40   READ A(J,K)
```

```
50    NEXT K
60    NEXT J
70    DATA 10, 11, 12, 13, 14, 15, 16, 17, 18
```

Our matrix in memory appears in *Figure 1-6.*

	Column		
	1	2	3
Row 1	A(1,1) = 10	A(1,2) = 11	A(1,3) = 12
Row 2	A(2,1) = 13	A(2,2) = 14	A(2,3) = 15
Row 3	A(3,1) = 16	A(3,2) = 17	A(3,3) = 18

Figure 1-6. *The matrix position and the data stored in each position.*

The word RESTORE in a program restores the data after it is read. For example, if we insert a line in the program, such as 65 RESTORE, all values in the matrix will assume the value of 10 because the data was restored.

After that rather long review, let's write a program that uses these words. The formula again is:

$$\text{Feed} = (D/.5)^{.8074} * .007$$

The printout should read as follows:

```
10    REM D = DRILL DIA. F = FEED
20    DIM D(6), F(6)
30    FOR I = 1 TO 6
40    READ D(I)
50    LET F(I) = ((D(I)/.5↑.8074)*.007
60    NEXT I
70    CLS
80    PRINT "DRILL SIZE", "FEED"
90    PRINT
100   FOR I = 1 TO 6
110   PRINT D(I),F(I)
120   NEXT I
130   DATA .125, .250, .375, .5, .625, .75
```

Line-by-Line Explanation of the Program

Line 10   REM D = DRILL DIA. F = FEED

The REM statement informs the reader what the variables are for this program.

10

Line 20   DIM D(6), F(6)

The DIM statement covered earlier in this chapter dimensions the array. The DIM statement is necessary only if the value of the dimension is greater than 10. The TRS-80[1] reserves memory for 10 positions by default, 1 through 10. It is good programming practice, nevertheless, to dimension all subscripted variables.

Line 30   FOR I = 1 TO 6

This starts the FOR-NEXT Loop.

Line 40   READ D(I)

First time through the loop, D(I) = D(1) = .125. Next time through the loop, D(I) = D(2) = .25, etc.

Line 50   LET F(I) = $((D(I)/.5)\uparrow^{.8074})*.007$

Note the parentheses. The drill size is first divided by .5, then carried to the exponent .8074 before it is multiplied by .007. The key on the keyboard for exponent is $\uparrow$ (arrow up).

Line 60   NEXT I

This continues the loop and directs the computer to go to line 30 for the second, third, fourth, etc. Line 40 for the READ statement and line 50 for the calculations.

Line 70   CLS

This line clears the screen for screen printing. Some computers do not have the CLS statement. In this case, clearing the screen can be completed by programming a FOR-NEXT Loop to clear the screen.

Line 70   FOR I = 1 TO 16:PRINT:NEXT I
Line 80   PRINT "DRILL SIZE", "FEED"

This statement prints drill size and feed at the top of the screen. Note the comma. The screen can be divided into four print columns of 16 PRINT characters each by using commas, which is a nice feature.

Line 90   PRINT

This PRINT statement skips a line on the screen.

Line 100 FOR I = 1 TO 6

The computer remembers the values calculated and assigned to the mailboxes, D(I) and F(I); this starts the printout loop.

Line 110 PRINT D(I), F(I)

Again, the comma lines up this data with the PRINT headings.

Line 120 NEXT I

This line directs the computer back to line 100 until the loop is complete.

Line 130 DATA .125, .250, .375, .5, .625, .75

---

[1]TRS-80 is a trademark of the Radio Shack Division of Tandy Corporation.

The drill sizes are stored in the program in the form of DATA statements. Note that each data statement must be separated by a comma.

By typing in RUN and pressing ENTER, the program is executed and the screen looks like

Drill Size	Feed
.125	2.28557E-03
.25	3.99988E-03
.375	5.5491E-03
.5	7E-03
.625	8.38192E-03
.75	9.71123E-03
READY	

Figure 1-7. Drill size and calculated feed.

The results are printed out on the screen in scientific notation.

Demonstration Three

Figure 1-8 reviews words, math symbols and the punctuation in the third demonstration.

Words Used	Math Symbols Used	Punctuation Used
1. ON...GOTO	1. equal =	1. colon :
2. GOSUB, RETURN	2. less than <	
3. IF THEN, ELSE	3. greater than >	
4. AND, OR, NOT	4. greater than or equal to >=	
	5. less than or equal to <=	
	6. not equal to <>	

Figure 1-8. Samples of the words, math symbols and punctuation in the third demonstration.

Review of Words Used

ON GOTO. The ON...GOTO statement is an unconditional branching statement. Unconditional means that the computer is directed to go to a line without any conditions. This statement is used typically in the menu structure of a program.

Example:

```
10    INPUT "TYPE IN THE MODULE YOU WISH TO USE", X
20    ON X GOTO 100, 200, 300, 400
```

If X = 3, the computer then counts to the third position and is directed to go to line 300 of the program.

GOSUB. The GOSUB statement directs the computer to a subroutine. The subroutine can be used several different ways, such as speeds and feeds data. After the computer completes the subroutine, it then encounters a RETURN statement and returns to the next line (where it originally went GOSUB).

Example:

```
100    GOSUB 1000
1000   REM SUBROUTINE FOR DATA
1010   A = 6:B=7:C=8:D=10:RETURN
```

In line 1010, the data or variables are separated by colons. Variables and entire lines of computer programs can be written this way. This method of programming is termed "compressed programming".

Example:

```
10    FOR I = 1 TO 10:A(I)=B(I):NEXT I
```

Compressed programming avoids the use of line numbers, but makes the program more difficult to understand, not for the computer, just for the reader.

IF THEN, ELSE. The IF THEN statement is a conditional branching statement and has wide use in programming. The IF THEN statement is a test, and if the test fails, the computer indexes to the next line of program.

Example:

```
10    INPUT "ENTER YOUR NUMBER";X
20    IF X = 6 THEN 100
30    IF X = 5 THEN 200
```

The ELSE statement is frequently used with the IF THEN statement to provide an alternative for the computer.

Example:

```
10    INPUT "TYPE IN THE NUMBER";X
20    IF X = 10 THEN 100 ELSE 200
```

The IF THEN, ELSE combination can also be used with other words.

Example:

```
10    CLS:GOTO 30
20    PRINT "A NUMBER LESS THAN 10 PLEASE"
30    INPUT "ENTER A NUMBER LESS THAN 10";X
40    IF X < 10 THEN 100 ELSE 20
```

In this example, the user is prevented from entering a value for X that is greater than 10.

AND, OR, NOT. AND, OR, NOT are tests that can be used for other types of sorting and somewhat follows Boolean logic.

Example:

```
 50   IF A > 5 AND B < = 6 THEN 100 ELSE 80
200   IF A = 3 OR B = 5 THEN 300
 40   IF A = > 7 AND NOT (B < 50) THEN 60 ELSE 100
110   IF A < > B AND C = 6 OR A=8 AND NOT (C=5) THEN 150
```

There are so many combinations possible for these tests, one could fill a book with logic programs that do nothing but sort variables. The important aspect for the beginning programmer to remember is that sorting and/or conditional branching is available in BASIC with the use of the following statements: IF THEN, AND, OR, NOT and ELSE.

Demonstration Four

Figure 1-9 lists some of the words used in this demonstration.

Words Used			
Group 1	Group 2	Group 3	Group 4
COS	SQR	ABS	RANDOM
SIN	EXP	CDBL	END
TAN	LOG	CSNG	SGN
ATN		INT	

Figure 1-9. *Words used by the computer in Demonstration Four.*

The math functions of the system are very powerful. While it would not be practical to write a single program that includes all the math functions, several short programs are included to serve as examples of statement usage. Other words not included in these programs are presented in one-line programs to illustrate their usage.

Group 1 Words

All trigonometry functions are calculated in radians, so a constant of .01745329 must be used to convert radians into degrees.

Demo Program 4

The following is a demonstration program.

```
 10   X = .01745329
 20   DIM A (60), B(60), C(60), D(60)
 30   LPRINT"ANGLE", "TAN", "COTAN", "SIN", "COS"
 40   INPUT "ENTER THE DEGREE FOR WHICH YOU WISH THE
      TABLE";N
 50   FOR I = N TO N + 1 STEP .0166667
 60   A(I) = TAN (I*X)
 70   B(I) = 1/(TAN(I*X))
 80   C(I) = SIN(I*X)
 90   D(I) = COS(I*X)

100   LPRINTI, A(I), B(I), C(I), D(I)
110   NEXT I
```

Program Comments

        Line 10   X = .01745329

This line is the constant to convert radians to degrees.

        Line 20   DIM A(60), B(60), C(60), D(60)

Line 20 sets up an array in memory or reserves 60 memory positions for each variable A, B, C, and D.

        Line 30   LPRINT "ANGLE", "TAN", "COTAN", "SIN", "COS"

This is the first time we have used the LPRINT statement. Remember the PRINT statement prints out information or data on the CRT screen. The LPRINT, or LINE PRINT, is used to direct the computer to print out information (hard copy) on a line printer. Also note that LLIST is the counterpart of LIST. LLIST prints out a hard copy of the program and LIST lists a program on the screen.

        Line 40   INPUT "ENTER THE DEGREE FOR WHICH YOU WISH THE TABLE"; N

This program calculates a single degree at a time.

        Line 50   FOR I = N TO N + 1 STEP .0166667

The step is based on $1/60$ = .0166667 which converts each step equal to N degrees plus one minute. To convert to minutes and seconds, the step would be $1/360$ = .00277778. Lines 60, 70, 80 and 90 demonstrate the use of TAN, SIN, COS, and of course 1/TAN equals COTAN.

        Line 110   NEXT I

This line directs the computer back to the start of the FOR-NEXT Loop for another calculation. The program printout is on the next page.

ATN(X) returns the arc tangent of X in radians. To convert radians into degrees, multiply by 57.29578.

Example:

        50   A = ATN(X)*57.29578

A will be expressed in decimal form and changes in the program would have to be made to convert A into degree, minute, second.

Group 2 Words

SQR(X) returns the square root of a number.

Example:

```
10   INPUT "ENTER A NUMBER";A
20   B = SQR(A)
30   PRINT B
```

Roots to other powers can be extracted by dividing 1 by the exponent.

ANGLE	TAN	COTAN	SIN	COS
5	.0874867	11.4303	.0871538	.996195
5.01667	.0877798	11.3921	.0874435	.99617
5.03333	.0880729	11.3542	.0877333	.996144
5.05	.0883661	11.3166	.0880231	.996118
5.06667	.0886593	11.2791	.0883128	.996093
5.08333	.0889524	11.242	.0886026	.996067
5.1	.0892457	11.205	.0888924	.996041
5.11667	.0895389	11.1683	.0891821	.996015
5.13334	.089832	11.1319	.0894717	.995989
5.15	.0901253	11.0957	.0897615	.995963
5.16667	.0904186	11.0597	.0900512	.995937
5.18334	.0907118	11.0239	.0903409	.995911
5.2	.0910051	10.9884	.0906306	.995885
5.21667	.0912984	10.9531	.0909203	.995858
5.23334	.0915918	10.918	.09121	.995832
5.25	.091885	10.8832	.0914996	.995805
5.26667	.0921784	10.8485	.0917893	.995779
5.28334	.0924718	10.8141	.0920789	.995752
5.3	.0927652	10.7799	.0923686	.995725
5.31667	.0930586	10.7459	.0926582	.995698
5.33334	.093352	10.7121	.0929479	.995671
5.35001	.0936454	10.6786	.0932375	.995644
5.36667	.0939388	10.6452	.093527	.995617
5.38334	.0942323	10.6121	.0938167	.99559
5.40001	.0945258	10.5791	.0941063	.995562
5.41667	.0948193	10.5464	.0943959	.995535
5.43334	.0951128	10.5138	.0946855	.995507
5.45001	.0954063	10.4815	.0949751	.99548
5.46667	.0956999	10.4493	.0952646	.995452
5.48334	.0959935	10.4174	.0955542	.995424
5.50001	.096287	10.3856	.0958437	.995396
5.51667	.0965805	10.3541	.0961332	.995369
5.53334	.0968742	10.3227	.0964228	.995341
5.55001	.0971678	10.2915	.0967123	.995312
5.56667	.0974615	10.2605	.0970018	.995284
5.58334	.0977551	10.2296	.0972914	.995256
5.60001	.0980488	10.199	.0975809	.995228
5.61668	.0983424	10.1686	.0978703	.995199
5.63334	.0986361	10.1383	.0981598	.995171
5.65001	.0989299	10.1082	.0984493	.995142
5.66668	.0992236	10.0782	.0987388	.995113
5.68334	.0995174	10.0485	.0990282	.995085
5.70001	.0998112	10.0189	.0993177	.995056
5.71668	.100105	9.98951	.0996072	.995027
5.73334	.100399	9.96029	.0998965	.994998
5.75001	.100693	9.93122	.100186	.994969
5.76668	.100986	9.90232	.100475	.99494
5.78334	.10128	9.87359	.100765	.99491
5.80001	.101574	9.84502	.101054	.994881
5.81668	.101868	9.81662	.101344	.994852
5.83335	.102162	9.78838	.101633	.994822
5.85001	.102456	9.7603	.101922	.994792
5.86668	.10275	9.73238	.102212	.994763
5.88335	.103044	9.70461	.102501	.994733
5.90001	.103338	9.677	.10279	.994703
5.91668	.103632	9.64955	.10308	.994673
5.93335	.103926	9.62225	.103369	.994643
5.95001	.10422	9.5951	.103658	.994613
5.96668	.104514	9.5681	.103948	.994583
5.98335	.104808	9.54126	.104237	.994553

Printout 1-1

Example:

```
10   INPUT "ENTER A NUMBER";A
20   INPUT "ENTER THE EXPONENT";B
30   C = A ↑ (1/B)
40   PRINT C
```

Examples of the program above:

ENTER A NUMBER	256	ENTER
ENTER THE EXPONENT?	8	ENTER
2		
RUN		ENTER
ENTER A NUMBER?	32767	ENTER
ENTER THE EXPONENT?	15	ENTER
2		
RUN		ENTER
ENTER A NUMBER?	27	ENTER
ENTER THE EXPONENT?	3	ENTER
3		

LOG(X) returns the natural logarithm of X or e based logs. To determine the logarithm for another base, the formula is LOG(X)/LOG(B) where B equals the base.

Example:

```
10   REM LOG TO ANY BASE
20   INPUT "ENTER A NUMBER";X
30   INPUT "ENTER THE BASE";B
40   A = LOG(X)/LOG(B)
50   PRINT "THE LOG OF";X;"TO BASE";B;"IS";A
60   GOTO 20
```

EXP(X) returns the natural exponent of X or e^X. This is the inverse of the LOG(X) function.

Example:

```
10   REM EXPONENT OF A NUMBER
20   INPUT "ENTER THE VALUE";A
30   X = EXP(A)
40   XI = EXP(—A)
50   X2 = EXP(LOG(A))
60   PRINT "THE NATURAL EXPONENTIAL OF";A;"IS";X
70   PRINT "THE NATURAL NEGATIVE EXPONENTIAL
     OF";A;"IS";X1
80   PRINT "THIS IS THE INVERSE OF THE LOG FUNCTION"
90   PRINT "THEREFORE";X2;"=";A
100  GOTO 20
```

Group 3 Words

The ABS(X) function returns the absolute value of X for X equal to or greater than 0. The INT(X) function returns the integer value of X and does not round up.

Example:

```
5    CLS
10   REM ABS AND INT FUNCTIONS
20   INPUT "ENTER A VALUE";A
30   X = ABS(A)
40   Y = INT(A)
50   PRINT "THE ABSOLUTE VALUE OF";A;"IS";X
60   PRINT "THE INTEGER VALUE OF";A;"IS";Y
```

A typical printout would look like this:

```
RUN
ENTER A VALUE?                          2.111   ENTER
THE ABSOLUTE VALUE OF                     2.111 IS 2.111
THE INTEGER VALUE OF                      2.111 IS 2.
RUN
ENTER A VALUE?                          -2.111   ENTER
THE ABSOLUTE VALUE OF                     -2.111 IS 2.111
THE INTEGER VALUE OF                      -2.111 IS -3.
RUN
ENTER A VALUE?                          .9999   ENTER
THE ABSOLUTE VALUE OF                     .9999 IS .9999
THE INTEGER VALUE OF                      .9999 IS 0.
```

The CDBL(X) and the CSNG(X) functions convert single precision numbers to double precision numbers and back again. The computer's normal operation, that is, without using CDBL(X) or CSNG(X), returns a six digit accuracy. In actual use, however, these two programming statements are limited. Executing the program below will show why.

```
10   X = .01745329
20    FOR I = 1 TO 10:P(I) = 1/I:NEXT
30    FOR I = 1 TO 10:Q(I)=TAN(I*X):NEXT
40    FOR I = 1 TO 10:R(I)=P(I)/Q(I): LPRINT I, "P", CDBL (P(I)):
     LPRINTI,"Q",CDBL(Q(I)):LPRINTI,"R",CDBL(R(I)):NEXTI
```

Double Precision

This program printout extends a number to what is called double precision. The program printout is shown on the following page. In reviewing the results of the program, the reader should note that the computer has calculated 1 divided by 3 as .3333333432674408 rather than a continuous string of 3's, and 1 divided by 10 as .1000000014901161. Needless to say, the programmer should be wary. The accuracy improvement changes from six significant digits to seven, eight, or nine, depending on the calculation. Nevertheless, there are several items of interest in the program shown above.

First, note that the "NEXT" does not say "NEXT I." The I is optional unless the program is a nested loop. Also note that the computer stores double precision in memory even when the CDBL statement is not used; i.e., line 20 omits its use and line 40 does not. The reader should also note that line 40 continues on and on past the point where a line of program would normally end. While this is possible, it is not considered good programming style because the program is difficult to read. For very long programs, there is a "packer" utility program

```
10  X=.01745329
20  FORI=1TO10:P(I)=1/I:NEXT
30  FORI=1TO10:Q(I)=TAN(I*X):NEXT
40  FORI=1TO10:R(I)=P(I)/Q(I):LPRINTI,"P",CDBL(P(I)):LPRINTI,"Q",CDBL(Q(I)):LPRIN
TI,"R",CDBL(R(I)):NEXTI
```

1	P	1
1	Q	.01745501533150673
1	R	57.29012298583984
2	P	.5
2	Q	.03492076694965363
2	R	14.31812763214111
3	P	.3333333432674408
3	Q	.05240781605243683
3	R	6.360374450683594
4	P	.25
4	Q	.06992680579423904
4	R	3.575166940689087
5	P	.2000000029802322
5	Q	.08748860657215119
5	R	2.286011934280396
6	P	.1666666716337204
6	Q	.1051042228937149
6	R	1.585727691650391
7	P	.1428571492433548
7	Q	.1227844953536987
7	R	1.16347873210907
8	P	.125
8	Q	.1405408382415772
8	R	.8894211649894715
9	P	.1111111119389534
9	Q	.1583844870328903
9	R	.7015277147293091
10	P	.1000000014901161
10	Q	.1763269752264023
10	R	.5671281814575195

Printout 1-2

available on the market that packs everything together to save the use of memory. The CSNG(X) statement converts a double precision number back to a six significant digit number.

One last comment should be made about FOR-NEXT Loops. It is not necessary to change the variable I just because it has been used before. Consider how this program is written. Lines 20, 30 and 40 all use FOR I =. Once the computer has completed the use of I, it sets I back to 1.

If subscripted variables are used in several FOR-NEXT Loops, the prime variable letter must be changed to store the data in separate places in memory.

Example:

```
10   FOR I = 1 TO 10
20   LET A(I) = X
30   NEXT
40   FOR I = 1 TO 10
50   LET B(I) = Y
60   NEXT
```

The INT(X) statement returns an integer value of a number, which can be of value when the trailing decimals are not required.

Example:

```
80   INPUT "ENTER";A
90   PRINT A
100  B=INT(A+.5)
110  PRINT B
```

In this example, the .5 rounds the number up to the next higher digit.

Group 4 Words

The word RANDOM is a complete statement in itself, rather than a function, and is used only once in a program to reseed the random number generator. RND(X), on the other hand, is required each time a program is executed to produce a random number. The random number generator and random numbers have value to the programmer who is writing a work sampling type program (see the program "RATIO").

```
10   CLS
20   RANDOM
30   PRINT "QUALITY AUDIT"
40   PRINT
50   PRINT "DEPARTMENT", "WORK HOUR",
     "MINUTES"
60   FOR I = 1 TO 4
70   A = RND(8):B=RND(60)
80   PRINT I,A,B,
90   NEXT I
RUN          ENTER
```

Quality Audit

Table 1-1 is produced by the nine-line program above. Many companies use the surprise quality audit as a technique of controlling quality. In this scheme, the quality control department assigns several inspectors to converge on a manufacturing department and take a surprise quality audit. *Table 1-1* shows that department one is to be audited starting 56 minutes after the start of the second work hour. The RND statements in line 70 provide the random hours and minutes.

Table 1-1
A Quality Audit

Department	Work Hour	Minutes
1	2	56
2	1	12
3	7	21
4	4	28

Demonstration Five

Figure 1-10 lists subjects and words used in Demonstration Five.

	Words	
Subjects	Group 1	Group 2
String I/O	RIGHT $	ASC
String space	LEFT $	INKEY $
String operation	MID $	LINE INPUT

Figure 1-10. *Words used by the computer in Demonstration Five.*

Strings

Without the ability to work with strings (words), the computer would be little more than a giant number cruncher. Strings give the computer the ability to input or output written messages. Moreover, strings can be manipulated in the computer by comparing, adding, subtracting and sorting. With the use of strings, word processing by a computer is made possible. String input and output are similar to numeric input and output, with the exception that several additional rules must be observed.

Maintenance Program

Before we start a line-by-line review of the program presented below, some description of what the program does is in order. This is a maintenance oiling program and can be used as the start of a preventative maintenance program for the maintenance department. A record of the machines which need oiling service each day is entered in the computer in the form of string instructions for each machine. At the beginning of each day, a printout of these instructions displaying machine name, location, type of oil and grease used to service the machine is also on the work form. This type of program is an easy way to create and maintain records in the department where the records are used by departmental personnel. From this general description, it is easy to see the future potential for this type of program. For example, an inventory record program could include all of the major inventory items in the maintenance department by machine and/or by description or part number. By reviewing the short program below, we will discover most of these rules.

```
10    CLEAR 100:CLS
20    REM PROGRAM FOR OILING SERVICE
30    PRINT "ENTER THE FIRST THREE LETTERS OF THE DAY"
35    PRINT "ENTER TODAY'S DATE, SEPARATE FROM THE
          DAY BY A COMMA"
40    INPUT D$, Y$
50    FOR Z = 1 TO 5
60    READ D1$, M1$, M2$, M3$
70    IF D1$ = D$ THEN 140 ELSE 80
80    NEXT I
90    DATA MON, T/L, ENGINE LATHE, DRILL PRESS
100   DATA TUE, 1S/C, LEBLOND, N/C DRILL
110   DATA WED, OD GRINDER, ID GRINDER, SURFACE GRINDER
```

```
120   DATA THU, ASSY. 1, ASSY. 2, ASSY. 3
130   DATA FRI, MILL, N/C MILL, HAND MILL
140   CLS: PRINT D1$, Y$
150   PRINT "MAINTENANCE FOR THIS DAY IS ON"
160   PRINT M1$
170   PRINT M2$
180   PRINT M3$
190   INPUT "TYPE  YES  FOR  ANOTHER  PRINTOUT";C$
200   IF C$ = "YES" THEN 10
210   END
```

Line-by-Line Explanation of the Program

Line 10   CLEAR 100:CLS

The CLEAR statement reserves computer memory for string storage. When booted up, the TRS-80 automatically sets aside 50 bytes for string storage. However, if more storage is required during the execution of a program, string storage must first be cleared. One other feature of the CLEAR statement is that all variables are set to 0.

Line 40   INPUT D$, Y$

This is a multiple input line whereby the first three letters of the day, such as MON, are typed in, followed by a comma to separate the strings, then the current date. It is important to note that the computer will accept a string with numbers in the string. For example, Y$ could be 01/01/81. There are restrictions, though, for string input. A comma cannot be part of the string unless the string is enclosed by quote marks on each side of the string. Without the quote marks, the computer reads the comma as a terminator.

Line 50   FOR I = 1 TO 5

This starts a loop to read the data in the program.

Line 60   READ D1$, M1$, M2$, M3$

Line 60 reads the data and places it in computer memory.

Line 70   IF D1$ = D$ THEN 140 ELSE 80

Strings can be tested for comparison to another string because strings are stored in computer memory in ASCII code (numbers). More about this later.

The reader should note two items of interest. First, subscripted variables are not used. This is not a programming requirement, merely a convenience because the user is looking for a specific day. Secondly, when a match is made, D1$ = D$, the computer "jumps" out of the loop and is directed to go to line 140 of the program. The ELSE part of this line is optional and is placed in the program for reader understanding.

The computer compares D1$ to D$: if the test passes, it continues to line 140. If the test fails, it will continue to the next line, 80.

Lines 90, 100, 110, 120, 130 = DATA statements

DATA Statements

DATA statements represent a very easy way to create files without knowing any of the computer's intricate filing language. This type of filing is recommended for the beginning programmer. Updating the data can be done by editing with the computer editing functions, or by retyping the entire line.

DATA statements in a program can include numbers as well as DATA strings. The numbers, as data, can be READ by the computer as string variables (such as the date presented earlier in the program), or as nonstring variables, such as A,B,C. If there is a mixture of string variables and nonstring variables in DATA statements, care must be taken in the programming to assure a proper match when reading data.

Line 140   CLS:PRINT D1$, Y$

This line prints out the day and date. If hard copy is desired, the statement would change to LPRINT rather than PRINT.

Lines 150, 160, 170, 180 PRINT statements

These lines print out the maintenance instructions for the day, and naturally would include much more detail than shown in this sample program.

Line 190   INPUT "TYPE YES FOR ANOTHER PRINTOUT";C$

This line is added to the program to demonstrate another type of test for strings.

IF C$ = "YES" THEN 10

String comparison can be made another way. Note that YES is inside quotes. If C$ = "YES" then proceed to line 10 and start over. If not (meaning if the test fails), proceed to line 120 which ends the program.

ASCII Codes and Sorting

Several comments about ASCII codes and sorting are in order. The computer stores all characters in number, or ASCII form. For this reason, sorting can be accomplished. The letter A, for example, is ASCII code 65, and when a line of computer program reads, IF A$ = "A" THEN -----, if A$ = A or 65 and "A" = 65 (ASCII code) then the test is a match and the computer is directed to do something by the statement THEN. To view some of the ASCII codes, type in the following program.

```
10   CLS
20   PRINT "ASCII CODES"
30   FOR I = 1 TO 52:READ A$: PRINT ASC(A$);A$,:NEXT
40   DATA !,#,$,%,&,',(,),*,-,.,/,0,1,2,3,4,5,6,7,8,9,<,=,>,?, A,B,C,D,E,F,G,H,
     I,J,K,L,M,N,O,P,Q,R,S,T,U,V,W,X,Y,Z
```

Group 1 Words

There are some other operations that can be performed on strings. Strings can be separated from right to left, or left to right, or even from the middle. The BASIC words that permit these operations are: RIGHT $, LEFT $ and MID $. To understand how these new statements are used, review the examples below.

```
10   INPUT "ENTER THE LAST NAME";A$
20   B$ = LEFT$(A$,2)
30   C$ = RIGHT$(B$,1)
```

```
40    C = ASC(C$)
50    D$ = LEFT$(A$,1)
60    D = ASC(D$)
70    B = C+D
80    PRINT A$, B$, C$, D$
90    PRINT , B, C, D
```

Line-by-Line Explanation of Program

Line 20   B$ = LEFT$(A$,2)

Line 20 separates the first two characters from left to right of A$. If A$ = JONES, then B$ becomes JO.

Line 30   C$ = RIGHT$(B$,1)

Line 30 separates the first character from right to left of B$. If B$ = JO then C$ becomes O.

Line 40   C = ASC(C$)

The letter O has the ASCII value of 79, therefore, C = 79.

Line 50   D$ = LEFT$(A$,1)

Line 50 separates the first character from left to right of A$, so D$ = J.

Line 60   D = ASC(D$)

The letter J has the ASCII value of 74, therefore, D = 74

Line 70   B = C+D, therefore B = 79+74, B = 153
Line 80   PRINT A$, B$, C$, D$

This line prints out the strings as separated.

Line 90   PRINT , B, C, D,

The first comma after the PRINT statement indexes the CRT to the second print column where B is printed beneath B$, and so on.

The reader might ask, of what value is this to an engineer? The answer lies in understanding the computer's filing system.

Filing System

If we were writing a random filing program for a vendor mailing list, we would like to have the ability to type in the vendor's last name and retrieve the full name, address, and phone number of that vendor without remembering where the data is placed on file. The random filing system is established by numerical record number and positions within a record number. Some means must be established to enter the file by number, then position number the string separation statements: corresponding ASCII code numbers give this ability. The MID string statement permits entering a string to retrieve a value or values inside a string. For example, the program above could be changed to read:

Delete Line 20
Change Line 30   C$ = MID$(A$2,1)

which would return 0 in Jones, or IF A$ = Adams would return

C$ = D

The CHR$(N) is the inverse of the ASC function because it returns the character assigned to the ASCII value. The argument has a range of 0 to 255. A short review of the ASCII codes is in *Figure 1-11.*

Decimal Code	Function
0-31	Control functions
32-95	Keyboard display characters
96-127	Lower case keyboard characters
128-191	Graphics characters
192-255	Space compression codes

Figure 1-11. *ASCII Codes.*

Type in the following program and run it.

```
10   PRINT "ASCII SYMBOLS FROM 0 TO 255"
20   PRINT "ENTER A STARTING VALUE AND ENDING VALUE"
30   INPUT "SEPARATE BY A COMMA";A,B
40   FOR I = A TO B
50   PRINT CHR$(I);I,
60   NEXT I
```

The short program above displays the ASCII characters. The graphics codes CHR$128-192 are of interest and will be discussed later in this chapter.

Group 2 Words

The INKEY$ is a very interesting word in BASIC. This function provides a continuous keyboard strobe and permits the user to press any key on the keyboard which is read into computer memory without pressing the ENTER key. The strobe time is very short, in the order of microseconds. While the major use of this function is in writing games for the computer, such as Star Wars, Tennis, and Return of the Empire, it does have some value to the engineer in his programming effort. Chapter Seven contains a time study program named "TIME". In this program, the computer is converted into a real time clock by the use of the INKEY$. For a short demonstration on how this function works, type in the following program.

```
10   CLS
20   A$=INKEY$:PRINT@ 540, A$:GOTO20
```

Type RUN and ENTER, then press any key.

Demonstration Six

Figure 1-12 lists words used to provide computer graphics.

Graphics

While many advancements have been made recently in computer graphics, and most computer magazines are filled with articles on how to produce 3-D drawings that rotate and new versions of the popular Star Wars-type games, the Manufacturing Engineer's use of

Group 1 Words	Group 2 Words
1. SET	1. POKE
2. RESET	2. PEEK
3. POINT	3. PRINT @
	4. TAB

Figure 1-12. Graphics words for the CRT.

graphics is fairly straightforward because his use of graphics is to convey instructions. Presently the microcomputer does not have the capability of replacing the CAD/CAM graphics systems now on the market, nor is that its interest. Graphics, nevertheless, can be an important part of the engineer's programming style and effort.

After reviewing this brief section on graphics codes and statements, the engineer should be able to understand basic graphics function. In Chapter Eight, Graphics, they will be reviewed in detail with examples using the screen printer to display scaled and non-scaled graphs. We will start with the video display worksheet shown on the next page in *Figure 1-13*.

Video Screen Numbering Systems

The video screen has three separate and different numbering systems. First, the screen is made up of 128 columns and 48 rows. In all computer applications, numbering starts with 0. Therefore, the X axis is numbered 0 through 127 and the Y axis is numbered 0 through 47. Each number corresponds to a block of six LED's called pixels. Each block of six LED's can be turned on (one at a time or all at once) in various patterns that represent the 64 graphics patterns available in the system.

Each graphics pattern then has a number by which it can be accessed. The reader should now review the graphics pattern shown on page 31. These LED's are turned on by the SET command and turned off by the RESET command. More about this later.

The second numbering system for the video screen is from 0 through 1023. The video screen is divided into 16 rows and 64 columns. This numbering system starts with 0 in the upper left-hand corner of the screen and then continues 0 through 63 for the first row, 64 through 127 for the second row, etc. Again, note the video worksheet. The use of this numbering system relates to the PRINT @ statement. Messages can be printed any place on the screen without disturbing another part of the screen using the PRINT @ location number.

The third numbering system relates to the video's screen in memory. The memory positions start with 15360 which again is the upper left-hand corner of the video screen and continues through 16383 which is the lower right-hand corner of the screen. Subtracting these two numbers indicates 1024 memory positions for the video screen or 1024 sets of six LED's, or 16 rows of 64 sets of six LED's. This numbering system relates to the graphics symbols mentioned earlier.

Group 1 Words

As stated earlier, the SET command turns on a LED located by X, Y coordinates using the first numbering system. The command RESET turns it off. The POINT command is a test statement that answers whether the LED is on or off.

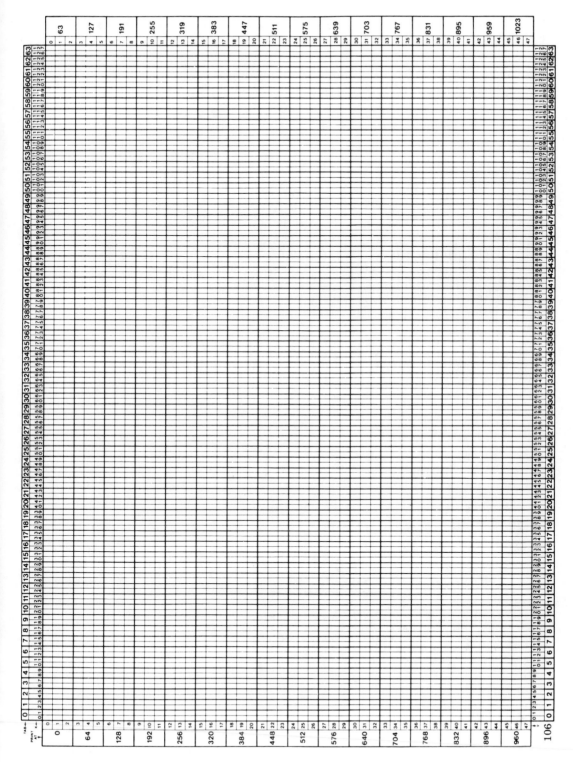

Figure 1-13. An E/Video Display Worksheet.

27

The short program that follows illustrates the language usage. A line-by-line explanation is shown below.

```
Line  5   CLS
Line 10   Y = 5
Line 20   FOR X =  10 TO 30
Line 30   SET(X,Y)
Line 40   NEXT X
```

```
5 CLS
10 Y=5
20 FORX=10TO30
30 SET(X,Y)
40 NEXTX
50 Y=10
60 FORX=10TO30
70 SET(X,Y)
80 NEXTX
90 X=10:FORY=5TO10:SET(X,Y):NEXTY
100 X=30:FORY=5TO10:SET(X,Y):NEXTY
101 Y=11:FORX=20TO40:SET(X,Y):NEXTX
102 Y=15:FORX=20TO40:SET(X,Y):NEXTX
103 X=20:FORY=11TO15:SET(X,Y):NEXTY
104 X=40:FORY=11TO15:SET(X,Y):NEXTY
105 Y=20:FORX=50TO70:SET(X,Y):NEXTX
106 Y=25:FORX=50TO70:SET(X,Y):NEXTX
107 X=50:FORY=20TO25:SET(X,Y):NEXTY
108 X=70:FORY=20TO25:SET(X,Y):NEXTY
110 FORY=0TO47
120 FORX=0TO79
130 IFPOINT(X,Y)THEN140ELSE155
140 LPRINT"*";:GOTO160
155 LPRINT" ";
160 NEXTX
180 NEXTY
```

```
A ********************** B
  *                    *
  *                    *
  *        BOX 1       *
  *                    *
  *                    *
C ********************** D
          **********************
          *                    *
          *                    *
          *        BOX 2       *
          *                    *
          **********************
```

```
                    **********************
                    *                    *
                    *                    *
                    *        BOX 3       *
                    *                    *
                    **********************
```

Printout 1-3

Line 10 establishes the location of the Y position and line 20 establishes the X position as shown in *Figure 1-14*. Also review the computer printout on page 28.

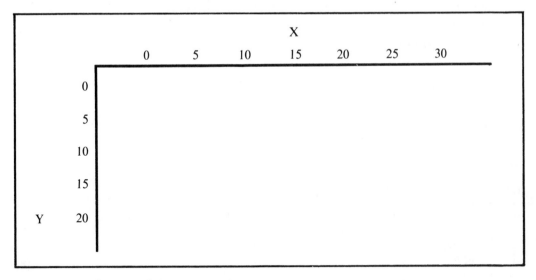

Figure 1-14. *The upper left corner of the CRT screen.*

Line 30 SET turns on the LED. The first time through the loop, X = 10, Y = 5. The second time through the loop, X = 11, Y = 5, and so on, until X = 30. These lines establish line A;B on BOX 1. Lines 50, 60, 70 and 80 establish line CD on BOX 1. (See computer *Printout 1-3).*

Line 90   X = 10:FOR Y=5 TO 10:SET(X,Y):NEXT Y

(Note: The entire loop here is written as one statement. The line establishes line A,C of BOX 1.)

Line 100   X = 30:FOR Y=5 TO 10:SET(X,Y):NEXT Y

This line establishes line B,D.

Lines 101, 102, 103 and 104 establish the same lines for BOX 2. Lines 105, 106, 107, 108 establish the lines for BOX 3. Lines 110-180 require a rather detailed explanation.

As mentioned earlier, the CRT has 128 X columns and 48 Y rows. The printer has 80 X columns and any number of Y rows. Lines 110 and 120 set up a matrix on the printer paper that is equal to the screen matrix.

Line 130   IF POINT (X,Y) THEN 140 ELSE 155

Line 130 is a test that asks if the LED is on for the X,Y coordinates. If so, then go to line 140. If not, go to line 155.

Line 140   LPRINT "*";:GOTO 160

If the LED is on, then PRINT *. Note the semicolon. This prevents the printer from indexing to the next line until all the X's in that row (Y) are printed; that is, if the LED's are on.

In line 155, if none of the LED's are on, the printer prints nothing but indexes to the next row of Y. Lines 160 and 180 complete the nested FOR-NEXT Loop.

This short subroutine can be used in a program to print out what is on the screen, provided turned on LED's are on the screen. There are limitations to what can be printed out because of the difference in the two numbering systems of the video screen and what is printed, such as 128 versus 80 columns. Nonetheless, it is a nice feature.

Printing Characters

Shown below is another short program that can print out on the screen for characters other than LED's. This program relates also to one of the other numbering systems.

```
2000    V = 15360
2010    FOR Y = 0 TO 15
2020    FOR X = 0 TO 63
2030    LPRINT CHR$(PEEK(V+64*Y+X));
2040    NEXT X
2050    LPRINT " "
2060    NEXT Y
```

Again, some detailed explanation is necessary. Remember we said earlier that the contents of memory which stores the screen's current data is from 15360 to 16383. This program peeks into memory, and if a keyboard character currently resides there, it prints it out. This program will print any character on the screen. Look at the example printout on the next page. You will observe that line 60 is an INPUT line asking a question. Because it is on the screen, it also is printed out on the printer.

```
5 CLS
10 PRINT"THIS IS A HANDY PROGRAM THAT CAN BE PLACED AT THE END OF A"
20 PRINT"LARGER PROGRAM , TO PRINT OUT WHAT EVER IS ON THE SCREEN"
30 PRINT@448,"ANY CHARACTER ON THE KEY BOARD CAN BE PRINTED"
40 PRINT@512,"FOR EXAMPLE: 1 2 3 4 5 6 7 8 9 0"
50 PRINT@576,"! # $ % & ' ( ) * = + < > ? @ , . /"
60 INPUT"ENTER ANY NUMBER TO PRINT OUT THE SCREEN";X
70 ONXGOTO2000
2000 V=15360
2010 FORY=0TO15
2020 FORX=0TO63
2030 LPRINTCHR$(PEEK(V+64*Y+X));
2040 NEXTX
2050 LPRINT" "
2060 NEXTY

THIS IS A HANDY PROGRAM THAT CAN BE PLACED AT THE END OF A
LARGER PROGRAM , TO PRINT OUT WHAT EVER IS ON THE SCREEN

ANY CHARACTER ON THE KEY BOARD CAN BE PRINTED
FOR EXAMPLE: 1 2 3 4 5 6 7 8 9 0
! # $ % & ' ( ) * = + < > ? @ , . /
ENTER ANY NUMBER TO PRINT OUT THE SCREEN? 1
```

Printout 1-4

Group 2 Words

The POKE statement is used in conjunction with the graphics characters shown on page 31. In all, there are 63 graphics characters produced by a block of six LED's of three rows and two columns. These graphics characters can be accessed from memory and used to display various shapes poked into the video memory mentioned earlier.

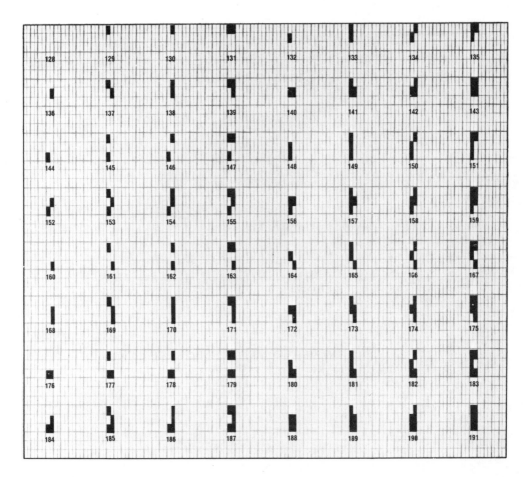

Figure 1-15. Graphics Characters.

Writing computer programs using POKE statements can be a very tedious process, but it is sometimes necessary to convey an idea of shape or form. One such example is included in Chapter Two in the "SFPM" program. This use of graphics describes the relationship of a mill cutter to the part being milled, which is necessary because there are five such relationships. The short program which follows demonstrates the use of the graphics characters and the PRINT @ statement. The subject selected is from the *Tool and Manufacturing Engineer's Handbook* and relates to development of blank sizes for drawn parts.

Totally, there are 12 different models, each having a different formula for calculation.

This example is typical of engineering graphics use because of the variety of different shapes. *Figure 1-16* shows what the user would see on the CRT screen.

ENTER ALL VALUES IN INCHES
ENTER THE VALUE OF D1?
ENTER THE VALUE OF D2?
ENTER THE VALUE OF H1?
ENTER THE VALUE OF H2?
THE BLANK DIAMETER IS

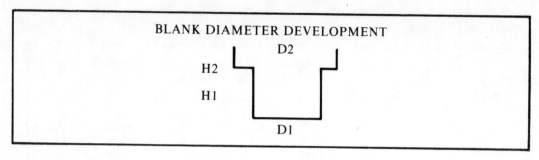

Figure 1-16. A flanged cup which is one of the 12 models.

It is easy to see that without the use of graphics to illustrate what the part looks like, flanged, not flanged and angled flanged parts would be difficult to describe. The computer program which produces the graphics follows:

```
10   CLS:REM CALCULATES BLANK DIAMETER
20   PRINT @ 5, "BLANK DIAMETER DEVELOPMENT"
30   PRINT @ 80, "D2"
40   PRINT @ 136, "H2"
50   PRINT @ 200, "H1"
60   PRINT @ 272, "D1"
70   FOR X = 15566 TO 15570:POKE X, 176:NEXT X
80   POKE 15565, 191:POKE 15571, 191
90   POKE 15501, 188:POKE 15507, 188
100  POKE 15500, 140:POKE 15508, 140
110  POKE 15499, 143:POKE 15509, 143
120  PRINT @ 451, "ENTER ALL VALUES IN INCHES"
130  INPUT "ENTER THE VALUE OF D1";D1
140  INPUT "ENTER THE VALUE OF D2";D2
150  INPUT "ENTER THE VALUE OF H1";H1
160  INPUT "ENTER THE VALUE OF H2";H2
170  B=SQR(D2/2+(4*((D1*H1)+(D2*H2))))
180  PRINT @ 835, "THE BLANK DIAMETER IS";B
```

Line-by-Line Explanation of the Program

Lines 20, 30, 40, 50 and 60 are PRINT @ statements that place the printed messages at specific locations on the CRT. Referring to the video map again, the numbering system used starts with 0 in the upper left-hand corner of the screen. There are 64 PRINT positions in the first row numbered 0 through 63. Therefore, the first PRINT @ 5, places the first letter in the fifth position of the first row. The process continues in a similar manner.

Line 70 is a FOR-NEXT Loop that places graphics character 176 in the five PRINT positions starting with 15566 and ending with 15570. Refer to the graphics characters to see what character 176 looks like. The reader should also take note that graphics can be poked on the video screen with a FOR-NEXT Loop.

Line 80 uses a single graphics character, number 191, in two different locations. Note that a FOR-NEXT Loop is not required for a single character. The process continues until the entire shape is displayed on the screen. Line 120 has an important function aside from conveying the message. The PRINT @ 451 is about halfway down the screen (line 8). This is a PRINT message that stops the computer from scrolling up and wiping out the graphics character. The inputs in lines 130-160 are displayed below line 120 while the screen is held steady. The graphics character itself is displayed in the upper left-hand corner of the screen. A programmer could easily produce six graphic characters on the screen at one time, and with two screen showings, display all 12 of the different figures for drawn shapes mentioned earlier.

Vertical Lines

Before leaving the subject of graphics, we should cover vertical lines because the program just reviewed has no such lines.

Type in the following lines of the program.

```
10   CLS:REM VERTICAL LINE
20   FOR X = 15392 TO 16352 STEP 64
30   POKE X, 149
40   NEXT X
50   GOTO 50
```

This program produces a vertical line in the center of the video screen. Note step 64 in the FOR-NEXT Loop. Now modify line 20 to step 63 and see what happens. Next modify line 20 to step 65. The brief introduction to computer graphics is just enough to get you started or hooked on what might be interesting possibilities.

Computer Filing

The last major section of computer language to review is computer filing. The statements and commands used for filing are for the most part stand-alone statements because they are used only for filing. These statements are reviewed in detail in Chapter Nine with programming examples of random and sequential filing.

For the reader who is not yet very familiar with programming in BASIC, this represents a good stopping point. Your next step should be to review some of the following chapters and use the skills acquired thus far to start writing programs. The lab exercises at the end of each chapter should be completed by the serious student before moving on to the next chapter.

Bibliography

Braden, William Jr. *Programming Techniques for Level II Basic.* Radio Shack, Tandy Corporation, 1980.

Dallas, Daniel B., Editor-in-Chief. *Tool & Manufacturing Engineer's Handbook,* 3rd Ed. Dearborn, MI: Society of Manufacturing Engineers, 1976.

Level II Basic Reference Manual, 2nd Ed. Radio Shack, a Division of Tandy Corporation, 1979.

Line Printer IV Reference Manual, Catalog No. 26-1159. Radio Shack, a Division of Tandy Corporation, 1979.

TRS DOS & Disk Basic Reference Manual, 1st Ed., Radio Shack, a Division of Tandy Corporation, 1979.

Wilson, Frank W., Editor-in-Chief. *Tool Engineer's Handbook,* 2nd Ed., Dearborn, MI: Society of Manufacturing Engineers, 1959.

CHAPTER 2

Cost Estimating

Cost estimating in a job shop has always been a costly and time consuming problem. Over the years, many attempts have been made to reduce the amount of engineering labor that is required to develop an estimate.

An Overview

Most companies attempt to establish some guidelines that represent a ratio of work quoted to work booked. As an example, if a company books only 2% of what it quotes, it suspects that the shop rate is too high or the work being quoted does not fit the plant's equipment. On the other hand, if a company books 20% of what it quotes, it suspects the work being quoted is priced too low or perhaps the estimating function has underestimated the amount of labor or material required.

Methods-Time Measurement[1] is not used for estimating a product because of the engineering time necessary to develop this level of detail. MTM can be used to illustrate the level of accuracy versus the amount of time necessary to develop an estimate. If an operation requires 1000 TMU's to perform and MTM is used to develop the estimate, then the engineer's effort spent using two levels of MTM might look like *Figure 2-1.*

	MTM-1	MTM-3*
Engineering time to develop estimate	3½ hours	½ hour
Resulting accuracy	± 7%	± 20%

Figure 2-1. MTM used to develop an estimate. Note that MTM-3 is a shorthand version of MTM-1.

The estimate's level of accuracy improves as the level of detail increases. Reviewing the estimating detail problem in this light and attempting to develop a table that represents the different ways a cost estimate can be developed, the problem can be seen more clearly.

As shown in *Table 2-1,* the level of detail has a dramatic effect on accuracy. Another consideration in estimating should be consistency. For example, an estimate for a drilling operation developed last week should have the same degree of consistency as an estimate for a drilling operation developed this week. If we can depend on some consistent level of accuracy, we might be able to predict the estimating error and adjust the estimate. To assist in controlling

[1]*MTM is a copyright of The MTM Association For Standards On Research.*

Table 2-1
Estimating Summary

Method	Level of Detail	Expected Accuracy
MTM	Very detailed	± 7%
Elements using standard data	Modest (load, process, unload)	± 10-15%
Operation	Summary detail (turn, mill, drill, bore)	± 15-20%
Part	No detail—judgement (make part, 5 hours set up and .5 hours per piece)	± 20-30%

this factor and to speed up the estimating process, most companies develop standard cost estimating forms. A sample form for milling is shown in *Figure 2-2*. While cost estimating forms serve the purpose of gaining consistency and speeding up the estimating process, they are not without their problems. To illustrate this point, one company uses over 20 different standard data estimating forms. A great deal of time is necessary to produce, reproduce and update such a book, as well as in the training necessary to use the forms properly. Using the preprinted form itself is a tedious problem. Cost estimating forms are designed to produce an estimate as fast as possible, usually sacrificing detail for speed. Using the idea offered earlier that a typical company books far less business than it quotes, speed in producing the estimate is justified. Once a company is awarded a contract based on the estimate, the next series of problems begin.

A Manufacturing Engineer is then given the new job to process. The amount and level of detail originally produced to estimate the job is virtually useless to the engineer doing the processing.

Computer Cost Estimating

When finally produced, it is not uncommon that the new part's process and actual cost show no resemblance to the original estimate. Computer cost estimating will not solve all of the problems; however, it does make major strides forward. Computer cost estimating can, if properly planned, reduce this problem. Before any attempt is undertaken to write cost estimating programs for the computer, a series of management decisions must be made to guide the engineer who will be writing the programs.

Parameters

Before we proceed with this idea, let's set some parameters on our estimate.

MILLING MACHINE RATE WORKSHEET
10-25-71

Machining Group Code _____
Date _____
Applicator _____
Part Name _____
Operation Description _____
Mat'l _____ Weight _____ Fixture No. _____
Cutter Dia _____ Cutter Mat'l _____ Cutter No. _____

Part No. _____
Dwg. No. _____
Oper. No. _____
Rev. No. _____

S.U. Hrs.	U.C. Hrs.

MACHINE TIME CALCULATIONS

No.	Cutter or Cut Descr.	Appr. + OT	Cut Length	Total 1 & 2	Mins/Inch	Freq.	Mach. Time	H.S.S. Factor	Mach. Time
1									
2									
3									
4									
				Total	1			2	

PRE-POST POSITION

				Accum. Total
To 5 lbs.	.079	Balance		
To 10 lbs.	.256	Pre-post Position		
To 20 lbs.	.306	File Part		
To 40 lbs.	.448	Inspect	Measure	
To 50 lbs.	.577		Finish	
Crane		Total		

Part Hndlg / Weight Factor

Part Hndlg	To 5#	To 10#	To 20#	To 40#	To 50#	Crane	2nd Vise	3rd Vise
Vise	.623	.704	.856	.967	1.160	4.114	.074	.148
Vise w/Layout	.976	1.058	1.221	1.698	1.881	4.835	.074	.148
	.607	.689	.874	1.022	1.305	4.259	.074	.148
Fixture Plug/An	.395	.433	.554	.698	.932	3.877		
Fixture Stops Rgh	.293	.343	.436	.550	.741	3.695		
Fixture Stops Fin	.373	.422	.550	.697	.923	3.877		
Jig on to Part	.395	.433	.554	.698	.932			
Table Rgh Surf	.210	.250	.337	.453	.584	3.568		
Table w/Layout	.850	.890	.989	1.461	1.592	4.572		
Table Fin. Surf.	.481	.521	.642	.794	1.016	3.998		
Table,Stops Rgh. Surf.	.222	.272	.365	.476	.611	3.568		
Table,Stops w/Layout	.862	.912	1.017	1.484	1.617	4.514		
Table, Stops Fin. Surf.	.493	.543	.670	.818	1.043	3.998		
Collet—Chuck	.382	.431	.562	.704	.943	3.877		

Securing / Number Required

Securing	1	2	3	4	5	6
Tighten & Loosen vise	.325	.658	.557			
Reset Vise to Rel. Strain	.173	.462	.433			
Pl—Sec—Rem Clamp	.337	.705	1.073	1.441	1.809	2.177
Reset to Rel Strain Add'l	.113	.226	.338	.451	.564	.677
	.244	.488	.733	.977	1.221	1.465
Set Screw Only	.205	.370	.535	.700	.865	1.030
Tighten & Loosen Star Wh'l	.452	.521	.922	.989	1.390	1.456
Betw. Centers	.945					
Lock & Unlock Quick Cam	.216					
	.392	.785	1.177	1.570	1.962	2.354
Nut & "C" Washer	.323	.646	.968	1.291	1.614	1.937
Lock & Unlock Zagar Fixt.	.068					
Clamp Assy On & Off	.385	.769	1.154	1.538	1.923	2.308
Pl—Sec—Rem Slide Clamp of Fixt. Clamp	.332	.600	.868	1.368	1.405	1.673
T & L Knurled Screw By Hand	.068	.068	.137	.137	.205	.205
Pl—Sec-Rem "C" Clamp	.166	.331	.497	.662	.828	.994

Misc. Handling

Misc. Handling		Min's	Freq	Total
Index Splined Index Plate Reposition Locating Pin		.692		
Place & Remove Splined Index Plate & Locating Pin		.159		
Index Zagar Fixture Per 90°		.103		
Change Tools		.788		
Index Radial	Rapid Return	.207		
Table	Rapid & Set to Dial	.319		
	Set to Dial Only	.112		
	Total			

Machine Handling

Machine Handling		Duplex	Vert.	Horiz.	Freq	Min's
Tool to Cut & Return	Lgdl	.291	.343	.343		
	Cross		.245	.245		
	Head or Knee		.362	.362		
Set Tool To Dial	Lgdl		.295	.295		
	Cross		.356	.356		
Mach. Nos. 1756, 8029, 8030 4644, 8006, 1632, 1633, 1376	Head or Knee	.267	.403	.403		
	Lgdl		.589			
Set Tool To Dial Step Cutting	Lgdl & Head or Knee		.938			
	Cross & Head or Knee		1.005	1.005		
Mach. Nos. 1756, 8029, 8030, 4644, 8006, 1632, 1633, 1376	Lgdl & Cross			.876		
	Lgdl & Head or Knee		1.231			
	Total					

Figure 2-2. A sample milling form.

PART Alignment (e) (Use only when actually observed)

		Min.	Freq	Total
Check With Dial Indicator Per Linear Inch of Travel		.015		
Check With Dial Indicator 1st Spot		.235		
Check Add'l Spot With Dial Indica.		.074		
Aligh Part to Square		.293		
Check With Feeler Guage		.153		
Drive Wedge Under Part		.119		
Place & Adjust Jack Under Part		.269		
Add'l When Jack is Reset		.112		
Place & Remove Jo-Block	Group "A"	.166		
	Group "B"	.512		
TOTAL				

Machine Handling Add'l (f)

		Dupx	Vert	Horz	Freq	Total
Start & Stop Mach		.076	.076	.076		
Change Feed	Group A		.178	.178		
	Group B		.037	.037		
	Group C		.260			
Change Speed	Group A		.164	.164		
	Group B		.245	.245		
Total						

MEASURING (g)

		+.005	+.001		Freq	Total
O.D. Micrometer	0-1 Inch	.204	.222	.241		
Size of Micrometer	2-4 Inch	.235	.253	.272		
	5-6 Inch	.268	.286	.305		
	7-8 Inch	.284	.302	.320		
	9-11 Inch	.307	.326	.344		
Depth Micrometer		.218	.237	.255		
	Add'l Loca.	.084	.102	.121		
Vernier	12 Inch	.215	.266			
Caliper	24 Inch	.286	.337			
(Size of Cal.)	36 Inch	.315	.366			
Pine Gage	First Loca.	.607	.626	.644		
	Add'l Loca.	.155	.173	.192		
	Total					

MEASURING

		Min.	Freq	Total
Check w/Gage Block	First Spot	.158		
	Add'l Spot	.046		
check w/Feeler	First Spot	.143		
Gage	Add'l Spot	.031		
Check w/Height	First Dim.	.313		
Gage & Dial Indicator		.066		
Check w/Depth	First Dim.	.161		
Scale	Add'l Dim.	.048		
Check w/6" Scale	First Dim.	.085		
	Add'l Dim.	.059		
Check w/Tape Rule	To 12"	.185		
(Length Checked)	12"-24"	.190		
	24"-36"	.195		
	Total			

SET UP

	Dupx	Vert	Horz	Sund	Total
Std. Set Up Allowance	34.50	19.90	20.90	32.50	I
Study Print Complex	3.00	3.00	3.00	3.00	
Inspection Complex	5.00	5.00	5.00	5.00	
Select Parallels Ea	1.00	1.00	1.00	1.00	
Set Up Clamp-WorkStop Ea	1.30	1.30	1.30	1.30	
Change Adaptor	2.00	2.00	2.00	2.00	
Cutter to Adapter EA					
Add'l Per Gang	5.00	5.00	5.00	5.00	
Cutter	10.00	10.00	10.00	10.00	
Change Face Mill 8"-10"	3.00	1.50	1.00	1.50	
Change Face Mill 12"-16"	4.00	3.00	2.00	3.00	
Change Arbor		5.00	6.00	6.00	
Set Over Arm & Supports			4.00	6.00	
Set Support Braces				2.00	
Indicate/Occurance	5.00	5.00	5.00	5.00	
Tail Stock	7.00	7.00	7.00	7.00	
Vise	5.00	8.00			
Fixture Simple	5.00	12.00			
Fixture Complex	8.00	15.00			
Dividing Head	8.00	15.00			
Angle Plate	3.00	6.00			
Test Cut (Mach Time 1st Pc)					I
Rev. 1			Total Set Up Min -46-		

Notes:

SUMMARY

		Total
A	Part Handling	
B	Securing	
C	Misc. Handling	
D	Machine Handling	
E	Part Alignment	
F	Add'l Machine Handling	
G	Measuring	
X	SUB-TOTAL (MIN.)	
I	Balance	
H_1	Machine Time	
Y	Total Unit Cycle	
X	SUB-TOTAL (MIN.)	
H_2	Machine Time H.S.S.	
Z	Total Unit Cycle HSS	

Part Name:

Set Up Hrs. __
Unit Cycle Hrs. __

Y

Z

Part No. __
Drwg. No. __

Figure 2-2. A sample milling form (reverse side).

Where:

  Turning a shaft

Assume:

Load	.250	minutes
Process	1.000	minutes
Unload	.250	minutes
	1.500	at standard
	.300	allowances 20%
	1.800	expected actual time

Note that the 20% figure includes scrap, rework, off-standard and personal time.

Table 2-2 below summarizes the estimate: assume an estimating accuracy of ±15% on the labor content and ±3% on the machine time. Also assume a ±5% absolute accuracy on the allowances.

Table 2-2
Limits of Accuracy

	Standard Time	Minimum Time	Maximum Time
Load	.250	-15% = .210	+15% = .290
Process	1.000	- 3% = .970	+ 3% = 1.030
Unload	.250	-15% = .210	+15% = .290
Total	1.500	1.390	1.610
Accuracy Limits		$\frac{1.390}{1.500} = -7\%$	$\frac{1.610}{1.500} = +7\%$
Allowances	.300	+15% = .210	+25% = .400
Grand Total	1.800	1.600 min.	2.010 max.
Original estimate	1.800		
Minimum estimate	1.600 = -12%		
Maximum estimate	2.010 = +12%		

Our estimate now has an accuracy of ±7% before adding any allowances. Our overall accuracy has improved because we have assumed a better level of accuracy on the machine time. Because it is a function of speeds and feeds, machine time lends itself to more accurate estimating. Based on the assumption, can a computer program be written to achieve an accuracy of ±3% or better in the speeds and feeds calculations section of the program? Then, can the estimate developed by the computer be of some value to the Process Engineer who must process the part after an order has been booked? The astute reader will observe: If the answers to these questions are positive, computer cost estimating should be of value. *Table 2-3* shows different approaches of writing a computer program to perform cost estimating for a simple

Table 2-3
Programming Time vs. Level of Detail

Information Required	TYPE I PROGRAM		TYPE II PROGRAM		TYPE III PROGRAM		TYPE IV PROGRAM	
	User Input	CPU Calc.	User Input	CPU Calc.	User Input	CPU Calc.	User Input	CPU Calc.
1 Starting Dia	x		x				x	
2 Finished Dia	x		x		x		x	
3 No. of Cuts		x	x		x			x
4 Depth of Cut		x	x					x
5 Feed	x		x		x			x
6 RPM		x		x		x		x*
7 Tool Material	x		x				x	
8 SFPM		x	x		x			x
9 Machine Time		x		x		x		x*
10 Type of Material	x		x				x	
11 Rev. Req.		x		x		x		x*
12 Machine Correction	-	-	-	-	-	-		x*
DATA TOTAL	IN 5	OUT 6	IN 8	OUT 3	IN 4	OUT 3	IN 4	OUT 8
**Approximate Programming Time	20 Hrs.		3 Hrs.		2 Hrs.		30 Hrs.	

* *(Machine RPM is corrected to reflect what a specific machine must use.)*
** *(The amount of programming time stated above is relative to input and output and is not reflective of any actual programs written.)*

turning operation. There are several points to be made concerning the amount of time necessary to write a computer program versus the accuracy achieved, which will have an influence on the management decisions necessary before implementing the programming effort.

A Type I program assumes that the computer will calculate the SFPM required—based on a depth of cut, feed, material type, hardness and tool material. This type of program, in effect, is a time saver for the engineer developing the cost estimate. And, of equal importance, the output data can be used in the process planning activity.

The importance of this idea should be restated. With no more time, effort or cost, an estimate for quoting can be produced to an accuracy level of ±5% (illustrative). Then, if awarded a contract, the Manufacturing Engineer processing the part can use the same data in his process planning. Thus, we have created an estimate that serves two functions. Nevertheless, the time necessary to write a computer program which calculates SFPM is not short.

A Type II program reflects the other end of the spectrum. The user is required to input eight elements of data while the computer calculates only three. If the estimator is required to use a handbook for speeds, feeds and SFPM, or enters the data from memory, little has been accomplished. The user would have been further ahead if he had used a hand-held calculator.

A Type III program is similar to a Type II program but additional programming shortcuts are taken.

A Type IV program resembles a Type I program, but it is more sophisticated. The row labeled machine correction is defined as computer testing to establish a specific RPM and feed rate for a specific machine and then corrects the time value. For example, if the computer calculates that 1000 RPM (ideal) is required but the machine to be used has a gear ratio that produces either 863 or 1126 RPM, the computer will make the decision which to use. The same logic can be applied to feed rates also. It could be titled "artificial intelligence" when the computer is taught to make intelligent decisions; programming time to achieve this increases dramatically. Other restrictions could also be programmed, such as not exceeding the horsepower of the machine, or a tool life factor or surface finish requirement.

Management Decisions

At this point, here is a summary of some questions concerning the management decisions which are necessary before a computer routine for cost estimating can be written.
1. Write a computer program for turning.
2. Write the program so that the level of detail is of value for the engineer who will process the job.
3. Program the computer to make as many decisions as possible; i.e., speeds, feeds, machine selection.
4. Program the computer to make corrections for RPM and feed for a specific machine and respond to other restrictions.

These management decisions are basic to achieving the desired goals and have a dramatic influence on the amount of time required to write the program. By now, the reader must be asking: Is it worth the time necessary to achieve the goals? The author's answer is an unqualified yes.

This chapter contains two computer programs for cost estimating.

Uses of "SFPM"

The first program, named "SFPM," has four modules. Each module is a study in computerized cost estimating. Module I is Carbide Turning. The user is asked to input the following data for roughing and finishing.
1. Starting diameter.
2. Finished diameter.
3. Depth of cut, roughing.
4. Feed for roughing.
5. Depth of cut, finishing.
6. Feed for finishing.
7. Shop rate dollars.
8. Cost of carbide insert, each side.
9. Tool change time.

During the execution of this module, the user is asked to select one of the 20 different materials by AISI number and hardness. Several typical program outputs are shown on pages 43 through 45 and a program listing is shown from page 48 to page 50. From a cost estimating point of view, this module is written with several important factors in mind.

First, one very time-consuming problem the cost estimator is confronted with is selection of the SFPM that matches the material being processed. This problem generally requires looking up data in a handbook such as the *Valenite Handy Reference*. [2]More often than not, because of the time required, the cost estimator will substitute a guesstimate for SFPM. The first program module calculates that the SFPM should be based on a depth of cut and feed rate for a given type material. Detail on how this is calculated is provided later in this chapter.

Secondly, one of the things a computer does best is "crunch numbers." Using this ability, the first module provides two sets of calculations as output. One set of data is for a tool life, entered by the user, and the second set of data is for 60 minutes of tool life. The selection of SFPM and tool life is a balance between the time it takes to produce the part versus cost of the tooling and time to change that tooling. In cost estimating, it is desirable to calculate several costs to assure that the least expensive cost is used. However, in developing an estimate by hand this is seldom done because of the time involved.

Sample printouts of the first program module appear on the next several pages.

Note that each printout is for the same type material and that all data input is held constant except roughing depth of cut. A summary is shown below in *Table 2-4*.

Table 2-4
Summary of Computer Printouts

| | | 60 Minute Tool Life | | |
Roughing Depth	Number of Cuts	SFPM Rough	RPM Rough	Parts per Hour
.075	6	459	876	68.6
.100	4	441	842	90.3
.125	3	427	815	107.6

Note that SFPM varies as a function of depth of cut.

[2]*TM Valenite—registered trademark of the Valeron Corporation.*

COST ESTIMATE — CARBIDE TURNING

PART NAME GEAR PART NUMBER 82100

DATE 01/01/81

THE FOLLOWING DATA IS FOR TWO SETS OF TOOL LIFE

	FOR 60 MIN TOOL LIFE	FOR 240 MIN TOOL LIFE
SFPM ROUGH	459	247
SFPM FINISH	1107	597
RPM ROUGH	876	471
RPM FINISH	2114	1140
TOTAL CUTTING TIME	.874146	1.62476 MIN. PER. PC.
TOTAL COST	$ .277056	$ .43846
PARTS PER HOUR	68.6384	36.9285

THE MATERIAL IS AISI 1018,1020--BHN 150
STARTING DIA. WAS 3 INCHES. FINISHED DIA. IS 2 INCHES
LENGTH OF CUT 4 INCHES

ROUGHING DEPTH .075 INCHES AT .04 FEED PER REV.

FINISHING DEPTH .01 INCHES AT .01 FEED PER REV

THE TOTAL NUMBER OF CUTS TAKEN IS 6

SHOP RATE $ 15.25 DOLLARS PER HOUR AND INSERT COST $ 2.75 PER SIDE
TOOL CHANGE TIME 4 MIN. PER CHANGE

Printout 2-1

COST ESTIMATE — CARBIDE TURNING

PART NAME GEAR PART NUMBER 82100

DATE 01/01/81

THE FOLLOWING DATA IS FOR TWO SETS OF TOOL LIFE

	FOR 60 MIN TOOL LIFE	FOR 240 MIN TOOL LIFE
SFPM ROUGH	441	238
SFPM FINISH	1107	597
RPM ROUGH	842	454
RPM FINISH	2114	1140
TOTAL CUTTING TIME .664274		1.23193 MIN. PER. PC.
TOTAL COST	$ .210538	$ .332451
PARTS PER HOUR	90.3242	48.7039

THE MATERIAL IS AISI 1018,1020--BHN 150
STARTING DIA. WAS 3 INCHES. FINISHED DIA. IS 2 INCHES
LENGTH OF CUT 4 INCHES

ROUGHING DEPTH .1 INCHES AT .04 FEED PER REV.

FINISHING DEPTH .01 INCHES AT .01 FEED PER REV

THE TOTAL NUMBER OF CUTS TAKEN IS 4

SHOP RATE $ 15.25 DOLLARS PER HOUR AND INSERT COST $ 2.75 PER SIDE
TOOL CHANGE TIME 4 MIN. PER CHANGE

Printout 2-2

COST ESTIMATE — CARBIDE TURNING

PART NAME GEAR PART NUMBER 82100

DATE 01/01/81

THE FOLLOWING DATA IS FOR TWO SETS OF TOOL LIFE

	FOR 60 MIN TOOL LIFE	FOR 240 MIN TOOL LIFE
SFPM ROUGH	427	230
SFPM FINISH	1107	597
RPM ROUGH	815	439
RPM FINISH	2114	1140
TOTAL CUTTING TIME	.557313	1.03425 MIN. PER. PC.
TOTAL COST	$ .176637	$ .279103
PARTS PER HOUR	107.659	58.0131

THE MATERIAL IS AISI 1018,1020--BHN 150
STARTING DIA. WAS 3 INCHES. FINISHED DIA. IS 2 INCHES
LENGTH OF CUT 4 INCHES

ROUGHING DEPTH .125 INCHES AT   .04 FEED PER REV.

FINISHING DEPTH .01 INCHES AT   .01 FEED PER REV

THE TOTAL NUMBER OF CUTS TAKEN IS 3

SHOP RATE $ 15.25 DOLLARS PER HOUR AND INSERT COST $ 2.75 PER SIDE
TOOL CHANGE TIME 4 MIN. PER CHANGE

Printout 2-3

Questions

Shown below are the questions asked by the computer and the answers supplied by the user for the printout in this example.

THIS PROGRAM CALCULATES SFPM, RPM, TIME AND PARTS PER HOUR FOR THE FOLLOWING OPERATIONS. TYPE IN THE MODULE NUMBER YOU WISH TO USE.

TURNING CARBIDE 1
TURNING HIGH SPEED STEEL 2
DRILLING—GANG DRILL 3
MILLING 4
? **1**

(Note: The bold figures are the input by user.)

THIS MODULE IS FOR CARBIDE TURNING. THE FINAL PRINTOUT WILL SHOW THE FOLLOWING DATA. SFPM IS CALCULATED BY THE COMPUTER. A COST SUMMARY IS DEVELOPED FOR TWO CUTTING CONDITIONS. THE COMPUTER WILL CALCULATE COSTS FOR 60 MINUTE TOOL LIFE AND THE USER IS ASKED TO INPUT A TOOL LIFE CONDITION THAT IS LESS THAN 240 MINUTES FOR WHICH THE COMPUTER WILL CALCULATE THAT COST ALSO.
TYPE 1 TO SEE THE MATERIAL LIST ? **1.**
TYPE IN THE NUMBER NEXT TO THE MATERIAL YOU WISH TO WORK WITH:

1. —1018—1020—BHN 150
2. —1040—BHN 180
3. —1045—BHN 270
4. —1050—1060—52100—BHN 225
5. —1095—BHN 225
6. —1335—BHN 209
7. —3140—BHN 275
8. —4130—4340—5132—BHN 200
9. —4140—4340—5132—BHN 300
10. —4150—4815—BHN 250
11. —4320—BHN 200
12. —8620—BHN 175
? **1.**

AFTER SELECTING THE MATERIAL, ANSWER THE FOLLOWING QUESTIONS.

LENGTH OF CUT?	**4**
STARTING DIAMETER?	**3**
FINISHED DIAMETER?	**2**
ROUGH CUT TOOL DEPTH?	**.075**
FEED FOR THE ROUGHING CUT?	**.040**
FINISH CUT TOOL DEPTH?	**.010**
FEED FOR THE FINISHING CUT?	**.010**
SHOP RATE COST PER HOUR?	**15.25**
TOOL CHANGE TIME IN MINUTES	**4**

TOOL LIFE DESIRED, LESS THAN 240 MINUTES	**240**
COST OF ONE SIDE, CARBIDE INSERT?	**2.75**

If a Manufacturing Engineer were to develop a cost study similar to this one, at least an hour of the engineer's time would be required to provide all the necessary calculations on a hand-held calculator, versus approximately two minutes of input and printout by the computer. An off-standard factor could be included by adding a line to the program to multiply the standard time by the user plant's off-standard to revise the output accordingly.

Additional comments about this module

After reviewing the printouts which demonstrate the first module's capability, several comments should be made. This program module or one like it could be modified or written to include any of the following features: cubic inch metal removal, horsepower calculations, limits on SFPM or RPM (for a specific machine tool). If the program is designed for a specific machine tool, other features could be added, such as machine and/or manual functions, change speed or feed, index turret, load and unload time. To accomplish this, a GOSUB table for the manual part of the operation could be added for each machine in the program. The engineer establishes the program limits.

One of the courses the author teaches is Cost Estimating. In this course, students are taught the mechanics of "building" a cost estimate from Standard Data Tables. The student spends hours mentally reviewing each operation in respect to the detail of how the operation must be performed and then selects time data from tables to build the estimate. Much of this logic can be inserted in a computer program reflecting the sequence in which it happens. For example, if a part is being produced on a turret lathe and a turret is selected to perform a drilling element, the computer can be made to understand the manual elements necessary to index the turret, advance and return each time the turret is chosen to perform some work. The computer also can be taught to recognize when work should be considered internal to another element.

Once this perception is developed by the student, the routine becomes somewhat boring because of the repetition involved. This boredom, of course, leads to errors and the development of "rules of thumb" which cause more errors. The student, however, must develop this level of understanding to take the next step—computer programming of cost estimating routines. The engineer working in the field should already understand these mechanics.

Module II—Turning High-Speed Steel

On the next page is an example of turning—high-speed steel. The high speed turning module was written using the same format as the carbide module. Again, the reader is reminded that each module in this program could be considered a stand alone program. Without a reminder of this fact, the reader who may not have much computer programming experience might become discouraged when the entire program is viewed. In reviewing this printout, note that calculations are made for 60 minutes of tool life only. The reason for this is that a high-speed steel tool in a turning application has relatively short life between resharpenings.

Another interesting feature of Module II is its ability to print out a chart (see *Printout 2-4*). This chart shows the exponential relationship of SFPM to feed. The details of charting on a computer will be given in Chapter Eight.

COST ESTIMATE — HIGH SPEED TURNING

PART NAME SHAFT PART NUMBER 32000

DATE 01/01/81

THE FOLLOWING DATA IS FOR HIGH SPEED STEEL
AND FOR 60 MIN. TOOL LIFE

SFPM FOR ROUGHING IS 62
SFPM FOR FINISHING IS 156

RPM FOR ROUGHING IS 118
RPM FOR FINISHING IS 297

TOTAL TIME FOR THE ROUGH & FINISH CUTS IS 3.04172 MIN. PER PC.
TOTAL OPERATION COST IS $ .773103 DOLLARS PER PART

PARTS PER HOUR ARE 19.7257

STARTING DIAMETER WAS 2.5 INCHES. FINISHED DIAMETER IS 2 INCHES
LENGTH OF CUT IS 4 INCHES
ROUGHING DEPTH IS .1 INCHES AT .04 FEED PER REV.
FINISHING DEPTH IS .01 INCHES AT .01 FEED PER REV.
THE MATERIAL IS AISI 1018,1020--BHN 150
SHOP RATE COST PER HOUR IS $ 15.25

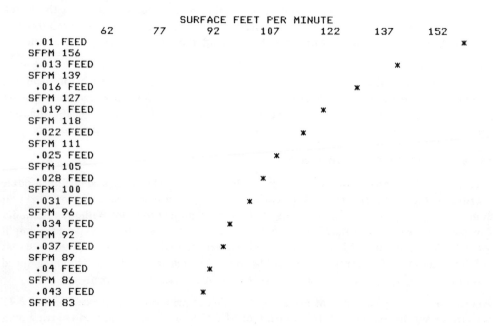

```
                          SURFACE FEET PER MINUTE
                62       77       92      107      122      137      152
  .01 FEED                                                              *
SFPM 156
  .013 FEED                                                    *
SFPM 139
  .016 FEED                                            *
SFPM 127
  .019 FEED                                    *
SFPM 118
  .022 FEED                               *
SFPM 111
  .025 FEED                          *
SFPM 105
  .028 FEED                       *
SFPM 100
  .031 FEED                    *
SFPM 96
  .034 FEED               *
SFPM 92
  .037 FEED              *
SFPM 89
  .04 FEED            *
SFPM 86
  .043 FEED          *
SFPM 83
```

Printout 2-4

COST ESTIMATE — HIGH SPEED TURNING

PART NAME SHAFT PART NUMBER 32101

DATE 01/01/81

THE FOLLOWING DATA IS FOR HIGH SPEED STEEL
AND FOR 60 MIN. TOOL LIFE

SFPM FOR ROUGHING IS 48
SFPM FOR FINISHING IS 121

RPM FOR ROUGHING IS   91
RPM FOR FINISHING IS 231

TOTAL TIME FOR THE ROUGH & FINISH CUTS IS 3.9294 MIN. PER PC.
TOTAL OPERATION COST IS $ .998724 DOLLARS PER PART

PARTS PER HOUR ARE 15.2695

STARTING DIAMETER WAS 2.5 INCHES. FINISHED DIAMETER IS 2 INCHES
LENGTH OF CUT IS 4 INCHES
ROUGHING DEPTH IS .1 INCHES AT .04 FEED PER REV.
FINISHING DEPTH IS .01 INCHES AT .01 FEED PER REV.
THE MATERIAL IS   AISI 1040--BHN 180
SHOP RATE COST PER HOUR IS $ 15.25

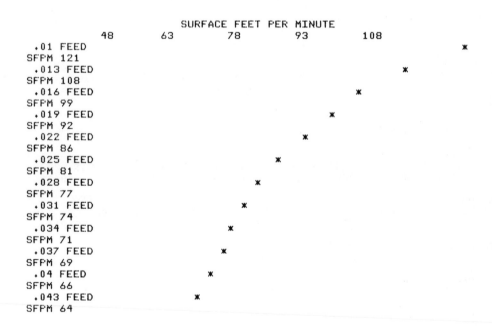

```
                       SURFACE FEET PER MINUTE
            48          63         78          93          108
 .01 FEED                                                              *
SFPM 121
 .013 FEED                                                        *
SFPM 108
 .016 FEED                                                   *
SFPM 99
 .019 FEED                                              *
SFPM 92
 .022 FEED                                         *
SFPM 86
 .025 FEED                                    *
SFPM 81
 .028 FEED                               *
SFPM 77
 .031 FEED                          *
SFPM 74
 .034 FEED                      *
SFPM 71
 .037 FEED                   *
SFPM 69
 .04 FEED               *
SFPM 66
 .043 FEED          *
SFPM 64
```

Printout 2-5

Module III—Gang Drilling

In several respects, Module III—Gang Drilling, is an example of a complete cost estimating routine and represents a completely different approach to computer programming.

First, it is a stand alone example of computer programming because it does not require the GOSUB routine from any of the other modules in the program. Secondly, in this module the user is asked to input the number of times he wishes to use other elements for each hole. For example, after the drill time has been calculated, the computer asks the user to type in the number of times he wishes to use the following elements: move jig, clean hole, inspect hole, spindle to and from work for each hole. Time values for each of these elements are in the computer program and then multiplied by the number of times the engineer wishes them to be used. At the end of the program, the user is asked to estimate the weight of the part. The computer program has load and unload time values in memory depending on the weight selected.

In the sample printout on this page, four holes are being drilled—1/4" (6.35 mm), 3/8" (9.525 mm), 1/2" (12.7 mm) and 3/4" (19.05 mm). The other elements include spindle to and from work and move the drill jig to the next spindle. A load and unload time of .3 minutes is included, and the drill time plus move time and load and unload are added together for a total of 1.927 minutes for the entire operation, or 31.13 parts per hour.

Also, note that setup allowances are included in this program. As stressed before, a computer should do what it does best and the engineer should do what he does best. The only user inputs necessary to execute this program are drill sizes and depth of holes. Selection of

```
COST  ESTIMATE  -  GANG  DRILLING
PART NAME BLOCK PART NUMBER 32110

                                     DATE 01/01/81

HOLE NUMBER 1
FOR A  .25  INCH DRILL 1  INCH HOLE LENGTH , USE 3.99988E-03 FEED 993.122 RPM
        DRILL TIME  .27062 OTHER ELEMENTS .1 TOTAL THIS HOLE .37062

HOLE NUMBER 2
FOR A  .375  INCH DRILL .5  INCH HOLE LENGTH , USE 5.5491E-03 FEED 662.081 RPM
        DRILL TIME  .166714 OTHER ELEMENTS .1 TOTAL THIS HOLE .266714

HOLE NUMBER 3
FOR A  .5  INCH DRILL 1  INCH HOLE LENGTH , USE 7E-03 FEED 496.561 RPM
        DRILL TIME  .330847 OTHER ELEMENTS .1 TOTAL THIS HOLE .430847

HOLE NUMBER 4
FOR A  .75  INCH DRILL 1.25  INCH HOLE LENGTH , USE 9.71123E-03 FEED 331.041 RPM
        DRILL TIME  .458814 OTHER ELEMENTS .1 TOTAL THIS HOLE .558814

TOTAL LOAD AND UNLOAD TIME IS .3
        TOTAL TIME FOR THE OPERATION IS 1.927

PARTS PER HOUR ARE 31.1366
TOTAL COST PER PART NOT INCLUDING SET UP IS $ .501019 DOLLARS PER PC.
TOTAL COST INCLUDING SET UP COSTS ARE:
    QUANITY THIS LOT 100 TOTAL $ .514019
    SET UP COSTS FOR THIS OPERATION ARE $  20.28
```

Printout 2-6

speeds and feeds is done internally by the program.

One last comment about the printer's role in this process. The engineer is not required to write any item on paper. The computer holds all the data in memory until the PRINT command is given. Writing is what the printer does best.

Module IV—Milling

For several reasons, writing a computer program for a milling operation is more difficult than might first appear.

First, the mill cutter approach must be calculated. There are five different variations of cutter approach and the user must choose the one he wishes to work with. Computer graphics is required to display the part cutter relationship on the screen for the user to view. The time required to write graphics can considerably extend the total programming time for the engineer. See Chapters One and Eight for a review of computer graphics.

Secondly, writing a program for milling operations is difficult because a milling machine can make a number of different types of cuts. Coupling this with both high-speed steel and carbide cutters provides a complex problem for speeds and feeds selection.

Module IV has the ability to calculate five different approaches for five different milling conditions for 10 different types of materials. While the program module itself is not very long, it should be pointed out that most of the programming effort went into writing the computer graphics part of the program.

When selecting this module, a graphics relationship of cutter-to-work is displayed on the screen. Examples of each of the five different cutter-part relationships are shown on the following pages along with the formulas necessary to calculate cutter approach. This program module shows five different milling conditions. The first is shown below.

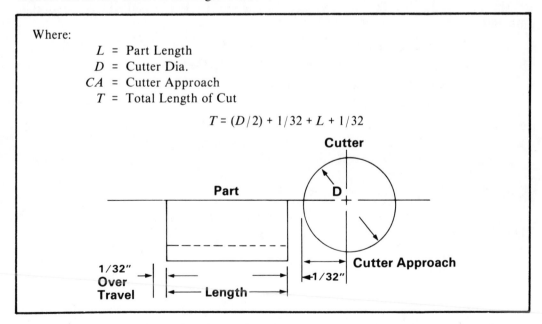

Where:

L = Part Length
D = Cutter Dia.
CA = Cutter Approach
T = Total Length of Cut

$$T = (D/2) + 1/32 + L + 1/32$$

Figure 2-3. This figure shows the relationship of the mill cutter to the work piece where the top of the work piece is on the center line of the cutter.

Where:

$$d = \text{Depth of Cut}$$
$$R = D/2$$
$$CA = \sqrt{R^2 - (R\text{-}d)^2}$$
$$T = CA + 1/32 + L + 1/32$$

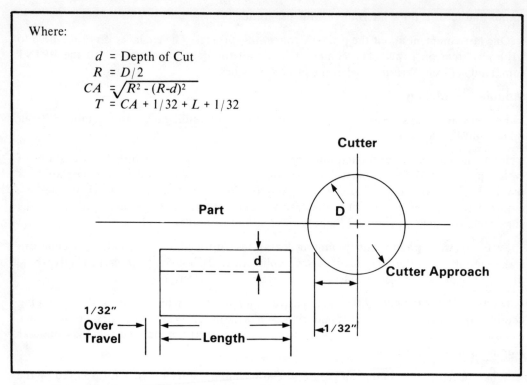

Figure 2-4. *In this cutter/part relationship, the part's top surface is below the center line of the cutter.*

There are several ways to show the round cutter on the CRT. The method selected for this program is shown in lines 6040 and 6050.

```
6040 FOR K = 4 TO 6 STEP .101: A = K * 3.14:
     R = 6: C = 2: D = C+ .101: X = D * (R * COS (A))

6050 Y = R * SIN (A): SET (X + 100, Y + 20):
     C = D: NEXT K
```

Where:

K = 4TO6 STEP .101 creates 10 steps in .1 increments.
A = K * 3.1417 starts the circle.
R = the circle radius.
Y = R * SIN(A) creates a sine curve.

The third and fourth graphics examples which appear on the screen are shown in *Figure 2-5* and *Figure 2-6.*

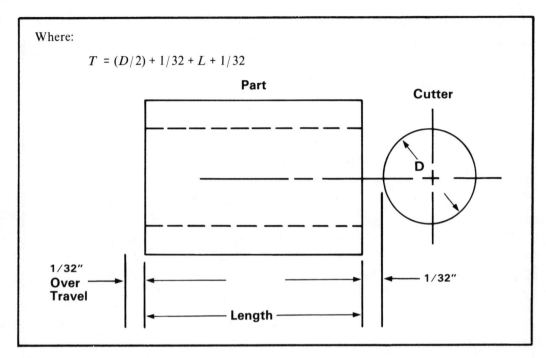

Where:

$$T = (D/2) + 1/32 + L + 1/32$$

Part

Cutter

D

1/32" Over Travel

1/32"

Length

Figure 2-5. This part/cutter relationship is valid for end milling or face milling.

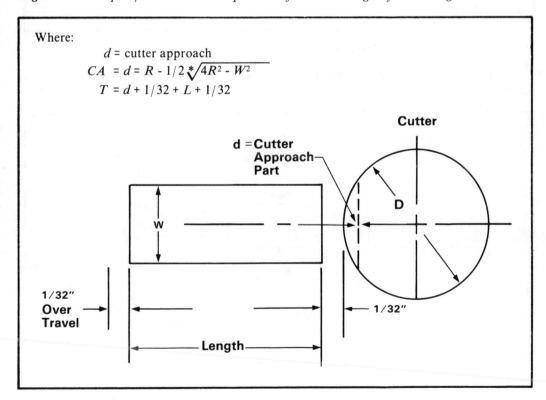

Where:

d = cutter approach

$$CA = d = R - 1/2 *\sqrt{4R^2 - W^2}$$

$$T = d + 1/32 + L + 1/32$$

Cutter

d =Cutter Approach

Part

D

W

1/32" Over Travel

1/32"

Length

Figure 2-6. The part center and cutter center lines are on the same plane.

The fifth example is shown in *Figure 2-7*.

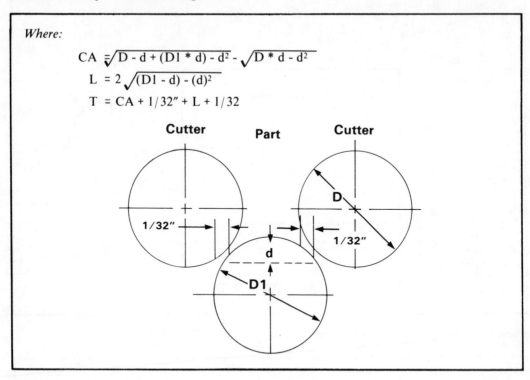

Where:

$$CA = \sqrt{D - d + (D1 * d) - d^2} - \sqrt{D * d - d^2}$$

$$L = 2\sqrt{(D1 - d) - (d)^2}$$

$$T = CA + 1/32'' + L + 1/32$$

Figure 2-7. *The part is round and the cutter produces a slot in the part.*

The printout for the milling module is for rough cutting and then finish cutting the part as shown below.

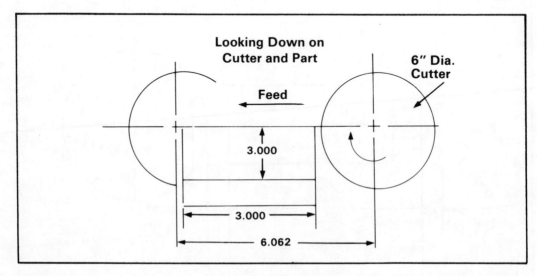

Figure 2-8. *This figure shows the relationship of a mill cutter to a workpiece as though you are looking down on the workpiece. The 6.062 is the total length of cut with approach and overtravel.*

```
COST ESTIMATE  -  MILLING
```

PART NAME BLOCK PART NUMBER 32109

DATE 01/01/81

THE FOLLOWING DATA IS FOR SLAB OR END MILLINGWITH A CARBIDE MILL - ROUGH CUT

THE TOTAL LENGTH OF CUT WITH APPROACH IS 6.062

RPM TO USE IS 95.4927

FEED IN INCHES PER MIN. IS 6.68449

TOTAL MILLING TIME IS .906875

TOTAL OPERATION TIME IS 1.21688

TOTAL PARTS PER HOUR ARE 49.3066

THE CUTTER DIA. IS 6
THE LENGTH OF CUT WITHOUT APPROACH IS 3
NUMBER OF TEETH IN THE CUTTER IS 10
LOAD AND UNLOAD TIME IS .25
NUMBER OF REVS REQUIRED IS 86.6

```
COST ESTIMATE  -  MILLING
```

PART NAME BLOCK PART NUMBER 32109

DATE 01/01/81

THE FOLLOWING DATA IS FOR SLAB OR END MILLINGWITH A CARBIDE MILL - FINISH CUT

THE TOTAL LENGTH OF CUT WITH APPROACH IS 6.062

RPM TO USE IS 127.324

FEED IN INCHES PER MIN. IS 6.11154

TOTAL MILLING TIME IS .991895

TOTAL OPERATION TIME IS 1.30189

TOTAL PARTS PER HOUR ARE 46.0867

THE CUTTER DIA. IS 6
THE LENGTH OF CUT WITHOUT APPROACH IS 3
NUMBER OF TEETH IN THE CUTTER IS 12
LOAD AND UNLOAD TIME IS .25
NUMBER OF REVS REQUIRED IS 126.292

Printout 2-7

This module is complete in the sense that it also includes other elements, load and unload as the gang drilling module did. The total roughing time on the first machine is 1.21688 minutes per piece. The total finishing time on the second machine is 1.30189 minutes per piece.

The "SFPM" program is reproduced in its entirety on the next several pages. Each module will be reviewed to point out the important aspects of computer programming in respect to the comments made earlier in this chapter concerning computer programs for cost estimating.

Program Name: "SFPM"

The memory required for this program is 17,251 bytes.

The "SFPM" program could be considered as four separate computer programs because each major module can be used by itself.

```
1 REM PROGRAM NAME SFPM
2 REM WRITTEN BY J.E.NICKS
3 REM COMPUTER APPLICATIONS FOR THE MANUFACTURING ENGINEER
4 REM COPYRIGHT 1981 ALL RIGHTS RESERVED
10 CLS
20 PRINT"THIS PROGRAM CALCULATES SFPM , RPM , TIME AND PARTS"
30 PRINT"PER HOUR FOR THE FOLLOWING OPERATIONS"
40 INPUT"ENTER THE PART NAME";W$
41 INPUT"ENTER THE PART NUMBER";X$
42 INPUT"ENTER TODAYS DATE I.E. 01/01/81";Y$
50 PRINT"TYPE IN THE MODULE NUMBER YOU WISH TO USE"
60 PRINT
70 PRINT"TURNING CARBIDE--------------------1"
80 PRINT"TURNING HIGH SPEED STEEL----------2"
90 PRINT"DRILLING --GANG DRILL------------3"
100 PRINT"MILLING---------------------------4"
110 INPUTN
120 ONNGOTO200,1000,2000,3000
200 REM TURNING CARBIDE
201 CLS
202 PRINT"THIS MODULE IS FOR CARBIDE TURNING"
203 PRINT"THE FINAL PRINT OUT WILL SHOW THE FOLLOWING DATA"
204 PRINT"SFPM IS CALCULATED BY THE COMPUTER"
205 PRINT"A COST SUMMARY IS DEVELOPED FOR 2 CUTTING CONDITIONS"
206 PRINT"THE COMPUTER WILL CALCULATE COSTS FOR 60 MIN. TOOL LIFE"
207 PRINT"AND THE USER IS ASKED TO INPUT A TOOL LIFE CONDITION"
208 PRINT"THAT IS LESS THEN 240 MIN.  FOR WHICH THE COMPUTER"
209 PRINT"WILL CALCULATE THAT COST ALSO":PRINT:PRINT:PRINT
210 INPUT"TYPE 1 TO SEE THE MATERIAL LIST";M
220 ONMGOSUB20000
221 CLS:PRINT"AFTER SELECTING THE MATERIAL , ANSWER THE FOLLOWING"
222 PRINT"QUESTIONS"
230 INPUT"LENGTH OF CUT";L
240 INPUT"STARTING DIAMETER";D1
250 INPUT"FINISHED DIAMETER";D2
260 INPUT"ROUGH CUT TOOL DEPTH";D3
270 INPUT"FEED FOR THE ROUGHING CUT";F1
280 INPUT"FINISH CUT TOOL DEPTH";D4
290 INPUT"FEED FOR THE FINISHING CUT";F2
300 INPUT"SHOP RATE COST PER HOUR";G
310 INPUT"TOOL CHANGE TIME IN MIN.";H
320 INPUT"TOOL LIFE DESIRED , LESS THEN 240 MIN. ";R4
325 INPUT"COST OF 1 SIDE ,CARBIDE INSERT";P
326 GOTO330
327 J=1
328 GOTO360
330 J1=(D1-D2)/2:J2=(J1-D4)/D3:J=INT(J2)
340 IFJ<1THEN327ELSE360
360 R1=D3/.03
370 S1=1/(R1[B)*C
380 R2=F1/.01
390 S2=INT(1/(R2[D)*S1)
400 R3=R4/60
410 S3=INT(1/(R3[A   )*S2)
420 Q1=D4/.03
430 S4=1/(Q1[B)*C
440 Q2=F2/.01
450 S5=INT(1/(Q2[D)*S4)
460 Q3=R4/60
470 S6=INT(1/(Q3[A)*S5)
```

User menu scrolls on the CRT (arrow pointing to lines 70–100)

Lines 360-470 calculate SFPM (arrow pointing to line 420)

Printout 2-8 continued

```
480  U1=INT(S2*3.8197/D2)
490  U2=INT(S5*3.8197/D2)          ◄─────── Lines 480-510 calculate RPM
500  U3=INT(S3*3.8197/D2)
510  U4=INT(S6*3.8197/D2)
520  V1=L/F1
530  V2=L/F2
540  W1=V1/U1
550  W2=V2/U2
560  W3=V1/U3
570  W4=V2/U4
580  W5=(W1*J)+W2               ◄─────── Lines 580-590 calculate time
590  W6=(W3*J)+W4
600  K=G/60
610  X1=K*W5
620  X2=K*W6
630  X3=K*H/(60/W5)
640  X4=K*H/(R4/W6)
650  X5=P/(60/W5)
660  X6=P/(R4/W6)
670  X7=X1+X3+X5
680  X8=X2+X4+X6
681  Z1=60/W5
682  Z2=60/W6
683  LPRINTCHR$(27);CHR$(14)"COST ESTIMATE - CARBIDE TURNING"
684  LPRINTCHR$(138):LPRINT"PART NAME ";W$;" PART NUMBER ";X$
685  LPRINTCHR$(138):LPRINT,,,"DATE ";Y$
686  FORI=1TO5:LPRINTCHR$(138):NEXTI
689  LPRINT"THE FOLLOWING DATA IS FOR TWO SETS OF TOOL LIFE"
690  LPRINT" "
691  LPRINTTAB(15);"FOR 60 MIN TOOL LIFE";TAB(40);"FOR";R4;"MIN TOOL LIFE"
692  LPRINT" "
700  LPRINT"SFPM ROUGH";TAB(18);S2;TAB(40);S3
710  LPRINT"SFPM FINISH";TAB(18);S5;TAB(40);S6
720  LPRINT" "
730  LPRINT"RPM ROUGH";TAB(18);U1;TAB(40);U3
740  LPRINT"RPM FINISH";TAB(18);U2;TAB(40);U4
750  LPRINT" "
760  LPRINT"TOTAL CUTTING TIME";TAB(18);W5;TAB(40);W6;" MIN. PER. PC."
761  LPRINT" "
770  LPRINT"TOTAL COST";TAB(18);"$";X7;TAB(40)"$";X8
780  LPRINT" "
790  LPRINT"PARTS PER HOUR";TAB(18);Z1;TAB(40);Z2
791  FORI=1TO3:LPRINT"  ":NEXTI
792  LPRINT"THE MATERIAL IS",A$
800  LPRINT"STARTING DIA. WAS";D1;" INCHES.  FINISHED DIA. IS ";D2; " INCHES"
810  LPRINT"LENGTH OF CUT";L;"INCHES"
811  LPRINT" "
820  LPRINT"ROUGHING DEPTH";D3;"INCHES AT ";F1;"FEED PER REV."
825  LPRINT" "
830  LPRINT"FINISHING DEPTH";D4;"INCHES AT ";F2;"FEED PER REV"
831  LPRINT" "
832  LPRINT"THE TOTAL NUMBER OF CUTS TAKEN IS";J
833  LPRINT" "
840  LPRINT"SHOP RATE $";G;"DOLLARS PER HOUR AND INSERT COST $";P;"PER SIDE"
850  LPRINT"TOOL CHANGE TIME ";H;" MIN. PER CHANGE"
851  INPUT" FOR ANOTHER CALCULATION TYPE 1 OR 2 TO EXIT";A
852  ONAGOTO4,860
860  END

1000 REM TURNING MODULE HHS
1010 PRINT"THIS HIGH SPEED TURNING MODULE PERMITS CALCULATION OF"
1020 PRINT"TIME,SPEED AND COST FOR 60 MIN. TOOL LIFE"
1021 INPUT"TYPE 1 TO SEE THE MATERIAL LIST";M
1030 IFM=1THEN1031
1031 GOSUB20000
```

Printout 2-8 continued

```
1032 CLS:PRINT"ENTER THE DATA FOR THIS OPERATION, AS ASKED FOR"
1033 PRINT:PRINT:PRINT
1040 INPUT"TYPE IN THE LENGTH OF CUT";L
1050 INPUT"TYPE IN THE STARTING DIAMETER";D1
1060 INPUT"TYPE IN THE FINISHED DIAMETER";D2
1070 INPUT"TYPE IN THE ROUGHING DEPTH OF CUT";D3
1080 INPUT"FEED FOR THE ROUGHING CUT";F1
1090 INPUT"TYPE IN THE FINISHING DEPTH OF CUT";D4
1100 INPUT"FEED FOR THE FINISHING CUT";F2
1110 INPUT"SHOP RATE, COST PER HOUR";G
1120 GOTO1150
1130 J=1
1140 GOTO1190
1150 J1=(D1-D2)/2
1160 J2=(J1-D4)/D3
1170 J=INT(J2)
1180 IFJ<1THEN1130
1190 R1=D3/.03
1200 S1=1/(R1[B)*C
1210 R2=F1/.01
1220 S2=INT(1/(R2[D)*S1)
1230 S3=INT(1 /(60[A1)*S2)
1240 Q1=D4/.03
1250 S4=1/(Q1[B)*C
1260 Q2=F2/.01
1270 S5=INT(1/(Q2[D)*S4)
1280 S6=INT(1/(60[A1)*S5)
1290 U3=INT(S3*3.8197/D2)
1300 U4=INT(S6*3.8197/D2)
1310 V1=L/F1
1320 V2=L/F2
1330 W3=V1/U3
1340 W4=V2/U4
1350 W6=(W3*J)+W4
1360 K=G/60
1370 X2=K*W6
1380 Z1=60/W6
1390 LPRINTCHR$(27);CHR$(14)"COST ESTIMATE - HIGH SPEED TURNING"
1391 LPRINTCHR$(138):LPRINT"PART NAME ";W$;" PART NUMBER ";X$
1392 LPRINTCHR$(138):LPRINT,,,"DATE ";Y$
1393 FORI=1TO5:LPRINTCHR$(138):NEXTI
1400 LPRINT"THE FOLLOWING DATA IS FOR HIGH SPEED STEEL"
1401 LPRINT"AND FOR 60 MIN. TOOL LIFE"
1410 LPRINT" "
1420 LPRINT"SFPM FOR ROUGHING IS";S3
1430 LPRINT"SFPM FOR FINISHING IS";S6
1440 LPRINT" "
1450 LPRINT"RPM FOR ROUGHING IS ";U3
1460 LPRINT"RPM FOR FINISHING IS";U4
1470 LPRINT" "
1480 LPRINT"TOTAL TIME FOR THE ROUGH & FINISH CUTS IS";W6;"MIN. PER PC."
1490 LPRINT"TOTAL OPERATION COST IS      $";X2;"DOLLARS PER PART"
1500 LPRINT" "
1510 LPRINT"PARTS PER HOUR ARE";Z1
1520 LPRINT" "
1530 LPRINT"STARTING DIAMETER WAS";D1;"INCHES. FINISHED DIAMETER IS";D2;"INCHES"
1540 LPRINT"LENGTH OF CUT IS";L;"INCHES"
1550 LPRINT"ROUGHING DEPTH IS";D3;"INCHES AT";F1;"FEED PER REV."
1560 LPRINT"FINISHING DEPTH IS";D4;"INCHES AT";F2;"FEED PER REV."
1570 LPRINT"THE MATERIAL IS  ";A$
1580 LPRINT"SHOP RATE COST PER HOUR IS      $";G
1585 CLS
1590 INPUT"TO PRODUCE A GRAPH OF SFPM VS. FEED TYPE 1";A4
1600 IFA4=1THEN1615
1610 IFA4<>1THEN1740
```

Printout 2-8 continued

```
1615 FORZ=1TO3:LPRINTCHR$(138):NEXTZ
1616 LPRINT"                    SURFACE FEET PER MINUTE"
1620 FORI=S3TOS6STEP15
1630 Z4=Z3+(X*50*(10/(S6-S3))+10):PRINTZ4,S6,S3,X
1631 LPRINTTAB(Z4);I;
1632 Z3=Z3+3
1640 X=X+1
1650 NEXTI
1660 LPRINT" "
1670 FORY=F2TOF1+.005STEP.003
1680 R2=Y/.01
1690 S2=INT(1/(R2[D)*S4)
1700 S7=INT(1/(60[A1)*S2)
1710 LPRINTY;TAB(5);"FEED";TAB((S7-S3)*(50/(S6-S3))+15);"*"
1720 LPRINT"SFPM";S7
1730 NEXTY
1740 END


2000 REM DRILLING MODULE
2001 CLS
2010 LPRINTCHR$(27);CHR$(14);"COST ESTIMATE - GANG DRILLING "
2011 LPRINTCHR$(138):LPRINT"PART NAME ";W$;" PART NUMBER ";X$
2012 LPRINTCHR$(138):LPRINT,,,"DATE ";Y$:FORI=1TO5:LPRINTCHR$(138):NEXTI
2015 PRINT"DRILLING MODULE"
2016 PRINT
2017 INPUT"ENTER SHOP RATE COST PER HOUR";Z
2018 INPUT"ENTER THE TOTAL QUANITY FOR THIS LOT";Z1
2020 PRINT"THIS PROGRAM CALCULATES TIME FOR GANG DRILLING"
2030 PRINT
2040 PRINT"UP TO 10 HOLES CAN BE ENTERED (PER SET UP)"
2045 PRINT"MATERIAL HARDNESS RANGE CAN BE FROM 150 TO 300 BHN"
2050 INPUT"TYPE IN MATERIAL HARDNESS BHN";H
2060 IFH=>150ANDH=<210THEN2110
2070 IFH=>211ANDH=<225THEN2120
2080 IFH=>226ANDH=<250THEN2130
2090 IFH=>251ANDH=<260THEN2140
2100 IFH=>261ANDH=<300THEN2150
2110 S=65:GOTO2160
2120 S=60:GOTO2160
2130 S=55:GOTO2160
2140 S=50:GOTO2160
2150 S=45:GOTO2160
2160 INPUT"HOW MANY HOLES ARE TO BE DRILLED IN THIS S/U";N
2161 SU=N*.25+.3
2170 PRINT"AFTER EACH ? TYPE IN THE SIZE OF THAT HOLE"
2180 PRINT"AND ANSWER THE OTHER QUESTIONS ASKED ON THE SCREEN"
2190 T=0:FORI=1TON
2200 INPUT"THE SIZE OF THIS HOLE IS";D(I)
2201 PRINT
2210 INPUT"THE LENGTH OF THIS HOLE IS";L
2219 REM FEED CALC
2220 F=((D(I)/.5)[.8074)*.007
2221 REM RPM
2230 R=S*3.8197/D(I)
2231 REM REV RQD
2240 L1=(L+(D(I)*.3))/F
2241 REM TIME
2250 T=L1/R:T1=T1+T
2251 PRINT
2260 PRINT"THE NEXT QUESTIONS ARE OTHER ELEMENTS FOR THIS HOLE"
2261 PRINT
2270 PRINT"ENTER THE TOTAL NO. OF TIMES USED OR 0 IF NOT USED"
2271 PRINT
2280 INPUT"CHANGE SPEED,FEED,ENGAGE FEED,COOLANT OFF OR ON";A
2281 PRINT
```

Lines 1615-1730 produce the graph

Lines 2060-2150—the computer selects SFPM based on materials hardness

Drill feed is calculated in Line 2220

Printout 2-8 continued

```
2290 A1=A*.05
2300 INPUT"MOVE JIG TO NEXT SPINDLE (INCLUDS TUMBLE)";B
2301 PRINT
2310 B1=B*.05
2320 INPUT"INSPECT HOLE AND OR CHANGE BUSHING";C
2321 PRINT
2330 C1=C*.1
2340 INPUT"SPINDLE TO , FROM , ON , OFF ";D
2341 PRINT
2350 D1=D1*.05
2360 INPUT"CLEAN HOLE";E
2370 E1=E*.1:F1=A1+B1+C1+D1+E1:G=F1+T1
2377 E1=E*.1:F1=A1+B1+C1+D1+E1:G=F1+T
2379 LPRINT"HOLE NUMBER";I
2380 LPRINT"FOR A ";D(I);" INCH DRILL";L;" INCH HOLE LENGTH , USE";F;"FEED";R;"R
PM"
2390 LPRINT"              DRILL TIME ";T;"OTHER ELEMENTS";F1;"TOTAL THIS HOLE";G
2395 LPRINT"          "
2400 T2=T2+G
2410 NEXTI
2420 PRINT"ESTIMATE THE PART WEIGHT & TYPE IN THE NUMBER THAT "
2421 PRINT
2430 PRINT"CORRESPONDS TO THE WEIGHT , FOR LOAD & UNLOAD"
2431 PRINT:PRINT
2440 INPUT"TO 5# (1): TO 10# (2): TO 20# (3): OVER 20# (4)";W
2450 ONWGOTO2460,2470,2480,2490
2460 W=.15:GOTO2491
2470 W=.3:GOTO2491        ◄──────── Lines 2460-2490 load and unload factors
2480 W=.55:GOTO2491
2490 W=1.05:GOTO2491
2491 LPRINT"TOTAL LOAD AND UNLOAD TIME IS";W
2492 LPRINT"              TOTAL TIME FOR THE OPERATION IS";T2+W
2501 LPRINTCHR$(138)
2510 T3=60/(T2+W)
2520 LPRINT"PARTS PER HOUR ARE";T3
2521 LPRINT"TOTAL COST PER PART NOT INCLUDING SET UP IS $";Z/T3;"DOLLARS PER PC.
"
2522 LPRINT"TOTAL COST INCLUDING SET UP COSTS ARE:"
2523 LPRINT"      QUANITY THIS LOT";Z1;"TOTAL $";(SU/Z1)+(Z/T3)
2525 LPRINT"      SET UP COSTS FOR THIS OPERATION ARE $ ";SU*Z
2530 INPUT"FOR ANOTHER SERIES OF HOLES FOR THIS PART   TYPE 1 OR 2 TO EXIT";X
2540 ONXGOTO2000,2550
2550 END


3000 REM MILLING MODULE:CLEAR100
3010 PRINT"THIS PROGRAM CALCULATES MILLING TIME FOR"
3020 PRINT"HSS AND CARBIDE CUTTERS & FOR 5 DIFFERENT"
3030 PRINT"MILLING CONDITIONS. TYPE 1 TO SEE THE FIRST CONDITION"
3040 PRINT"OR TYPE 1 TO 5 TO SEE ANY OF THE CONDITIONS"
3050 INPUTN:ONNGOTO3060,3150,3270,3390,3490
3060 GOSUB6000
3070 FORX=15956TO15971:POKEX,176:NEXTX
3080 FORY=15828TO15956STEP64:POKEY,170:NEXTY
3090 FORY=15843TO15971STEP64:POKEY,149:NEXTY
3100 PRINT@768,"FOR THIS 1ST CONDITION THE PART IS ON THE SAME"
3110 PRINT@832,"CENTER AS THE CUTTER. THIS CONDITION IS VALID"
3120 PRINT@896,"FOR SLAB OR END MILLING"
3130 PRINT@960,"FOR THE NEXT CONDITION TYPE 2":INPUTN
3140 ONNGOTO3150
3150 GOSUB6000
3160 FORX=15829TO15842:POKEX,176:NEXTX
3170 FORX=15956TO15971:POKEX,176:NEXTX
3180 FORX=15892TO15907:POKEX,136:NEXTX
3190 FORY=15892TO15956STEP64:POKEY,170:NEXTY
3200 FORY=15907TO15971STEP64:POKEY,149:NEXTY
```

Printout 2-8 continued

```
3210 X=15828:POKEX,160:X=15843:POKEX,144
3220 PRINT@768,"FOR THIS 2ND CONDITION THE PART IS BELOW"
3230 PRINT@832,"THE CENTER LINE OF THE CUTTER. THIS CONDITION"
3240 PRINT@896,"IS VALID FOR SLOT MILLING"
3250 PRINT@960,"FOR THE NEXT CONDITION TYPE 3 ":INPUTN
3260 ONNGOTO3270
3270 GOSUB6000
3280 FORX=15572TO15587:POKEX,131:NEXTX
3290 FORX=15636TO15651:POKEX,130:NEXTX
3300 FORX=15956TO15971:POKEX,176:NEXTX
3310 FORX=15892TO15907:POKEX,144:NEXTX
3320 FORY=15572TO15956STEP64:POKEY,170:NEXTY
3330 FORY=15587TO15971STEP64:POKEY,149:NEXTY
3340 PRINT@768,"FOR THIS 3RD CONDITION THE PART IS WIDER"
3350 PRINT@832,"THEN THE CUTTER. THIS CONDITION IS VALID"
3360 PRINT@896,"FOR FACE MILLING OR END MILLING"
3370 PRINT@960,"FOR THE NEXT CONDITION TYPE 4":INPUTN
3380 ONNGOTO3390
3390 GOSUB6000
3400 FORX=15700TO15715:POKEX,176:NEXTX
3410 FORX=15828TO15843:POKEX,176:NEXTX
3420 FORY=15764TO15828STEP64:POKEY,191:NEXTY
3430 FORY=15779TO15843STEP64:POKEY,191:NEXTY
3440 PRINT@768,"FOR THIS 4TH CONDITION THE PART IS ON THE SAME"
```

Graphics showing part-cutter relationship is generated by poke statements

```
3450 PRINT@832,"CENTER AS THE CUTTER AND IS SMALLER THEN THE"
3460 PRINT@896,"CUTTER. THIS CONDITION IS VALID FOR FACE OR "
3470 PRINT@960,"END MILLING. FOR THE LAST CONDITION TYPE 5":INPUTN
3480 ONNGOTO3490
3490 GOSUB6000
3500 FORX=15956TO15976:POKEX,140:NEXTX
3510 FORK=4TO6STEP.101:A=K*3.14:R=6:C=2:D=C+.101:X=D*(R*COS(A))
3520 Y=R*SIN(A):SET(X+60,Y+28):C=D:NEXTK
3525 FORX=15898TO15906:POKEX,132:NEXTX
3530 PRINT@768,"FOR THIS LAST CONDITION THE PART IS ROUND"
3540 PRINT@832,"THIS CONDITION IS VALID FOR SLOT MILLING"
3550 PRINT@896,"TYPE IN THE CONDITION YOU WISH TO WORK WITH"
3560 PRINT@960,"OR TYPE 6 TO START OVER"
3570 INPUTN
3580 ONNGOTO3730,3780,3840,3840,3890
3730 REM LC FOR COND
3731 ZZ$="SLAB OR END MILLING"
3732 PRINTZZ$
3740 INPUT"THE CUTTER DIA";D
3750 INPUT"THE LENGTH OF CUT TO BE MILLED IS";L
3760 L1=L+(D/2)+.062
3770 GOTO3965
3780 REM LC FOR COND 2
3781 ZZ$="SLOT MILLING"
3790 INPUT"THE CUTTER DIA. IS";D
3800 INPUT"LENGTH OF THE WORK TO BE MILLED ";L
3810 INPUT"WIDTH OF THE MILL CUT";W
3811 R2=D/2:R3=R2[2:R4=R2-W:R5=R4[2:R6=SQR(R3-R5)
3820 L1=L+R6+.062
3830 GOTO3965
3840 REM LC FOR COND 3&4
3841 ZZ$="FACE OR END  MILLING"
3850 INPUT"THE CUTTER DIA. IS";D
3851 INPUT"LENGTH OF THE PART TO BE MILLED";L
3860 INPUT"THE WIDTH OF THE SLOT OR PART (COND 3 OR 4) IS";W
3861 R2=D/2:R3=(R2[2)*4:W1=W[2:R4=SQR(R3-W1)/2
3862 R5=R2-R4:L1=L+R5+.062
```

Printout 2-8 continued

```
3880 GOTO3965
3890 REM LC FOR COND 5
3891 ZZ$="SLOT MILLING OF A ROUND PART"
3900 INPUT"CUTTER DIA. IS";D
3910 INPUT"DEPTH OF THE MILLED SLOT IS";D1
3920 INPUT"DIA. OF THE WORK IS";D2
3930 D3=D2/2:D4=D1[2:D5=(2*D1*D3)-D4
3931 L=SQR(D5)*2
3932 A1=D-D1+(D2*D1)-D1[2:A2=SQR(A1)
3933 A3=(D*D1)-D1[2:A4=SQR(A3):A5=A2-A4
3950 L1=L+A5+.062
3960 GOTO3965
3965 INPUT"TYPE 1 TO SEE THE MATERIAL LIST";X
3966 IFX=1THEN3971
3971 GOSUB4000
3972 PRINT"THERE ARE 5 TYPES OF MILLING CONDITIONS THE PROGRAM CALCULATES"
3973 PRINT"TYPE IN THE NUMBER AFTER THE CONDITION YOU WISH"
3974 PRINT"1------CARBIDE FACE MILLING , ROUGH CUT"
3975 PRINT"2------CARBIDE FACE MILLING , FINISH CUT"
3976 PRINT"3------CARBIDE END MILLING" ,
3977 PRINT"4------HIGH SPEED STEEL FACE MILLING"
3978 PRINT"5------HIGH SPEED END MILLING"
3979 INPUTN
3980 ONNGOTO5000,5040,5080,5120,5160
4000 PRINT"MATERIAL SELECTION AND HARDNESS"
4010 PRINT"TYPE IN THE MATERIAL NO. YOU WISH TO WORK WITH"
4020 PRINT"1----ALUMINUM OR MAGNESIUM BHN 21-118"
4030 PRINT"2---BRASS OR BRONZE "
4040 PRINT"3---CAST IRON BHN 150-180"
4050 PRINT"4---CAST OR MALLEABLE IRON BHN 180-225"     ← Lines 4000-4120
4060 PRINT"5---CAST IRON BHN 225-350"                      material menu
4070 PRINT"6---CAST STEEL."
4080 PRINT"7---STEEL BHN 100-150"
4090 PRINT"8---STEEL BHN 150-250"
4100 PRINT"9---STEEL OR STAINLESS BHN 250-350"
4110 PRINT"10--STEEL BHN 350-450"
4120 INPUTN
4130 ONNGOTO4150,4160,4170,4180,4190
4140 ONN-5GOTO4200,4210,4220,4230,4240
4141 REM A=FEED RC,B=SFPM RC,C=FEED FC,D=SFPM FC
4142 REM E=FEED EM =C,F=SFPM EM=D
4143 REM MG=HSSRSFPM,H=HSSRFEED,I=HSSFSFPM,J=HSSFFEED
4150 A=.02:B=1500:C=.007:K=2250:E=C:F=K:G=.02:H=400:I=.01:J=700
4151 RETURN
4160 A=.015:B=350:C=.007:K=500:E=C:F=K:G=.009:H=200:I=.005:J=300
4161 RETURN
4170 A=.02:B=325:C=.01:K=500:E=C:F=K:G=.016:H=80:I=.008:J=120    ← Lines 4150-4241
4171 RETURN                                                        contain all
4180 A=.011:B=230:C=.007:K=350:E=C:F=K:G=.013:H=60:I=.007:J=110    speeds and feeds
4181 RETURN                                                        for the milling
4190 A=.007:B=150:C=.004:K=200:E=C:F=K:G=.011:H=50:I=.006:J=90     module
4191 RETURN
4200 A=.008:B=150:C=.005:K=300:E=C:F=K:G=.012:H=50:I=.006:J=80
4201 RETURN
4210 A=.012:B=600:C=.007:K=700:E=C:F=K:G=.01:H=90:I=.005:J=120
4211 RETURN
4220 A=.012:B=375:C=.007:K=500:E=C:F=K:G=.008:H=80:I=.004:J=90
4221 RETURN
4230 A=.012:B=250:C=.003:K=350:E=C:F=K:G=.006:H=70:I=.003:J=80
4231 RETURN
4240 A=.012:B=150:C=.007:K=225:E=C:F=K:G=.004:H=150:I=.002:J=60
4241 RETURN
5000 PRINT"THIS SECTION CALCULATES CARBIDE FACE MILLING , ROUGH"
5001 ZX$="WITH A CARBIDE MILL - ROUGH CUT"
5010 INPUT"NUMBER OF TEETH IN THE CUTTER";N
```

Printout 2-8 continued

```
5020 R=(B*12)/(D*3.1416):F1=A*N*R:R1=L1/(A*N):T=R1/R
5030 GOTO5200
5040 PRINT"THIS SECTION CALCULATES CARBIDE FACE MILLING , FINISH"
5041 ZX$="WITH A CARBIDE MILL - FINISH CUT"
5050 INPUT"NUMBER OF TEETH IN THE CUTTER";N
5060 R=(K*12)/(D*3.1416):F1=C*N*R:R1=L1/(C*N):T=R1/R
5070 GOTO5200
5080 PRINT"THIS SECTION CALCULATES CARBIDE END MILLING"
5081 ZX$="USING A CARBIDE END MILL"
5090 INPUT"NUMBER OF TEETH IN THE CUTTER";N
5100 R=(F*12)/(D*3.1416):F1=E*N*R:R1=L1/(E*N):T=R1/R
5110 GOTO5200
5120 PRINT"THIS SECTION CALCULATES HSS FACE MILLING"
5121 ZX$="USING A HIGH SPEED FACE MILL"
5131 INPUT"NUMBER OF TEETH IN THE CUTTER";N
5140 R=(H*12)/(D*3.1416):F1=G*N*R:R1=L1/(G*N):T=R1/R
5150 GOTO5200
5160 PRINT"THIS SECTION CALCULATES HSS END MILLING"
5161 ZX$="USING A HIGH SPEED END MILL"
5170 INPUT"NUMBER OF TEETH IN THE CUTTER";N
5180 R=(J*12)/(D*3.1416):F1=I*N*R:R1=L1/(I*N):T=R1/R
5190 GOTO5200
5200 REM OTHER ELEMENTS
5210 PRINT"THE NEXT SERIES OF QUESTIONS ARE FOR OTHER ELEMENTS"
5220 PRINT"TYPE IN THE NUMBER OF TIMES YOU WISH"
5230 PRINT"EACH ELEMENT TO BE USED OR 0 IF NOT USED"
5241 INPUT"RAPID ADVANCE TO OR FROM WORK";M
5250 M1=M*.03
5260 INPUT"COOLANT ON OR OFF OR ADJUSTED";P
5270 P1=P*.04
5280 INPUT"START AND OR STOP CYCLE";Q
5290 Q1=Q*.03
5300 PRINT"LOAD AND UNLOAD"
5310 PRINT"TYPE IN THE NUMBER THAT CORRESPONDS TO THE PART WEIGHT"
5320 INPUT"TO 5# (1),TO 10# (2),TO 15# (3),OVER 20# (4)";U
5330 ONUGOTO5340,5341,5342,5343
5340 U=.25:GOTO5350
5341 U=.4:GOTO5350
5342 U=.9:GOTO5350
5343 U=1.15:GOTO5350
5350 T2=T+U+M1+P1+Q1
5351 LPRINTCHR$(27);CHR$(14)"COST ESTIMATE - MILLING"
5352 LPRINTCHR$(138):LPRINT"PART NAME ";W$;" PART NUMBER ";X$
5353 LPRINTCHR$(138):LPRINT,,,"DATE ";Y$:FORI=1 TO 5 :LPRINTCHR$(138):NEXTI
5360 LPRINT"THE FOLLOWING DATA IS FOR ";ZZ$ ; ZX$
5361 LPRINT:LPRINT" "
5370 LPRINT"THE TOTAL LENGTH OF CUT WITH APPROACH IS";L1
5380 LPRINTCHR$(138)
5390 LPRINT"RPM TO USE IS";R
5400 LPRINTCHR$(138)
5410 LPRINT"FEED IN INCHES PER MIN. IS ";F1
5420 LPRINTCHR$(138)
5430 LPRINT"TOTAL MILLING TIME IS";T
5440 LPRINTCHR$(138)
5450 LPRINT"TOTAL OPERATION TIME IS";T2
5460 LPRINTCHR$(138)
5470 LPRINT"TOTAL PARTS PER HOUR ARE";60/T2
5471 LPRINTCHR$(138)
5472 LPRINT"THE CUTTER DIA. IS";D
5473 LPRINT"THE LENGTH OF CUT WITHOUT APPROACH IS";L
5474 LPRINT"NUMBER OF TEETH IN THE CUTTER IS";N
5475 LPRINT"LOAD AND UNLOAD TIME IS";U
5476 LPRINT"NUMBER OF REVS REQUIRED IS";R1
5480 INPUT"TO CALCULATE ANOTHER CUT TYPE 1 OR 2 TO EXIT";Z
5490 ONZGOTO3000,5500
```

Printout 2-8 continued

```
5500 END
6000 CLS
6010 PRINT@148,"PART":PRINT@165,"CUTTER"
6020 FORX=15744TO15807:POKEX,176:NEXTX
6030 FORY=15538TO16050STEP64:POKEY,170:NEXTY
6040 FORK=4TO6STEP.101:A=K*3.14:R=6:C=2:D=C+.101:X=D*(R*COS(A))
6050 Y=R*SIN(A):SET(X+100,Y+20):C=D:NEXTK
6060 RETURN
```

Lines 6000-6060 are the graphics that produce the mill and cutter circle. It is used six times from one GOSUB

```
20000 PRINT"TYPE IN THE NUMBER NEXT TO THE MATERIAL"
20001 PRINT"YOU WISH TO WORK WITH"
20010 PRINT"1--1018--1020--BHN 150"
20020 PRINT"2--1040--BHN--180I"
20030 PRINT"3--1045--BHN 270"
20040 PRINT"4--1050--1060--52100--BHN 225"
20050 PRINT"5--1095--BHN 225"
20055 PRINT"6--1335 BHN 209"
20060 PRINT"7--3140--BHN 275"
20080 PRINT"8--4130--4340--6150--BHN 200"
20090 PRINT"9--4140--4340--5132--BHN 300"
20100 PRINT"10-4150--4815--BHN 250"
20110 PRINT"11-4320--BHN 200"
20120 PRINT"12-8620--BHN 175"
20130 INPUTM
20140 ONMGOTO20170,20180,20190,20200,20210
20150 ONM-5GOTO20220,20230,20240,20250,20260
20160 ONM-10GOTO20270,20280
20170 A=.4445:B=.1423878:C=947:D=.4274194:A1=.478
20171 A$="AISI 1018,1020--BHN 150":RETURN
20180 A=.4445:B=.1403315:C=766:D=.4268478:A1=.488
20181 A$="AISI 1040--BHN 180":RETURN
20190 A=.4445:B=.144557:C=451:D=.4244958:A1=.415
20191 A$="AISI 1045--BHN 270 ":RETURN
20200 A=.4445:B=.1398564:C=552:D=.4295068:A1=.425
20201 A$="AISI 1050,1060,52100--BHN 225":RETURN
20210 A=.4445:B=.1403514:C=507:D=.4276384:A1=.44
20211 A$="AISI 1095--BHN 225":RETURN
20220 A=.4445:B=.1416237:C=631:D=.4285519:A1=.449
20221 A$="AISI 1335--BHN 209":RETURN
20230 A=.4445:B=.1415539:C=428:D=.4249875:A1=.425
20231 A$="AISI 3140--BHN 275":RETURN
20240 A=.4445:B=.1412583:C=654:D=.427253:A1=.457
20241 A$="AISI 4130,4340,6150--BHN 200":RETURN
20250 A=.4445:B=.1424077:C=383:D=.4275653:A1=.454
20251 A$="AISI 4140,4340,5132--BHN 300":RETURN
20260 A=.4445:B=.143763:C=485:D=.424931:A1=.454
20261 A$="AISI 4150,4815--BHN 250":RETURN
20270 A=.4445:B=.1411354:C=676:D=.4268544:A1=.445
20271 A$="AISI 4320--BHN 200":RETURN
20280 A=.4445:B=.142019:C=800:D=.4276947:A1=.475
20281 A$="AISI 8620--BHN 175":RETURN
20290 END
```

This sub routine contains all of the exponents for the SFPM calculations. Also note that this section of the program can be used in any turning program.

Printout 2-8 continued

Program Summary

There are four possible methods that "SFPM" can be handled by the programmer.
1. Let the user (engineer) look up the SFPM for the material being used. If guess work is used, the computer is not necessary.
2. Write the program with a shortcut version of "SFPM". The drilling module is an example of this method. Reference is made to lines 2060 through 2150. Based on the material's brinell hardness, the computer selects one of five preprogrammed "SFPM's".
3. Write the program with a massive GOSUB where speeds and feeds are in memory. The milling module is written in this manner. Reference is made to lines 4000 through 4241. In this section of the program, the user selects one of 10 different types of materials. After the user enters the material number, the computer selects all of the fixed variables from a GOSUB table. Lines 4141 through 4143 define these variables with REM statements. Only those variables needed for a specific type cut and cutter are used. Others are discarded in memory.
4. Modules I and II contain the feature of calculating surface feet-per-minute. There is very little in print on this subject. However, the steps necessary to perform these calculations are on the next several pages.

Steps for calculating constants in "SFPM" program

Modules I & II

The *Valenite Handy Reference* was used as a reference. As an example: AISI 1018-1020 BHN 150 shows a relationship of 947 SFPM for .010 feed and .030 depth of cut. The constants used in the "SFPM" program are a series of exponents for each type material and are calculated as follows :

1. Hold feed constant and calculate the exponent for depth of cut. At .010 feed:

$$\text{Hi SFPM} = 947 \ @ \ .030 \text{ depth of cut} = DC \ 1$$
$$\text{Lo SFPM} = 858 \ @ \ .060 \text{ depth of cut} = DC \ 2$$

Where:

$$DC \ 2 = 2 * DC \ 1$$

$$\frac{947}{858} = \frac{.030}{.060} = \frac{H}{L} = \left(\frac{DC \ 2}{DC \ 1}\right)^{-b} = X = (2)^{-b}$$

$$\frac{947}{858} = \frac{.030}{.060} = \frac{\log X}{\log 2} = {}^{-b(exp)}$$

$$\frac{\log 1.10372}{\log 2} = \frac{.042863}{.30103} = .1423878^{-b \ (exp)}$$

2. Hold depth of cut constant and determine exponent for feed (same formula). At .060 depth of cut:

$$\frac{858}{638} = \frac{.010 \text{ feed}}{.020 \text{ feed}} = \frac{H}{L} = \left(\frac{f1}{f2}\right)^{-b} = X = (2)^{-b}$$

$$\frac{858}{638} = \frac{.010}{.020} = \frac{\log X}{\log 2} = {}^{-b \ (exp)}$$

$$\frac{\log 1.3448275}{\log 2} = \frac{.121666}{.030103} = .4274191 ^{-b \ (exp)}$$

3. Determine exponent for tool life.

$$Y = a \ N^b$$

Where:

Y = SFPM at 240 minute tool life
a = starting SFPM
N = ratio of desired tool life/60
$-b$ = exponent = -.4445

Example:

AISI 1018 at 150 BHN = 947 SFPM.

Where:

Feed = .010 and depth of cut = .030 at 60 minute tool life.
$$Y = 947 * (240/60)^{-.4445}$$
$$947 * 4^{-.4445} = 511.3$$

In this case, the *Valenite Handy Reference* booklet uses 511.

The "SFPM" program uses these exponents and constants to calculate any point in the Valenite table. Line 20170 in the program states:

A = .4445 (tool life constant exponent)
B = .1423878 (exponent for depth of cut)
C = 947 (starting SFPM)
D = .4274191 (exponent for feed)

The A1 constant is used for high-speed steel only. Because the computer will not calculate negative exponents, all factors are converted to positive exponents and the equation is divided into 1 in the program. Approximately the same figures can be calculated using log-log paper and the graphing method. However, this method is not as accurate as calculating them by computer.

In the main body of the program, the INT (X) (integer statement) is used to remove the decimal points. Therefore, the final SFPM figures produced are nearly the same as the Valenite booklet.

Program Name: "FORGE"

This program requires 11,500 bytes.

The program is an important example of cost estimating. This program was developed and written by two of my engineering students, Mark Pulsipher and Edward Petee, and follows the cost estimating form shown on page 69.

Note the programming style used to write this program. First, typical operations are presented in "menu" style. Forging processes such as block, forge, restrike and trim are shown in the menu. When the user has completed "processing" the forging, he types *8* which terminates the FOR-NEXT loop. This programming approach is important to review because it represents the way most cost estimating programs should be written.

The next important feature about the "FORGE" program is that the user is asked to input a production rate for each operation selected; (i.e., what are the number of pieces per hour?). This approach demonstrates that there is more than one way an estimate can be made. This comment is made to call attention to the fact that developing a computer estimating routine in this manner has some of the inaccuracies that standard data estimating forms have.

The engineering students who wrote this program were asked to develop it using the cost estimating form as their programming format. This explains the reason for treating the production rate as they did. These same two students demonstrated the program at a forging convention. The reaction of some of the attendees was one of amazement. The attendees reviewing the program output were amazed that a microcomputer could develop an estimate including all the cost factors in such a short period.

One last comment about programming style using the "FORGE" program as an example. All costs per hour for each machine, operator and operator's helper are programmed. This reduces the input by the user. Once each quarter these figures can be edited and updated as new accounting figures are available.

```
5 REM LIST OF VARIBLES
10 A$ = "*** FORGE ESTIMATE ***":B$="DATE OF INQUIRY":C$="CUSTOMERS NAME"
15 D$="CUSTOMERS ADDRESS":E$="ANNUAL QUANTITY":F$="PART NAME":G$="PART NUMBER":H
$="OPERATION SELECTION"
20 K$="1) BLANK OR BLOCK":L$="2) FORGE":M$="3) UPSET":N$="4) RESRIKE"
25 O$="5) TRIM (HOT-COLD)":P$="6) PUNCH":Q$="7) ROUGH GRIND":R$="8) SELECTION OF
 OPERATIONS COMPLETED"
100 CLS:PRINT:PRINT,A$
102 PRINT:PRINT"TO CLEAR SREEN OF INSTRUCTIONS ENTER -1- "
105 PRINT:PRINT"YOU MAY USE UP TO THREE DIFFERENT RUN QUANTITIES TO COMPARE THE
COST AND TIME REQD.  THE FIRST TIME THRU THE PROGARM YOU WILL BEREQUIRED TO ENTE
R THE NECESSARY DATA.  THE COMPUTOR WILL THEN   CALCUL. THE OTHER RUN QUANTITIES
 AND";
110 PRINT" GIVE A TOTAL SUMMARY."
115 PRINT:PRINT"AS YOU GO THRU THE PROGRAM FOLLOW THE INSTRUCTIONS AND ENTER THE
CORRECT DATA ASKED FOR.  AFTER YOU HAVE ENTERED THE DATA REQD.  PRESS -ENTER-.
**THANK-YOU**"
117 INPUT IC
200 CLS:PRINT,A$:PRINT
205 PRINTB$"    (I.E. (MM/DD/YY)":INPUTB1$:PRINTC$:INPUTC1$
210 PRINTD$:INPUTD1$:PRINTE$:INPUTE1
215 PRINTF$:INPUTF1$:PRINTG$:INPUTG1$
220 GOSUB 1600
225 GOSUB 1100
230 GOSUB 1640
235 CLS:PRINT:INPUT"HOW MANY DIFFERENT RUN (SIZE) QUANTITIES DO YOU WISH TO USE
;    THE LIMIT IS THREE ";DJ
240 FORDC=1TODJ
245 PRINT:PRINT"WHAT IS THE QUANTITY FOR RUN --";DC:INPUTX(DC)
250 NEXT DC
255 FORY=1TO8:CLS:PRINT,A$:PRINT:PRINTH$:PRINT:PRINTK$
260 PRINTL$:PRINTM$:PRINTN$:PRINTO$:PRINTP$:PRINTQ$:PRINTR$
265 PRINT:INPUT"TYPE IN THE NO. CORRESPONDING WITH OPERATION DESIRED. ";AA
280 LET V(Y)=AA
282 IFAA=8THEN 355
285 REM MACH. SELECTION LIST
```

Printout 2-9

FORGE ESTIMATE

CUSTOMER _____ DATE OF INQUIRY_____

ADDRESS _____ QUANTITY_____

PART NAME _____ PART NUMBER _____

	OPERATION	Equipment Used	Prod. Per Hr.	Total Hrs.	Mach. Rate	RUN Cost	RUN Prod. per Hr.	RUN Total Hrs.	Cost	RUN Prod. per Hr.	RUN Total Hrs.	Cost
MACHINE BURDEN	1. Blank or Block											
	2. Forge											
	3. Upset											
	4. Restrike											
	5. Trim (Hot-Cold)											
	6. Punch											
	7. Rough Grind											
	8.											
	9.											

		Operators No. Men	Operators Rate per 100 Pcs.	Helpers No. Men	Helpers Rate per 100 Pcs.	Total per 100 Pcs.							
LABOR	1. Blank or Block												
	2. Forge												
	3. Upset												
	4. Restrike												
	5. Trim (Hot-Cold)												
	6. Punch												
	7. Rough Grind												
	8.												
	9.												

		Units	Rate per 100				
MAT'L HANDLING	Cutting & Handling						
	Product Handling						
	Laboratory						
	Shipping						

SPEC. OPER.	Pickle				
	Tumble-S. B.				
	Heat Treat				
	Ann.-Norm.				

		Hrs. per Set-Up	Rate Labor	Rate Burden	Pcs. per Set-Up	
SET-UP	Burden					
	Labor					

Die Maintenance	per 100 Pcs.		

SUMMARY	Total Conversion Cost			
	Material	lbs. @		
	Material Quantity Extra			
	Sub-Total			
	Rejections	% of Sub-Total		
	Factory Cost			
	Administrative and Selling			
	Total Cost			
	Cost per 100 Pcs.			
	Quote Dies	Profit		
		Freight		
		Die Amortization		
		Cash Discount		
		Selling Price		

Figure 2-9. Forge Estimate.

DIE-A   **DIE ESTIMATE**   DIE-B

Type of Die _____ Pieces per Sinking _____   Type of Die _____ Pieces per Sinking _____

Impressions Block _____ Impressions Finish _____   Impressions Block _____ Impressions Finish _____

MATERIAL

Article	Type of Steel	Size	Weight	Price Per Lb.	Amount	Article	Type of Steel	Size	Weight	Price Per Lb.	Amount
Blocks						Blocks					
Trimmers						Trimmers					
Punch						Punch					
TOTAL						TOTAL					

Sinkings per Block _____ Material per Sinking _____   Sinkings per Block _____ Material per Sinking _____

LABOR AND BURDEN

Operation	Hours	Labor		Burden		Operation	Hours	Labor		Burden	
		Rate	Amount	Rate	Amount			Rate	Amount	Rate	Amount
Planing						Planing					
Sinking						Sinking					
Edger						Edger					
Trimmer						Trimmer					
Punch						Punch					
Bender						Bender					
Hardening						Hardening					
TOTALS						TOTALS					

Labor and Burden per Sinking _____   Labor and Burden per Sinking _____

DIE MAINTENANCE

	Die "A"	Die "B"	Die "C"	Die "D"	Total
Material per Sinking					
Labor per Sinking					
Burden per Sinking					
TOTALS					
Pieces per Sinking					
Die Main per 100 Pcs.					

INITIAL DIE COST

Items	Amount
Original Blocks—Trimmer Steel	
Die Labor—First Sinking	
Die Burden on First Sinking	
TOTAL	

ESTIMATED WEIGHT OF FORGING

Size	Weight per Inch	Length	Weight of Section

MATERIAL

	Carbon	Mang.	Phos.	Sul.	Sil.	Nickel
Type _____			Chrome	Van.	Molyb.	
S.A.E.						

Size Material	STEEL PRICE PER CWT.	
	Base at	
Cut in Multiples of	Freight (if not above)	
	Carbon Extra	
Gross Weight per Piece	Size Extra	
	Forge Quality Extra	
Net Weight per Piece		
	TOTAL	

Remarks

Weight Calculated by _____ Estimated by _____ Checked by _____

Figure 2-10. Die Estimate.

```
290 CLS:PRINT,"*** EQUIPMENT ***":PRINT
295 PRINT"1) 2000 LB. BOARD DROP HAMMER","10) 1500 TON FORGE PRESS"
300 PRINT"2) 3000 LB. BOARD DROP HAMMER","11) 3000 TON FORGE PRESS"
305 PRINT"3) 5000 LB. BOARD DROP HAMMER","12) 1000 TON COINING PRESS"
310 PRINT"4) 3000 LB. STEAM DROP HAMMER","13) 50 TON TRIM PRESS"
315 PRINT"5) 6000 LB. STEAM DROP HAMMER","14) 100 TON TRIM PRESS"
320 PRINT"6) 12000 LB. STEAM DROP HAMMER","15) 50 TON COLD TRIM PRESS"
325 PRINT"7) 20000 LB. STEAM DROP HAMMER","16) 100 TON COLD TRIM PRESS"
330 PRINT"8) 3-INCH FORGE MACHINE","17) SNAGING OR GRINDING"
335 PRINT"9) 6-INCH FORGE MACHINE"
340 PRINT:INPUT"TYPE IN THE NO. CORRESPONDING WITH DESIRED EQUIP. ";W(Y)
345 INPUT"WHAT IS THE PROD. / HR. FOR THIS EQUIP. ";U(Y)
350 NEXTY
355 FOR EE=1TODJ
360 PRINT"THIS IS A SUMMARY FOR RUN SIZE"X(EE)
362 LPRINT" ":LPRINT"          SUMMARY OF DATA FOR SELECTED OPERATION":LPRINT" "
364 LPRINT"THIS IS A SUMMARY FOR RUN SIZE OF "X(EE):LPRINT" "
365 LET TC=0:RC=0
370 FOR X=1TO8
371 IF V(L)=8THEN645
372 IF V(X)=8THEN645
375 ON W(X) GOTO 395,405,415,425,435,445
380 ON W(X)-6 GOTO 455,465,475,485,495,505
385 ON W(X)-12 GOTO 515,525,535,550,560
390 REM DATA FOR EQUIP.
395 LETY=15.00:F=9.00:T=1:R=5.50:H=2:W=3.5:S=65
400 Z$="2000 LB. BOARD DROP HAMMER":GOTO570
405 LET Y=21:F=12:T=1:R=5.5:H=2:W=3.5:S=90
410 Z$="3000 LB. BOARD DROP HAMMER":GOTO570
415 LET Y=34:F=14:T=1:R=5.5:H=2:W=3.5:S=140
420 Z$="5000 LB. BOARD DROP HAMMER":GOTO 570
425 LET Y=36:F=14:T=1:R=5.5:H=2:W=3.5:S=140
430 Z$="3000 LB. STEAM DROP HAMMER":GOTO570
435 LET Y=5:F=18:T=1:R=5.5:H=2:W=3.5:S=200
440 Z$="6000 LB. STEAM DROP HAMMER":GOTO570
445 LET Y=75:F=23:T=1:R=5.5:H=2:W=3.5:S=400
450 Z$="12000 LB. STEAM DROP HAMMER":GOTO570
455 LET Y=100:F=35:T=1:R=5.5:H=2:W=3.5:S=800
460 Z$="20000 LB. STEAM DROP HAMMER":GOTO570
465 LET Y=20:F=10:T=1:R=5.5:H=2:W=3.5:S=150
470 Z$="3-INCH FORGE MACHINE":GOTO570
475 LET Y=55:F=25:T=1:R=5.5:H=2:W=3.5:S=300
480 Z$="6-INCH FORGE MACHINE":GOTO570
485 LET Y=40:F=15:T=1:R=5.5:H=2:W=3.5:S=150
490 Z$="1500 TON FORGE PRESS":GOTO570
495 LET Y=20:F=0:T=1:R=5.5:H=2:W=3.5:S=50
500 Z$="3000 TON FORGE PRESS":GOTO570
505 LET Y=20:F=10:T=1:R=5.5:H=2:W=3.5:S=150
510 Z$="1000 TON COINING PRESS":GOTO570
515 LET Y=40:F=15:T=1:R=5.5:S=250
520 Z$="50 TON HOT TRIM PRESS":GOTO570
525 LET Y=30:F=15:T=1:R=5.5:S=200
530 Z$="100 TON HOT TRIM PRESS":GOTO570
535 LET Y=50:F=0:T=1:R=5.5:S=300
540 Z$="50 TON TRIM PRESS":GOTO570
550 LET Y=50:F=0:T=1:R=5.5:H=2:W=3.5:S=300
555 Z$="100 TON TRIM PRESS":GOTO810
560 LET Y=6:T=1:R=5.5:Z$="SNAGGING OR GRINDING":GOTO570
565 REM CALCUL. COST
570 LET Z=X(EE)/U(X):R=R*T:W=W*H
575 LET RC=(Z*Y)+(Z*F)+(Z*R)+(Z*W)+S
580 LET TC=TC+RC
585 REM PRINT DATA
590 CLS:PRINT:PRINT"          SUMMARY OF DATA FOR SELECTED OPERATION"
591 LPRINT" "
```

Printout 2-9 continued

```
595 ON V(X) GOTO 1060,1065,1070,1075,1080,1085,1090
600 PRINT "EQUIPMENT USED",,Z$:LPRINT "EQUIPMENT USED",,Z$
605 PRINT "PROD./HR.",,U(X):LPRINT "PROD./HR. ",,U(X)
610 PRINT "MACHINE RATE",,"$"Y"/HR.":LPRINT "MACHINE RATE",,"$"Y"/HR."
615 PRINT "SET UP COST",,"$"S:LPRINT "SET UP COST",,"$"S
620 PRINT "NO. OF OPER.","      "T,"RATE/HR.","$"R:LPRINT "NO. OF OPER.","      "T
,"RATE/HR.","$"R
625 PRINT "NO. OF HEPLERS","       "H,"RATE/HR.","$"W:LPRINT "NO. OF HEPLERS","
  "H,"RATE/HR.","$"W
630 PRINT "TOTAL HRS./OPER.",Z:LPRINT "TOTAL HRS./OPER.",Z
635 PRINT "RUN COST/OPER.",,"$"RC:LPRINT "RUN COST/OPER.",,"$"RC
640 NEXT X
645 LET TC(EE)=TC
650 NEXT EE
651 STOP
700 REM OTHER ADDED COST
702 LPRINT" ":LPRINT" ":LPRINT,"ADDED OPERATIONS":LPRINT" "
705 FOR I=1TO8
710 CLS:PRINT "**** OTHER ADDED COST ****":PRINT
715 PRINT "1) CUTTING AND HANDLING":PRINT "2) PRODUCT HANDLING AND SHIPPING"
720 PRINT "3) LABORATORY":PRINT "4) PICKLING":PRINT "5) TUMBLE OR SAND BLAST"
725 PRINT "6) HEAT TREAT":PRINT "7) ANN. - NORM.":PRINT R$
730 PRINT:PRINT "TYPE IN THE NO. CORRESPONDING WITH THE OPERATION":PRINT "YOU DE
SIRE TO HAVE ADDED TO EXISTING OPERATIONS."
740 INPUT G(I)
742 IFG(I)=8THEN745
743 NEXT I
744 STOP
745 FOR BB=1TODJ
748 LPRINT" ":LPRINT"ADDED COST FOR THE RUN SIZE OF "X(BB):LPRINT" "
750 FOR J=1TO8:IFV(J)=8THEN800
752 ON G(J) GOTO 755,760,765,770,773,775,780
755 LET AD=(.1*NW)*X(BB)
756 LPRINT"THE COST OF CUTTING AND HANDLING IS $"AD:GOTO 790
760 LET AD=(.15*NW)*X(BB)
762 LPRINT"THE COST OF PRODUCT HANDLING AND SHIPPING IS $"AD:GOTO790
765 LET AD=(.01*NW)*X(BB)
767 LPRINT"THE COST OF LABORATORY WORK IS $"AD:GOTO790
770 LET AD=(.02*NW)*X(BB)
772 LPRINT"THE COST OF PICKLING IS $"AD:GOTO790
773 LET AD=(.05*NW)*X(BB)
774 LPRINT"THE COST OF TUMBLE OR SAND BLAST CLEANING IS $"AD:GOTO790
775 LET AD=(.08*NW)*X(BB)
776 LPRINT"THE COST OF HEAT-TREATMENT IS $"AD:GOTO 790
780 LET AD=(.06*NW)*X(BB)
782 LPRINT"THE COST OF ANN. - MORM. IS $"AD:GOTO790
785 REM ACCUM. ADDED COST
790 LET AD1=AD1+AD
795 NEXT J
800 LET AD(BB)=AD1
805 LPRINT" ":LPRINT"OTHER ADDED COST FOR THE RUN QUAINTY OF"X(BB)"=$ "AD(BB):LP
RINT" "
810 NEXT BB
820 LET LN=(E1/200)*CK
825 LET MT=(LN*350)
827 IF LN<1THENLN=1
828 LPRINT" ":LPRINT" ":LPRINT,"DIE MAINTENACE":LPRINT" "
830 LPRINT" ":LPRINT "THERE WILL BE APPROXMATELY "LN" TIMES THE DIES WILL BE DOW
N FOR MAINTENANCE"
835 LPRINT"THE COST OF DIE MAINTENANCE WILL BE $ "MT
840 REM CALCUL. FOR SUMMARY
845 FOR PP=1TODJ
850 PRINT:PRINT,"*** SUMMARY ***":LPRINT" ":LPRINT,"*** SUMMARY ***":LPRINT" "
852 PRINT"FOR THE RUN SIZE OF"X(PP):PRINT:LPRINT"FOR THE RUN SIZE OF "X(PP):LPRI
NT" "
```

Printout 2-9 continued

```
855 PRINT"THE TOTAL CONVERSION COST IS "TC(PP)+AD(PP)+MT:LPRINT"THE TOTAL CONVER
SION COST IS $ "TC(PP)+AD(PP)+MT
860 PRINT"THE TOTAL MAT'L WEIGHT IS "NW*X(PP)" LBS. @ $ "ST*X(PP):LPRINT"THE TOT
AL MAT'L WEIGHT IS "NW*X(PP)" LBS. @ $ "ST*X(PP)
865 PRINT"THE REJECTION RATE IS AT 3% OF THE SUB-TOTAL, WHICH IS $"((ST*X(PP))+T
C(PP)+AD(PP)+MT)*.03:LPRINT"THE REJECTION RATE IS 3% OF THE SUB-TOTAL, WHICH IS
$ "((ST*X(PP))+TC(PP)+AD(PP)+MT)*.03
870 PRINT "THE FACTORY COST IS $ "((ST*X(PP))+AD(PP)+MT+TC(PP))*1.03:LPRINT"THE
FACTORY COST IS $ "((ST*X(PP))+AD(PP)+MT+TC(PP))*1.03
875 PRINT"THE SALES & ADMINISTRATIVE COST IS $ "(((ST*X(PP))+TC(PP)+AD(PP)+MT)*1
.03)*.15:LPRINT"THE SALES & ADMIMSTRATIVE COST IS $ "(((ST*X(PP))+TC(PP)+AD(PP)+
MT)*1.03)*.15
880 PRINT"THE TOTAL COST IS $ "(((ST*X(PP))+AD(PP)+TC(PP)+MT)*1.03)*1.15:LPRINT"
THE TOTAL COST IS $ "(((ST*X(PP))+AD(PP)+TC(PP) +MT)*1.03)*1.15
882 NEXT PP
885 PRINT:INPUT"DO YOU WISH TO RUN THIS PROGRAM AGAIN, IF SO TYPE IN - Y - FOR Y
ES ELSE - N - FOR NO. ";EL$
890 IF EL$="Y"THEN200
895 END
1060 PRINT:PRINT H$,K$   :LPRINT H$,K$: GOTO  600
1065 PRINT:PRINT H$,L$ :LPRINT H$,L$: GOTO 600
1070 PRINT:PRINT H$,M$   :LPRINT H$,M$: GOTO  600
1075 PRINT:PRINT H$,N$   :LPRINT H$,N$: GOTO  600
1080 PRINT:PRINT H$,O$   :LPRINT H$,O$: GOTO  600
1085 PRINT:PRINT H$,P$   :LPRINT H$,P$: GOTO  600
1090 PRINT:PRINT H$,Q$   :LPRINT H$,Q$: GOTO  600
1100 CLS:PRINT"          ** CALCUL. OF SLUG WEIGHT **"
1105 PRINT:PRINT,"MATL. SELECTION"
1110 PRINT:PRINT"1) ALUMINUM",,"6) MOLYBDENUM"
1115  PRINT"2) BRASS,FORGING","7) MONEL"
1120 PRINT"3) COPPER,FORGING","8) STEEL(CAST,CARBON,ALLOY,CR.)"
1125 PRINT "4) IRON,WROGHT",,"9) STEEL,14% TUNGSTEN"
1130 PRINT "5) MAGNESIUM",,"10) STEEL,22% TUNGSTEN"
1135 PRINT:PRINT"TYPE IN THE NO. CORRESPONDING WITH THE MAT'L"
1140 INPUT"OF WHICH FORGING WILL BE MADE OF. ";MS
1142 ON MS GOSUB 1300,1305,1310,1315,1320,1325,1330,1335,1340,1345
1144 CLS:PRINT:PRINT"         *** CALCUL. OF SLUG WEIGHT CONT. ***"
1145 PRINT:PRINT"           GEOMETRIC SHAPE OF SLUG "
1146 PRINT:PRINT"1) RECTANGULAR PRISM OR SQUARE"
1147 PRINT "2) RIGHT CYLINDER"
1148 PRINT "3) TRIANGULAR PRISM"
1149 PRINT:PRINT "TYPE IN THE NO. CORRESPONDING WITH THE GEOMETRIC"
1150 INPUT "SHAPE BEST SUITED FOR FORGING SLUG. ";SH
1151 ON SH GOSUB 1160,1355,1480
1155 RETURN
1160 CLS:FOR L5= 15 TO 30
1161 PRINT @ 273,"-C-"
1165 SET(L5,5) : SET(L5,20)
1170 NEXT L5
1175 FOR M5=5 TO 20
1180 SET(15,M5):SET(30,M5)
1185 NEXT M5
1190 FOR A5=60 TO 120
1195 SET(A5,5):SET(A5,20)
1200 NEXT A5
1205 FOR B5=5 TO 20
1210 SET(60,B5):SET(120,B5)
1215 NEXT B5
1220 FOR J5 = 22 TO 25
1225 SET(15,J5):SET(30,J5):SET(60,J5):SET(120,J5)
1230 NEXT J5
1235 FOR K5=33 TO 38
1240 SET(K5,5):SET(K5,20)
1245 NEXT K5
1255 PRINT @ 522,"-A-"
```

Printout 2-9 continued

```
1260 PRINT @ 555,"-B-"
1265 PRINT @ 704, :INPUT"WHAT IS DIM. -A-    (IN DECIMAL INCHES (I.E. 2.5) ";GA
1270 PRINT @ 768, :INPUT"WHAT IS DIM. -B-    (IN DECIMAL INCHES (I.E. 3.0) ";CO
1275 PRINT @ 832, :INPUT"WHAT IS DIM. -C-    (IN DECIMAL INCHES (I.E. 5.75) ";RS
1276 LETNW=(GA*CO*RS)*BS
1277 LETST=NW*DA
1280 RETURN
1300 LET J$="ALUMINUM":BS=.098:DA=2:CK=.5:RETURN
1305 LET J$="BRASS,FORGING":BS=.305:DA=2:CK=.9:RETURN
1310 LET J$="COPPER,FORGING":BS=.325:DA=2:CK=.9:RETURN
1315 LET J$="IRON,WROGHT":BS=.285:DA=.6:CK=1.2:RETURN
1320 LET J$="MAGNESIUM":BS=.063:DA=3.5:CK=.5:RETURN
1325 LET J$="MOLYBDENUM":BS=.368:DA=4:CK=1.2:RETURN
1330 LET J$="MONEL":BS=.320:DA=3:CK=1.8:RETURN
1335 LET J$="STEEL(CAST,CARBON,ALLOY,CR.)":BS=.283:DA=.6:CK=1:RETURN
1340 LET J$="STEEL,14% TUNGSTEN":BS=.312:DA=.7:CK=1.1:RETURN
1345 LET J$="STEEL,22% TUNGSTEN":BS=.321:DA=.8:CK=1.16:RETURN
1350 REM CYLINDER CALCUL.
1355 CLS:FOR K8=4 TO 6 STEP .101
1360 LET A8=K8*3.14
1365 LET R8=6
1366 C8=2
1370 D8=C8+.101
1375 LET X8=D8*(R8*COS(A8))
1380 LET Y8=R8*SIN(A8)
1385 SET(X8+25,Y8+15)
1390 C8=D8
1391 NEXT K8
1395 FOR A5= 60 TO 120
1400 SET(A5,9):SET(A5,20)
1405 NEXT A5
1410 FOR B5=9 TO 20
1415 SET(60,B5):SET(120,B5)
1420 NEXT B5
1425 FOR CR=20 TO 25
1430 SET(12,CR):SET(38,CR)
1435 NEXT CR
1440 FOR J5=22 TO 25
1445 SET(60,J5):SET(120,J5)
1450 NEXT J5
1455 PRINT @ 523,"-A-"
1460 PRINT @ 555,"-B-"
1465 PRINT @ 704,:INPUT"WHAT IS DIM. -A-    (IN DECIMAL INCHES (I.E. 2.5) ";AG
1470 PRINT @ 768,:INPUT"WHAT IS DIM. -B-    (IN DECIMAL INCHES (I.E. 5.75) ";CO
1472 LETNW=(.7854*(AG[2)*CO)*BS
1473 LET ST=NW*DA
1475 RETURN
1477 REM TRIANGLE CALCUL.
1480 CLS:X3=20:Y3=5:K3=15
1481 PRINT @ 260,"-C-"
1485 FOR L3=0 TO K3
1490 SET(X3+L3,Y3+L3):SET(X3,Y3+L3):SET(X3+L3,Y3+K3)
1495 NEXT L3
1500 FOR A5=60TO120
1505 SET(A5,5):SET(A5,20)
1510 NEXT A5
1515 FOR B5=5TO20
1520 SET(60,B5):SET(120,B5)
1525 NEXTB5
1530 FOR J5=22TO25
1535 SET(20,J5):SET(35,J5):SET(60,J5):SET(120,J5)
1540 NEXT J5
1545 FOR CC=10 TO 16
1550 SET(CC,5):SET(CC,20):NEXT CC
1555 PRINT @ 524,"-A-"
```

Printout 2-9 continued

```
1560 PRINT @ 555,"-B-"
1565 PRINT @ 704,:INPUT"WHAT IS DIM. -A-  (IN DECIMAL INCHES (I.E. 1.25) ";GA
1570 PRINT @ 768,:INPUT"WHAT IS DIM. -B-  (IN DECIMAL INCHES (I.E. 5.75) ";CO
1575 PRINT @ 832,:INPUT"WHAT IS DIM. -C-  (IN DECIMAL INCHES (I.E. 3.0) ";RS
1577 LET NW=(((GA*RS)/2)*CO)*BS
1578 LET ST=NW*DA
1580 RETURN
1600 LPRINT,CHR$(30)A$CHR$(29):LPRINT" "
1605 LPRINTB$,,B1$
1610 LPRINTC$,,C1$
1615 LPRINTD$,D1$
1620 LPRINTE$,,E1
1625 LPRINTF$,,F1$
1630 LPRINTG$,,G1$
1635 RETURN
1640 LPRINT" ":LPRINT" ":LPRINT,"MATERIAL DATA "
1645 LPRINT" ":LPRINT"THE MATERIAL SELECTED IS "J$
1650 LPRINT"THE MATERIAL IS $ "DA"/LB."
1655 LPRINT"THE SLUG WEIGHT IS "NW
1660 LPRINT"THE SLUG COST IS $ "ST
1665 RETURN
1670 END
```

*** FORGE ESTIMATE ***

DATE OF INQUIRY	01/01/81
CUSTOMERS NAME	B.R.MACHINE
CUSTOMERS ADDRESS	120 PERE MARQUETTE
ANNUAL QUANTITY	3000
PART NAME	GEAR
PART NUMBER	82100

MATERIAL DATA

THE MATERIAL SELECTED IS STEEL(CAST,CARBON,ALLOY,CR.)
THE MATERIAL IS $ .6 /LB.
THE SLUG WEIGHT IS 4.00083
THE SLUG COST IS $ 2.4005

SUMMARY OF DATA FOR SELECTED OPERATION

THIS IS A SUMMARY FOR RUN SIZE OF 1000

OPERATION SELECTION		2) FORGE	
EQUIPMENT USED		2000 LB. BOARD DROP HAMMER	
PROD./HR.		100	
MACHINE RATE		$ 15 /HR.	
SET UP COST		$ 65	
NO. OF OPER.	1	RATE/HR.	$ 5.5
NO. OF HEPLERS	2	RATE/HR.	$ 7
TOTAL HRS./OPER.		10	
RUN COST/OPER.		$ 430	

OPERATION SELECTION		4) RESRIKE	
EQUIPMENT USED		1000 TON COINING PRESS	
PROD./HR.		125	
MACHINE RATE		$ 20 /HR.	
SET UP COST		$ 150	
NO. OF OPER.	1	RATE/HR.	$ 5.5
NO. OF HEPLERS	2	RATE/HR.	$ 7
TOTAL HRS./OPER.		8	
RUN COST/OPER.		$ 490	

Printout 2-9 continued

```
OPERATION SELECTION                    5) TRIM (HOT-COLD)
EQUIPMENT USED                         100 TON HOT TRIM PRESS
PROD./HR.                               125
MACHINE RATE                           $ 30 /HR.
SET UP COST                            $ 200
NO. OF OPER.              1            RATE/HR.         $ 5.5
NO. OF HEPLERS           2            RATE/HR.         $ 14
TOTAL HRS./OPER.                        8
RUN COST/OPER.                         $ 716


             SUMMARY OF DATA FOR SELECTED OPERATION

THIS IS A SUMMARY FOR RUN SIZE OF   2000

OPERATION SELECTION                    2) FORGE
EQUIPMENT USED                         2000 LB. BOARD DROP HAMMER
PROD./HR.                               100
MACHINE RATE                           $ 15 /HR.
SET UP COST                            $ 65
NO. OF OPER.              1            RATE/HR.         $ 5.5
NO. OF HEPLERS           2            RATE/HR.         $ 7
TOTAL HRS./OPER.                        20
RUN COST/OPER.                         $ 795


OPERATION SELECTION                    4) RESRIKE
EQUIPMENT USED                         1000 TON COINING PRESS
PROD./HR.                               125
MACHINE RATE                           $ 20 /HR.
SET UP COST                            $ 150
NO. OF OPER.              1            RATE/HR.         $ 5.5
NO. OF HEPLERS           2            RATE/HR.         $ 7
TOTAL HRS./OPER.                        16
RUN COST/OPER.                         $ 830


OPERATION SELECTION                    5) TRIM (HOT-COLD)
EQUIPMENT USED                         100 TON HOT TRIM PRESS
PROD./HR.                               125
MACHINE RATE                           $ 30 /HR.
SET UP COST                            $ 200
NO. OF OPER.              1            RATE/HR.         $ 5.5
NO. OF HEPLERS           2            RATE/HR.         $ 14
TOTAL HRS./OPER.                        16
RUN COST/OPER.                         $ 1232


             SUMMARY OF DATA FOR SELECTED OPERATION

THIS IS A SUMMARY FOR RUN SIZE OF   3000

OPERATION SELECTION                    2) FORGE
EQUIPMENT USED                         2000 LB. BOARD DROP HAMMER
PROD./HR.                               100
MACHINE RATE                           $ 15 /HR.
SET UP COST                            $ 65
NO. OF OPER.              1            RATE/HR.         $ 5.5
NO. OF HEPLERS           2            RATE/HR.         $ 7
TOTAL HRS./OPER.                        30
RUN COST/OPER.                         $ 1160


OPERATION SELECTION                    4) RESRIKE
EQUIPMENT USED                         1000 TON COINING PRESS
PROD./HR.                               125
MACHINE RATE                           $ 20 /HR.
SET UP COST                            $ 150
```

Printout 2-9 continued

75

```
NO. OF OPER.            1         RATE/HR.        $ 5.5
NO. OF HEPLERS          2         RATE/HR.        $ 7
TOTAL HRS./OPER.                  24
RUN COST/OPER.                    $ 1170

OPERATION SELECTION               5) TRIM (HOT-COLD)
EQUIPMENT USED                    100 TON HOT TRIM PRESS
PROD./HR.                         125
MACHINE RATE                      $ 30 /HR.
SET UP COST                       $ 200
NO. OF OPER.            1         RATE/HR.        $ 5.5
NO. OF HEPLERS          2         RATE/HR.        $ 14
TOTAL HRS./OPER.                  24
RUN COST/OPER.                    $ 1748



            *** SUMMARY ***

FOR THE RUN SIZE OF   1000

THE TOTAL CONVERSION COST IS $  7286.08
THE TOTAL MAT'L WEIGHT IS  4000.83  LBS. @ $  2400.5
THE REJECTION RATE IS 3% OF THE SUB-TOTAL, WHICH IS $  290.597
THE FACTORY COST IS $  9977.18
THE SALES & ADMIMSTRATIVE COST IS $  1496.58
THE TOTAL COST IS $  11473.8



            *** SUMMARY ***

FOR THE RUN SIZE OF   2000

THE TOTAL CONVERSION COST IS $  8907.17
THE TOTAL MAT'L WEIGHT IS  8001.66  LBS. @ $  4801
THE REJECTION RATE IS 3% OF THE SUB-TOTAL, WHICH IS $  411.245
THE FACTORY COST IS $  14119.4
THE SALES & ADMIMSTRATIVE COST IS $  2117.91
THE TOTAL COST IS $  16237.3



            *** SUMMARY ***

FOR THE RUN SIZE OF   3000

THE TOTAL CONVERSION COST IS $  10528.2
THE TOTAL MAT'L WEIGHT IS  12002.5  LBS. @ $  7201.49
THE REJECTION RATE IS 3% OF THE SUB-TOTAL, WHICH IS $  531.892
THE FACTORY COST IS $  18261.6
THE SALES & ADMIMSTRATIVE COST IS $  2739.25
THE TOTAL COST IS $  21000.9
```

Printout 2-9 continued

```
                  ADDED OPERATIONS


ADDED COST FOR THE RUN SIZE OF   1000

THE COST OF HEAT-TREATMENT IS $ 320.066
THE COST OF ANN. - MORM. IS $ 240.05
THE COST OF TUMBLE OR SAND BLAST CLEANING IS $ 200.041

OTHER ADDED COST FOR THE RUN QUAINTY OF 1000 =$   400.083


ADDED COST FOR THE RUN SIZE OF   2000

THE COST OF HEAT-TREATMENT IS $ 640.133
THE COST OF ANN. - MORM. IS $ 480.099
THE COST OF TUMBLE OR SAND BLAST CLEANING IS $ 400.083

OTHER ADDED COST FOR THE RUN QUAINTY OF 2000 =$   800.166


ADDED COST FOR THE RUN SIZE OF   3000

THE COST OF HEAT-TREATMENT IS $ 960.199
THE COST OF ANN. - MORM. IS $ 720.149
THE COST OF TUMBLE OR SAND BLAST CLEANING IS $ 600.124

OTHER ADDED COST FOR THE RUN QUAINTY OF 3000 =$   1200.25


             DIE MAINTENACE


THERE WILL BE APPROXMATELY  15  TIMES THE DIES WILL BE DOWN FOR MAINTENANCE
THE COST OF DIE MAINTENANCE WILL BE $   5250
```

Printout 2-9 continued

General Comments, Computerized Cost Estimating Routines

In the past several years, many magazine articles and chapters in books have been written about computerized cost estimating. They extol the wonders of speed, decision making and complexity of such activities. Most of these articles fail to mention that writing computer programs to perform cost estimating chores are among the most complex of computer applications in the Manufacturing Engineering field. Unlike many computer applications, when confronted with writing programs to perform estimating work, there sometimes seems to be no beginning or no end.

Start simply and, as your programming skills improve, write more complex programs. The objectives must be ever present in the mind of the engineer-programmer and his company's management. The objective should not be how to replace a hand-operated cost estimating system with a computerized system in 1000 easy steps. The objective should be to assist the engineer with the aid of the computer, not to replace him.

While it should be evident, at this point, that the computer has the ability to make intelligent decisions—these decisions must be programmed. Cost-effective decisions should be made to determine what part the computer should play and how long it will take to achieve this level. These decisions must be reviewed periodically as engineering programming skills improve.

Complicated cost estimating systems will evolve soon enough. The first effort should be to get value from your new investment (the computer) and not to see how complex programming can become.

Some consideration also should be given to modular style programming for use later in compiling routines for more complicated work. But the first effort should be to analyze what the engineer can do best and what the computer can do best and then proceed with simple programs.

One last comment about programming style. Most professionally written programs contain fail-safe language to prevent the user from making errors. While it is necessary to write computer programs to prevent miscalculations and errors that will produce incorrect results, it is not necessary to fail-safe every input. The effort should be to write simple programs that work correctly.

Bibliography

Horton, Holbrook L., Editor. *Machinery's Handbook*, 19th Ed. New York: Industrial Press, Inc., 1974.

Jenson, Jon E., Editor. *Forging Industry Handbook*, 2nd Ed. Cleveland: Forging Industry Association, 1970.

Valenite Handy Reference, The Valeron Corporation, 1976.

Vernon, Ivan R., Editor. *Realistic Cost Estimating for Manufacturing*. Dearborn, MI: Society of Manufacturing Engineers, 1968.

Optional Lab Assignments

Lab Assignment 2-1 (least difficult)
Write a cost estimating program for a cylindrical grinder. All speeds, feeds and manual time values should be stored in the form of a GOSUB routine.

Lab Assignment 2-2 (moderate)
Write a computer program for a gang drilling machine that has four spindles. This program should include typical operations that a gang drill can perform; i.e., drill, ream, counterbore, countersink and tap. The program should include all speeds and feeds calculations internally and all standard data for other machine and manual functions, loading, unloading, inspection, etc.

Lab Assignment 2-3 (difficult)
Write a computer program for a multiple spindle screw machine. All speeds and feeds for each typical operation should be chosen by the computer and reconciled to speeds and feeds for the specific machine being tooled.

Lab Assignment 2-4 (difficult)
Write a computer program using the milling standard data sheet presented earlier in the text *(Figure 2-1)*. In writing this program, the graphics used in the SFPM milling module should be used. The speeds and feeds GOSUB module can also be used.

CHAPTER 3

Learning Curves and Launching Costs

In Chapter Two, we discussed how the microcomputer can be used for cost estimating, and we examined in detail a lengthy computer program that develops cost estimates for turning, drilling and milling. Another facet of cost estimating is the use of learning curves and the development of launching costs. In this chapter, we shall explore the use of the microcomputer as a tool for revising a product cost estimate and massaging the numbers of the estimate to include the effect of learning.

Every person and/or manufacturing activity learns at a different rate or speed. Even in high-production, such as automotive production, when a new model year begins, costs are higher in the early stages of production compared to later stages. The degree or amount of learning that takes place is referred to as the slope of the learning curve. The broad objectives of learning curves are three-fold.

1. Predict with some degree of accuracy what future costs might be as product continues to be produced, while understanding that as product is produced, costs tend to reduce themselves by the dynamics of learning.
2. If costs tend to reduce themselves as a product is produced, then it should be predictable what extra costs there will be if the quantity of product decreases rather than increases. In other words, what would costs be if we revised the process?
3. Objectives One and Two imply that cost forms some type of curve. If this is true, and if we can measure this curve, then we should be able to calculate costs above some point (referred to as standard) and identify these costs as launching costs or one-time nonrecurring costs associated with the early stages of production.

Principles

Learning curves and launching costs are not new theories. They were developed in the 1940's by the aircraft industry to provide methods for engineers to make cost predictions years in advance of production of a specific aircraft. These methods are still used today by the aerospace industry, and in some cases, are required by the government. The use of these principles has been adopted by other industries. Launching costs specifically have been used in the automotive industry to calculate the cost effect of new products. It should also be mentioned that prior to the advent of the small desk-type engineering computer, these costs were calculated by using log-log paper, a practice now obsolete.

Before the computer program which calculates learning curves and launching costs is examined, a review of the basic principles is in order.

Principle Number 1

As the quantity of product doubles, costs are reduced by "learning" at some steady rate called "learning rate". This learning rate can be expressed as a percentage.

In the example shown in *Table 3-1,* if the first unit costs one hour to produce, and the learning rate is 90%, then the average accumulated time through the second unit produced is .9 hours. As the volume of production again doubles, i.e., from two units to four units, the average accumulated cost per unit is reduced by learning (.9000 hours times 90% equals .81000 hours).

Table 3-1
Learning Rate

Units Produced	Learning Rate	Average Accumulated Cost per Unit
1	90%	1.0000 Hour
2	90%	.9000 Hours
4	90%	.8100 Hours
8	90%	.7290 Hours
16	90%	.6561 Hours

The exponent for the curve can be calculated:

$$Y1/Y2 = (a/N1^b)/(a/N2^b) = N2^b/N1^b = (2N1/N1)^b$$

Where:

$N2 = 2N1$
$Y1 = $ time or percent (greater)
$Y2 = $ time or percent (lesser)
$N1 = $ number of units produced (greater)
$N2 = $ number of units produced (lesser)
$a = $ time for the first unit
$b = $ exponent for the curve

Example:

If the second unit produced has an average accumulated time of 80 hours, and if the fourth unit produced has an average accumulated time of 64 hours then:

$$80/64 = (4/2)^b = 1.25 = 2^b$$

$$b = \log 1.25/\log 2 = .0969/.3010 = .322 = b$$

$$64/80 = 80\% \text{ curve, or } 1/1.25 = 80\% \text{ curve}$$

The learning rate of this product is 80% and the exponent associated to an 80% curve is .322.

Principle Number 2

The cost for an individual unit is:

$$1 - b * Y = N3$$

For very low quantities, the formula above produces a very slight error. To correct this use:

$$N3 = Y(N\text{-}1)\left[\left(\frac{N}{N\text{-}1}\right) - \left(\frac{N\text{-}1}{N}\right)^{-b}\right]$$

Example:

      If using a 90% curve, b = .152, and the average accumulated time through the 16th unit is .6561, then the time for the 16th unit only is:

$$(1 - .152) * .6561 = .5564$$

Principle Number 3

Average accumulated time for the Nth unit is:

$$Y = a * (N^{-b})$$

Where:

      Y = average accumulated time for the Nth unit
      N = number of units produced
      a = time for the first unit
      $-b$ = exponent for the curve

Example:

      a = 1st unit = 1 hour
      N = 4th unit
      $-b$ = exponent for a 90% curve = -.152

Then:

$$1 * (4^{-.152}) = .81004$$

(Note: .81000 vs. .81004 is a rounding error at the fifth decimal.)

Principle Number 4

Rearrangement of the formula above yields:

$$a = 1/(N^{-b}) * Y = \text{time for the first unit}$$

Example:

      Job shop standard data is usually "set" at some base that fits the shop and standard data may or may not include some off standard factors. The word "set" implies standard data is "adjusted" in a job shop to reflect most nearly what the average quantity of production is. This adjustment may be made consciously or unconsciously. The idea, of course, is not to estimate costs at the million level when the average lot size is 50. For example, assume that the standard data is "set" at 256 units, i.e., the shop would reach standard time when the 256th unit is produced. What would the time be for the first unit if our shop has a 90% learning rate?

      b = -.152 = exponent for a 90% curve
      Y = 1.58 = time developed from the standard data
      N = 256
      a = $1/(256^{-.152}) * 1.58 = 3.67$ = time for the first unit

Principle Number 5

Solving for N:

$$(Y/a)^{-1/b} = N$$

Example:

If the average accumulated time for the Nth unit is .96, and the time for the first unit is 1.5, using a 95% learning curve $b = .074$, then what is the Nth unit?

$$(.96/1.5)^{-(1/.074)} = 416$$
$$or$$
$$(.96/1.5)^{-13.5135} = 416$$

The Nth unit is 416 when the average accumulated time is .96.

Principle Number 6

The general idea of launching costs is used in a wide variety of industries. It attempts to predict how much cost will be associated in launching a new product or model.

The basic idea can be understood by reviewing *Figure 3-1*.

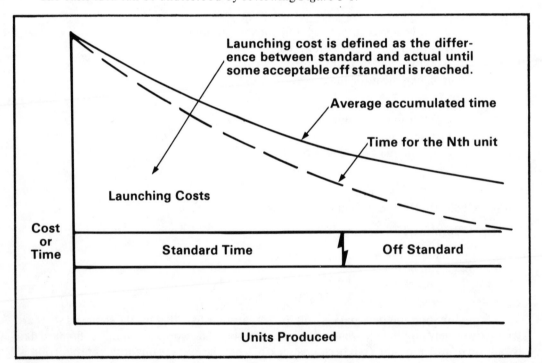

Figure 3-1. Launching Costs.

The theory of launching costs further assumes that after learning has reached some future point when the reduction of costs is minor due to the affect of doubling quantity, (for example: from two million units to four million units), then other dynamics must produce cost reduction. The factors may include: the reduction of standards through methods improvement, cost reduction programs or product redesign review. When this occurs, the curve might look similar to the diagram in *Figure 3-2*.

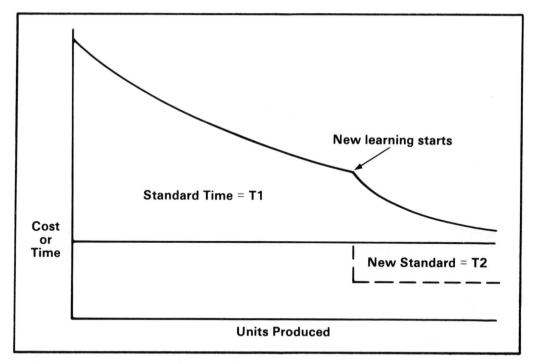

Figure 3-2. *A sample of launching costs.*

At this point, the concept of launching costs divides into two separate theories.

The first theory states that new learning starts from the point at which standard is reduced, starting a new curve for only that part of the unit cost that has been reduced. The part of standard that has not been reduced is not affected and continues at the same learning rate. That part of standard that has been affected starts a new learning cycle where the Nth unit now becomes the first unit.

The second theory states that learning continues but at some new learning rate, i.e., an entirely new exponent.

Arguments can be made for both of these theories to determine how many hours or dollars this launching cost will be. The true value of this approach is a measure of improvement from a management point of view and/or prediction of early costs for accounting purposes.

Using the previous example shown above, if .96 is the averge accumulated time for the Nth unit which is 416, then:

$$Y * (1-b) = Y3, \text{ or time for the } N\text{th unit only}$$

$$.96 * (1 - .074) = .8889 = Y3$$

Then:

$$Y = .96 \text{ (average accumulated time for all lots to 416)}$$
$$\underline{-Y3 = -.89} \text{ (time for the 416th unit only)}$$
$$.07$$

$$.07 * 416 = 29.12 \text{ hours} * \$15.00 = \$436.80$$

Where:

$15.00 = shop rate
436.80 = launching costs through the 416th unit

Another way to analyze the problem is to ask, when will standard be reached for the Nth unit if learning continues?

$$((STD/1-b)/a)^{-(1/b)} = N2$$

If the standard cost is .8, then:

$$((.8/.926)/1.5)^{-13.5135} = N2 = 1729$$

The standard should be reached at the 1729th unit. The percent off standard is derived by:

$$\text{Actual}/\text{Standard} - 100 * 100 = \text{percent off standard}$$

Example:

.89/.8*100-100 = 11.25% off standard. Or, stated in other words, when the 416th unit as an individual is reached, the off standard at that point is 11.25%.

The next section of this chapter displays the computer program for learning curves and includes several examples.

Program Name: "LEARN"

The memory required for this program is 4136 bytes.

This program has four separate parts combined in one program. When "booted up" the user selects the module or routine he wishes to work with. The four sections of this program are:
1. Calculate the exponent for a curve.
2. Calculate time for the first unit.
3. Calculate time for the Nth unit.
4. Calculate launching costs.

Some microcomputers calculate log base 10 directly; the TRS-80[1] microcomputer works in e based logs and it is necessary to write the calculations using $\log(x)/\log(10)$. The program is presented in its entirety on the next several pages.

```
3 REM PROGRAM NAME LEARN
4 REM WRITTEN BY J.E.NICKS
5 REM COMPUTER APPLICATIONS FOR THE MANUFACTURING ENGINEER
6 REM COPYRIGHT 1981 ALL RIGHTS RESERVED
10 CLS
20 PRINT"THIS PROGRAM CALCULATES"
21 PRINT"LEARNING CURVES AND LAUNCHING COSTS"
22 PRINT"INPUT THE SUB PROGRAM YOU WISH TO USE"
23 PRINT:PRINT
30 PRINT"CALCULATE THE EXPONENT FOR A CURVE-----------1"
40 PRINT"CALCULATE THE TIME FOR THE FIRST UNIT--------2"
50 PRINT"CALCULATE THE TIME FOR THE N TH. UNIT--------3"
60 PRINT"CALCULATE LAUNCHING COST---------------------4"
70 INPUTN
```

Printout 3-1

[1]TRS-80 is a trademark of the Radio Shack Division of Tandy Corporation.

```
80 ONNGOTO90,250,410,600
81 CLS
90 PRINT"THIS ROUTINE CALCULATES EXPONENTS FOR A LEARNING CURVE"
91 PRINT
92 PRINT"THE NUMBER OF UNITS PRODUCED (LARGER) MUST BE"
93 PRINT"2 TIMES THE NUMBER OF UNITS PRODUCED (SMALLER)"
94 PRINT
100 INPUT"TIME OR PER CENT (LARGER)";Y1
110 INPUT"NUMBER OF UNITS PRODUCED (LARGER)";N1
120 INPUT"TIME OR PER CENT (SMALLER)";Y2
130 INPUT"NUMBER OF UNITS PRODUCED (SMALLER)";N2
140 A=Y1/Y2:A1=LOG(A)/LOG(10)  ←——————
150 C=N1/N2:C1=LOG(C)/LOG(10)  ←——————
160 B=A1/C1:B1=Y2/Y1
170 LPRINT CHR$(27);CHR$(14);"LEARNING CURVE EXPONENTS"
171 LPRINT" "
180 LPRINT"THE LARGER TIME OR % WAS";Y1;"THE SMALLER WAS";Y2
181 LPRINT" "
190 LPRINT"LARGER UNITS PRODUCED WAS";N1;"THE SMALLER WAS";N2
191 LPRINT" "
200 LPRINT"THIS IS A ";B1;"% LEARNING CURVE"
201 LPRINT" "
210 LPRINT"THE EXPONENT FOR THIS CURVE IS";B
220 CLS:INPUT"FOR ANOTHER CALCULATION TYPE 1 OR 2 TO EXIT";X
230 ONXGOTO10,240
240 END

241 CLS
250 PRINT"THIS ROUTINE CALCULATES TIME OF THE FIRST UNIT"
260 INPUT"THE AVERAGE ACCUM QUANTITY IS ";Q
270 PRINT"THE AVERAGE ACCUM TIME FOR ";Q;"QUANTITY IS"
280 INPUTY
290 PRINT"TO CHOOSE THE LEARNING CURVE YOU WISH TO WORK WITH"
300 INPUT"TYPE 1";Z
310 IFZ=1THEN320
320 GOSUB2000
330 A=(Q[B)*Y
335 LPRINT CHR$(27);CHR$(14);"TIME FOR THE FIRST UNIT"
336 LPRINT" "
340 LPRINT"THE AVERAGE ACCUM TIME FOR THE";Q;"UNIT"
350 LPRINT"WAS";Y
355 LPRINT" "
360 LPRINT"TIME FOR THE FIRST UNIT USING A ";C;"% CURVE"
370 LPRINT"IS ";A
380 INPUT"FOR ANOTHER CALCULATION TYPE 1 OR 2 TO EXIT";X
390 ONXGOTO10,400
400 END

401 CLS
410 PRINT"TIME FOR THE N TH UNIT"
420 INPUT"NUMBER OF UNITS PRODUCED, THE N TH UNIT IS";P
430 INPUT"TIME FOR THE FIRST UNIT";A
440 PRINT"TO CHOOSE THE LEARNING CURVE YOU WISH TO WORK WITH"
450 INPUT"TYPE 1";Z
460 IFZ=1THEN470
470 GOSUB2000
480 Y=(P[-B)*A
490 Y1=(1-B)*Y
500 LPRINT CHR$(27);CHR$(14);"TIME FOR THE N TH UNIT"
505 LPRINT" "
510 LPRINT"WHERE TIME FOR THE FIRST UNIT IS ";A
520 LPRINT"USING A";C;"% LEARNING CURVE"
525 LPRINT" "
530 LPRINT"THE AVERAGE ACCUM TIME FOR THE N TH UNIT";P
540 LPRINT"IS";Y
```

Lines 140 and 150 convert natural logs to base 10 logs

Printout 3-1 continued

```
545 LPRINT" "
550 LPRINT"AND THE TIME FOR THE N TH ";P;" UNIT ONLY"
560 LPRINT"IS";Y1
570 PRINT"FOR ANOTHER CALCULATION TYPE 1 OR 2 TO EXIT"
571 INPUTX
580 ONXGOTO10,590
590 END


600 CLS
601 PRINT"THIS ROUTINE CALCULATES LAUNCHING COSTS"
610 INPUT"TIME IN HOURS FOR THE FIRST UNIT IS";A
620 INPUT"STANDARD TIME IN HOURS PER UNIT ";S
630 INPUT"SHOP RATE DOLLARS IS";R
640 PRINT"TO CHOOSE THE LEARNING CURVE YOU WISH TO WORK WITH"
650 INPUT"TYPE 1";Z
660 IFZ=1THEN670
670 GOSUB2000
680 B1=-1/B:B2=1-B
690 P=((S/B2)/A)[B1
700 Y=(P[-B)*A
710 O=((Y/S)*100)-100
720 L=(Y-S)*P*R
730 LPRINT CHR$(27);CHR$(14);"LAUNCHING COSTS"
731 LPRINT" "
740 LPRINT"TIME FOR THE FIRST UNIT IS";A;"HOURS"
750 LPRINT"STANDARD TIME IS";S;"HOURS PER UNIT"
760 LPRINT"SHOP RATE IS $";R;" DOLLARS"
761 LPRINT" "
770 LPRINT"USING A ";C;"% LEARNING CURVE"
780 LPRINT"STANDARD IS REACHED AT THE ";P;"UNIT"
781 LPRINT" "
790 LPRINT"WHEN THE ";P;"UNIT IS REACHED AS A UNIT"
800 LPRINT"THE AVERAGE ACCUM TIME UP TO THE ";P;"UNIT"
810 LPRINT"IS";Y
811 LPRINT" "
820 LPRINT"AND THE OFF STANDARD IS";O;"PER CENT"
821 LPRINT" "
822 LPRINT" "
830 LPRINT CHR$(27);CHR$(14);"LAUNCHING COSTS ARE $";L;"DOLLARS"
840 INPUT"FOR ANOTHER CALCULATION TYPE 1 OR 2 TO EXIT";X
850 ONXGOTO10,860
860 END


2000 CLS
2010 PRINT"THE FOLLOWING CURVES ARE AVAILABLE TO WORK WITH"
2030 PRINT"TYPE IN THE NUMBER YOU WISH TO USE
2040 PRINT"1   = 98%-------------2   = 96%"
2050 PRINT"3   = 95%-------------4   = 94%"
2060 PRINT"5   = 92%-------------6   = 90%"
2070 PRINT"7   = 88%-------------8   = 96%"
2080 PRINT"9   = 85%-------------10  = 84%"
2090 PRINT"11  = 82%-------------12  = 80%"
2100 PRINT"13  = 78%-------------14  = 76%"
2110 PRINT"15  = 75%"
2120 INPUTN
2130 ONNGOTO2160,2170,2180,2190,2200
2140 ONN-5GOTO2210,2220,2230,2240,2250
2150 ONN-10GOTO2260,2270,2280,2290,2300
2160 B=.029146:C=98:RETURN
2170 B=.058894:C=96:RETURN
2180 B=.074:C=95:RETURN
2190 B=.089267:C=94:RETURN
2200 B=.120294:C=92:RETURN
2210 B=.152003:C=90:RETURN
2220 B=.184425:C=88:RETURN
```

Printout 3-1 continued

```
2230 B=.217591:C=86:RETURN
2240 B=.234465:C=85:RETURN   ◄──────── Sub-routine contains exponents for
2250 B=.251539:C=84:RETURN                the last three modules
2260 B=.286304:C=82:RETURN
2270 B=.321928:C=80:RETURN
2280 B=.358453:C=78:RETURN
2290 B=.395929:C=76:RETURN
2300 B=.415038:C=75:RETURN
```

Printout 3-1 continued

Program Notes

No attempt will be made to review this program line by line, but several points should be made. This program is written using as few BASIC statements and symbols as possible, (eleven BASIC statements). This approach provides the engineer, who may not have much experience writing computer programs, with an understanding that rather complex routines can be accomplished on the microcomputer without much computer training. For those who do have some training, this program, of course, is very elementary.

Lines 10 to 240 provide the user with a menu of four options that can be performed. In this module, the user should note that all calculations for exponents are completed in only three lines—140, 150 and 160.

Lines 241 to 400 provide the user with "time for the first unit" by inputting variable Q for quantity and variable Y for average time. The user should note line 320. This is a subroutine statement that allows the exponents to be stored as data type statements. It should also be pointed out that there are other ways to write this section of the program.

In lines 401 to 590, note that line 480 shows the printer symbol for an exponent after the P in the formula.

Lines 600 to 680 comprise the module that is the most important in this program because it has the ability to calculate launching costs.

GOSUB Section

Lines 2000 to 2300 of this program form the GOSUB routine. A user might ask, why have a GOSUB routine at all? Why not calculate the exponent with the computer if the computer has that much power? There are two reasons for writing the program this way. First, from the learning curve review, remember that four factors must be known to calculate the exponent:
1. Time or percent (larger).
2. Time or percent (smaller).
3. Units produced (larger).
4. Units produced (smaller).

These factors are not always known when calculating the answers to later questions. Secondly, from a programmer's point of view, it is good programming style to reduce the number of inputs by the user whenever possible to reduce errors of user input.

By studying the three example printouts, the reader should be impressed that the computer developed each printout in less than one minute. If an engineer were to make the same calculations, using a hand-held calculator, each set of calculations might take as much as an hour, unless the engineer making the calculations is very familiar with the formulas.

After reviewing the following example printout, the user should review *Figure 3-3,* which graphically illustrates what the launching cost part of the printout is showing.

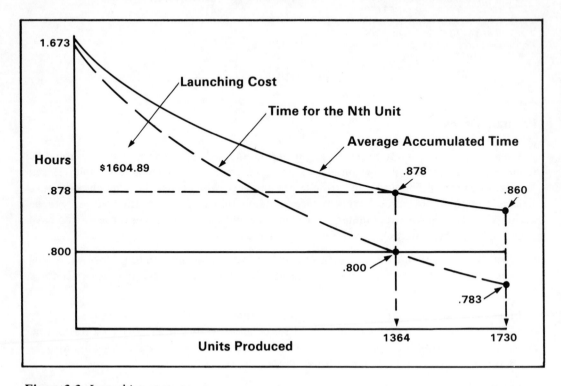

Figure 3-3. Launching costs.

An interesting aside, one of the advantages of a microcomputer is that it performs repititions of calculations in seconds. An example of this is shown in the eight line program named "Learn 2".

The interesting aspect of this short program is that the program took only three minutes to write, no more than five minutes to type into the computer and it took the computer less than 30 seconds to calculate and produce the 25 lines shown in the following printout.

Break-even Analysis

One of the most fundamental questions faced by the Manufacturing Engineer is: "Which is the least expensive machine on which to produce a part?" Often it is only a guess to determine which machine is the least costly.

Some years ago, in a paper written for the Society of Manufacturing Engineers, I developed a system for making a decision regarding machine selection using the Break-even Chart. Shown on page 95 is how the chart works.

Example:

350 parts are to be produced. Machines One and Two can produce the required operation. However, each has a different setup time, run time and shop rate. Which machine

LEARNING CURVE EXPONENTS

THE LARGER TIME OR % WAS .86 THE SMALLER WAS .8

LARGER UNITS PRODUCED WAS 1730 THE SMALLER WAS 865

THIS IS A .930233 % LEARNING CURVE

THE EXPONENT FOR THIS CURVE IS .104337

TIME FOR THE FIRST UNIT

THE AVERAGE ACCUM TIME FOR THE 1730 UNIT
WAS .86

TIME FOR THE FIRST UNIT USING A 94 % CURVE
IS 1.6732

TIME FOR THE N TH UNIT

WHERE TIME FOR THE FIRST UNIT IS 1.6732
USING A 94 % LEARNING CURVE

THE AVERAGE ACCUM TIME FOR THE N TH UNIT 1730
IS .859998

AND THE TIME FOR THE N TH 1730 UNIT ONLY
IS .783228

LAUNCHING COSTS

TIME FOR THE FIRST UNIT IS 1.6732 HOURS
STANDARD TIME IS .8 HOURS PER UNIT
SHOP RATE IS $ 15.25 DOLLARS

USING A 94 % LEARNING CURVE
STANDARD IS REACHED AT THE 1364.47 UNIT

WHEN THE 1364.47 UNIT IS REACHED AS A UNIT
THE AVERAGE ACCUM TIME UP TO THE 1364.47 UNIT
IS .878413

AND THE OFF STANDARD IS 9.80165 PER CENT

LAUNCHING COSTS ARE $ 1631.64 DOLLARS

Printout 3-2

should be used? The data can be reduced to a chart.

In the data presented on the next page, the break-even quantity is 264, which indicates three things. If the quantity to be produced is 264, either machine could be used. If the quantity to be produced is less than 264, then Machine Two should be used, and if the quantity is greater than 264, Machine One should be used. However, as handy as this decision tool is, it takes time to calculate and most Manufacturing Engineers just estimate which machine to use.

The example could become more involved if an off standard is added and if different learning rates for each machine are used.

LEARNING CURVE EXPONENTS

THE LARGER TIME OR % WAS .75 THE SMALLER WAS .65

LARGER UNITS PRODUCED WAS 500 THE SMALLER WAS 250

THIS IS A .866667 % LEARNING CURVE

THE EXPONENT FOR THIS CURVE IS .206451

TIME FOR THE FIRST UNIT

THE AVERAGE ACCUM TIME FOR THE 500 UNIT
WAS .75

TIME FOR THE FIRST UNIT USING A 88 % CURVE
IS 2.35949

TIME FOR THE N TH UNIT

WHERE TIME FOR THE FIRST UNIT IS 2.35949
USING A 88 % LEARNING CURVE

THE AVERAGE ACCUM TIME FOR THE N TH UNIT 500
IS .749999

AND THE TIME FOR THE N TH 500 UNIT ONLY
IS .61168

LAUNCHING COSTS

TIME FOR THE FIRST UNIT IS 2.35949 HOURS
STANDARD TIME IS .6 HOURS PER UNIT
SHOP RATE IS $ 18.75 DOLLARS

USING A 88 % LEARNING CURVE
STANDARD IS REACHED AT THE 555.1 UNIT

WHEN THE 555.1 UNIT IS REACHED AS A UNIT
THE AVERAGE ACCUM TIME UP TO THE 555.1 UNIT
IS .735678

AND THE OFF STANDARD IS 22.6129 PER CENT

LAUNCHING COSTS ARE $ 1412.15 DOLLARS

Printout 3-3

LEARNING CURVE EXPONENTS

THE LARGER TIME OR % WAS 10.187 THE SMALLER WAS 8.698

LARGER UNITS PRODUCED WAS 2000 THE SMALLER WAS 1000

THIS IS A .853833 % LEARNING CURVE

THE EXPONENT FOR THIS CURVE IS .227974

TIME FOR THE FIRST UNIT

THE AVERAGE ACCUM TIME FOR THE 2000 UNIT
WAS 10.187

TIME FOR THE FIRST UNIT USING A 85 % CURVE
IS 60.5372

TIME FOR THE N TH UNIT

WHERE TIME FOR THE FIRST UNIT IS 60.5372
USING A 85 % LEARNING CURVE

THE AVERAGE ACCUM TIME FOR THE N TH UNIT 2000
IS 10.187

AND THE TIME FOR THE N TH 2000 UNIT ONLY
IS 7.79851

LAUNCHING COSTS

TIME FOR THE FIRST UNIT IS 60.5372 HOURS
STANDARD TIME IS 8.5 HOURS PER UNIT
SHOP RATE IS $ 22.25 DOLLARS

USING A 85 % LEARNING CURVE
STANDARD IS REACHED AT THE 1385.12 UNIT

WHEN THE 1385.12 UNIT IS REACHED AS A UNIT
THE AVERAGE ACCUM TIME UP TO THE 1385.12 UNIT
IS 11.1033

AND THE OFF STANDARD IS 30.6276 PER CENT

LAUNCHING COSTS ARE $ 80232.1 DOLLARS

Printout 3-4

93

```
1 REM PROGRAM NAME LEARN2
2 REM WRITTEN BY J.E.NICKS
3 REM COMPUTER APLICATIONS FOR THE MANUFACTURING ENGINEER
4 REM COPYRIGHT 1981 ALL RIGHTS RESERVED
5 LPRINT"THIS PROGRAM CALCULATES LEARNING CURVE EXPONENTS"
6 LPRINT" "
10 FORX=75TO100
20 A=100/X
30 B=LOG(A)/LOG(10):C=LOG(2)/LOG(10)
40 D=B/C
50 LPRINT"FOR A";X;"% LEARNING CURVE USE EXPONENT B =";D
60 NEXTX
```

```
THIS PROGRAM CALCULATES LEARNING CURVE EXPONENTS

FOR A 75 % LEARNING CURVE USE EXPONENT B = .415038
FOR A 76 % LEARNING CURVE USE EXPONENT B = .395929
FOR A 77 % LEARNING CURVE USE EXPONENT B = .37707
FOR A 78 % LEARNING CURVE USE EXPONENT B = .358454
FOR A 79 % LEARNING CURVE USE EXPONENT B = .340076
FOR A 80 % LEARNING CURVE USE EXPONENT B = .321928
FOR A 81 % LEARNING CURVE USE EXPONENT B = .304006
FOR A 82 % LEARNING CURVE USE EXPONENT B = .286304
FOR A 83 % LEARNING CURVE USE EXPONENT B = .268817
FOR A 84 % LEARNING CURVE USE EXPONENT B = .251539
FOR A 85 % LEARNING CURVE USE EXPONENT B = .234465
FOR A 86 % LEARNING CURVE USE EXPONENT B = .217591
FOR A 87 % LEARNING CURVE USE EXPONENT B = .200913
FOR A 88 % LEARNING CURVE USE EXPONENT B = .184425
FOR A 89 % LEARNING CURVE USE EXPONENT B = .168123
FOR A 90 % LEARNING CURVE USE EXPONENT B = .152003
FOR A 91 % LEARNING CURVE USE EXPONENT B = .136061
FOR A 92 % LEARNING CURVE USE EXPONENT B = .120294
FOR A 93 % LEARNING CURVE USE EXPONENT B = .104697
FOR A 94 % LEARNING CURVE USE EXPONENT B = .0892672
FOR A 95 % LEARNING CURVE USE EXPONENT B = .0740005
FOR A 96 % LEARNING CURVE USE EXPONENT B = .0588936
FOR A 97 % LEARNING CURVE USE EXPONENT B = .0439431
FOR A 98 % LEARNING CURVE USE EXPONENT B = .0291464
FOR A 99 % LEARNING CURVE USE EXPONENT B = .0144991
FOR A 100 % LEARNING CURVE USE EXPONENT B = 0
```

Printout 3-5

Table 3-2
Break-even Chart

Data	Machine One	Machine Two
Setup hours	4.00	3.00
Run time per pc. (min.)	1.50	1.90
Work center cost per hr.	$15.00	$14.00
Setup cost	$60.00	$42.00
Run cost per pc.	1.5/60 * $15.00 = $.375 ea.	1.9/60 * $14.00 = $ .4433 ea.

Therefore:

$$\$60.00 + .375\chi = \$42.00 + .4433\chi$$
$$\$18.00 = .0683\chi$$
$$264 = \chi$$

The above calculations are based on the equation:
$$y = a + bx$$

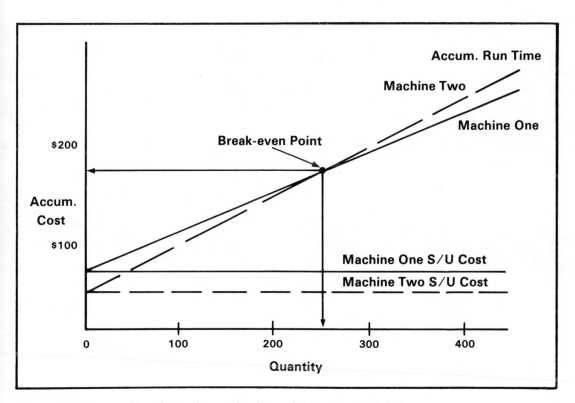

Figure 3-4. *The graphic relationship of the data calculated in Table 3-2.*

Program Name: "B.E.P"

The memory required for this program is 1956 bytes.

This program calculates the break-even point and instructs the user to use either Machine One or Two, if quantities are either more or less than the break-even point. The program also tests the hypothesis (that is, is there a break-even point?) If it is not true, the printout states so and defines which machine is the least expensive to use.

The calculation is structured so that if the break-even point is a positive number, then there is no break-even point and the program is directed to line 300 which calculates some sample cost plus or minus 10 parts from what has been calculated to determine which machine is the least expensive. Then lines 320 and 330 provide another test to discover which machine is the least expensive and directs the computer to print out the answer.

Line 180 then corrects the negative number to a positive number and proceeds with another test (lines 200 to 210) which directs the computer to print out the answer of the break-even point and which machine to use if the quantity is more or less than the break-even point.

This page shows a printout of the program "B.E.P." and following the program are four sample printouts. The reader should note than on each printout the original input data is shown for review purposes.

```
BREAK  EVEN  ANALYSIS


THE BREAK EVEN POINT IS 260.714 PARTS
FOR LESS THAN 260.714 QUANTITY USE THE GISHOLT  TURRET LATHE
FOR MORE THAN 260.714 QUANTITY USE THE W & S TURRET LATHE


FOR THE W & S TURRET LATHE THE ORIGINAL DATA WAS
SET UP HOURS 4 AND RUN TIME PER PC OF 1.5
COST PER HOUR OF $ 15.25


FOR THE GISHOLT  TURRET LATHE THE ORIGINAL DATA WAS
SET UP HOURS 3 AND RUN TIME PER PC OF 1.9
COST PER HOUR OF $ 14.25



BREAK  EVEN  ANALYSIS


THE BREAK EVEN POINT IS 768.749 PARTS
FOR LESS THEN  768.749 QUANTITY USE THE T LATHE
FOR MORE THEN 768.749 QUANTITY USE THE SP LATHE


FOR THE T LATHE THE ORIGINAL DATA WAS
SET UP HOURS 3.75 AND RUN TIME PER PC OF .5
COST PER HOUR OF $ 12.5


FOR THE SP LATHE THE ORIGINAL DATA WAS
SET UP HOURS 4 AND RUN TIME PER PC OF .45
COST PER HOUR OF $ 13
```

Printout 3-6

BREAK EVEN ANALYSIS

THERE IS NO BREAK EVEN POINT
THE N/C DRILL IS ALWAYS LESS EXPENSIVE

FOR THE GANG DRILL THE ORIGINAL DATA WAS
SET UP HOURS 3 AND RUN TIME PER PC OF 3
COST PER HOUR OF $ 12.5

FOR THE N/C DRILL THE ORIGINAL DATA WAS
SET UP HOURS 2 AND RUN TIME PER PC OF 2
COST PER HOUR OF $ 12

BREAK EVEN ANALYSIS

THE BREAK EVEN POINT IS 102.703 PARTS
FOR LESS THAN 102.703 QUANTITY USE THE GANG DRILL
FOR MORE THAN 102.703 QUANTITY USE THE N/C DRILL

FOR THE N/C DRILL THE ORIGINAL DATA WAS
SET UP HOURS 4 AND RUN TIME PER PC OF .85
COST PER HOUR OF $ 15.75

FOR THE GANG DRILL THE ORIGINAL DATA WAS
SET UP HOURS 3.5 AND RUN TIME PER PC OF 2.1
COST PER HOUR OF $ 12.11

——————————————— **Printout 3-6 continued** ———————————————


```
1 REM PROGRAM NAME BEP
2 REM WRITTEN BY J.E.NICKS
3 REM COMPUTER APPLICATIONS FOR THE MANUFACTURING ENGINEER
4 REM COPYRIGHT 1981 ALL RIGHTS RESERVED
10 CLS
11 PRINT"THIS PROGRAM CALCULATES THE BREAK EVEN POINT"
12 PRINT"FOR MACHINE OPERATIONS"
13 PRINT"AND DETERMINES WHICH MACHINE TO USE FOR A GIVEN QUANITY"
20 FORI=1TO5:PRINT:NEXT
30 PRINT"ENTER THE DATA FOR THE FIRST MACHINE"
40 INPUT"TYPE IN THE NAME OF THE FIRST MACHINE";A$
50 INPUT"SET UP HOURS FOR MACHINE 1 IS";A1
60 INPUT"RUN TIME IN MIN. PER PC. MACHINE 1 IS";A2
70 INPUT"COST PER HOUR MACHINE 1 IS";A3
75 CLS:FORI=1TO8:PRINT:NEXT
80 PRINT"ENTER THE DATA FOR THE SECOND MACHINE"
90 INPUT"TYPE IN THE NAME OF THE SECOND MACHINE";B$
```

Printout 3-7

```
100 INPUT"SET UP HOURS FOR MACHINE 2 IS";B1
110 INPUT"RUN TIME IN MIN. PER PC. MACHINE 2 IS";B2
120 INPUT"COST PER HOUR MACHINE 2 IS";B3
121 REM A4=HR PER PC,A5=S/U COST
130 A4=A2/60:B4=B2/60:A5=A1*A3:B5=B1*B3
140 REM A6=RUN COST
150 A6=A4*A3:B6=B4*B3
160 C=A5-B5:D=A6-B6:E=C/D
165 LPRINTCHR$(27);CHR$(14);"BREAK EVEN ANALYSIS"
166 FORI=1TO2:LPRINT" ":NEXT
170 IFE>1THEN300
180 E=ABS(E)
190 F=E+10:A7=A5+(A6*F):B7=B5+(B6*F)
200 IFA7>B7THEN220
210 IFA7<B7THEN260
220 LPRINT"THE BREAK EVEN POINT IS";E;"PARTS"
230 LPRINT"FOR LESS THEN ";E;"QUANTITY USE THE ";A$
240 LPRINT"FOR MORE THEN";E;"QUANTITY USE THE ";B$
250 GOTO400
260 LPRINT"THE BREAK EVEN POINT IS";E;"PARTS
270 LPRINT"FOR LESS THAN";E;"QUANTITY USE THE ";B$
280 LPRINT"FOR MORE THAN";E;"QUANTITY USE THE ";A$
290 GOTO400
300 F=E+10:F1=E-10:A7=A5+(A6*F):A8=A5+(A6*F1):A9=A7+A8
310 B7=B5+(B6*F):B8=B5+(B6*F1):B9=B7+B8
320 IFA9<B9THEN340
330 IFA9>B9THEN370
340 LPRINT"THERE IS NO BREAK EVEN POINT"
350 LPRINT"THE ";A$;" IS ALWAYS LESS EXPENSIVE"
360 GOTO400
370 LPRINT"THERE IS NO BREAK EVEN POINT"
380 LPRINT"THE ";B$;" IS ALWAYS LESS EXPENSIVE"
390 GOTO400
400 FORI=1TO2:LPRINT" ":NEXT
401 LPRINT"FOR THE ";A$;" THE ORIGINAL DATA WAS"
410 LPRINT"SET UP HOURS";A1;"AND RUN TIME PER PC OF";A2
420 LPRINT"COST PER HOUR OF $";A3
425 FORI=1TO2:LPRINT" ":NEXT
430 LPRINT"FOR THE ";B$;" THE ORIGINAL DATA WAS"
440 LPRINT"SET UP HOURS";B1;"AND RUN TIME PER PC OF";B2
450 LPRINT"COST PER HOUR OF $";B3
460 INPUT"TYPE 1 FOR ANOTHER CALCULATION OR 2 TO EXIT";Z
470 ONZGOTO10,480
480 END
```

Printout 3-7 continued

Bibliography

Konz, Stephan. *Work Design*. Columbus, OH: Grid Publishing, Inc., 1979.

Nicks, J.E. *Numerical Control for Profit*. Dearborn, MI: Society of Manufacturing Engineers, 1966.

Ostwald, Phillip F., Editor. *Manufacturing Cost Estimating*. Dearborn, MI: Society of Manufacturing Engineers, 1980.

Optional Lab Assignments

Lab Assignment 3-1 (least difficult)
Write a computer program that calculates the weight of bar stock for a multiple spindle screw machine. This program should also permit the user to input a part length, cut off tool width and material cost per pound. The printout should include the following:
1. The number of parts per bar
2. The cost per piece (including scrap and offal).
3. Bar end length.

Lab Assignment 3-2 (moderate)
In Chapter Two we reviewed how the computer can be used to produce cost estimates. Write a computer program that makes a cost estimate and also combines elements of learning curves. The user should have the option of determining what the quote quantity is and what learning curve percent to use. The computer should then adjust the quote figures to reflect a new quantity. Example: More time for a lesser quote quantity or less time for a larger quantity, depending on the quote quantity being less than or greater than where the standard data is set.

Lab Assignment 3-3 (difficult)
Write a computer program that calculates the break-even points for three machines. The user input for each machine should include the following:
1. Set up hours.
2. Run time per piece.
3. Special tooling dollars (for that machine).
4. A shop rate for each machine.

CHAPTER 4

Machine Capability Studies

An important aspect of manufacturing process planning is the establishment of process dimensions and process tolerances. A process dimension is defined as a dimension that differs from the finished blueprint dimension in that additional work must be performed on that surface of the part to produce the desired finished part dimension. Examples are rough turn, semifinish grind and finish grind. A process tolerance is defined as the tolerance associated with a process dimension. The problem of establishing process length dimensions and tolerances becomes more acute when the engineer processing the part realizes that in many cases the length tolerance must be shared or budgeted from the finished blueprint tolerance. Additional information on this subject is defined in Chapter 11.

At this point in the process development, the age-old problem of determining whether the machine being used can hold these tolerances becomes a factor. One of the most important duties of the Manufacturing Engineer doing process planning work is to establish process tolerances that can be maintained on the shop floor. While there are many good textbooks on the subject of statistical quality control, many fail to stress this important aspect of manufacturing.

The objective of this chapter is three-fold. First, it explores the need for some method of establishing a systematic way to determine process capabilities. Then, we will review the math necessary and present a hand-calculated example of a typical capability study. Lastly, we will review a short computer program which calculates process capabilities.

Quality

Only very large companies have Quality Control or Quality Assurance Engineers. Companies that do not have these functions require the Manufacturing Engineer to be responsible for some, if not all, of the Quality Control Engineering duties. This responsibility is often shunned because the Manufacturing Engineer may not be trained to do this type of work, or the nature of this responsibility may not be well defined.

For most of us, the term, Quality Control, implies floor inspection. Floor inspection, of course, is fast becoming an obsolete practice whereby the floor inspector checks the work of a production operator once in the morning and again in the afternoon, whether it is necessary or not. This comment might sound overly critical of the inspection department's efforts, and it is intended to be. Magazine articles and editorials have been written recently on the question: "Why can't American industry produce a quality product?" During the past year, Japanese manufacturing specialists have been invited to this country to speak to our American automobile manufacturers on the subject of producing a quality automobile. This is true irony.

Machine Capability Studies

While this chapter makes no pretense of solving all of the quality problems that exist in America today, it does set forth the basic idea of responsibility for quality, from an engineering viewpoint, and a very simple method of answering fundamental questions. It is the author's opinion that subjects such as planning for quality, types of gaging, gaging frequency and machine capability studies are the direct responsibility of the Manufacturing Engineer in companies that do not have Quality Assurance Engineering functions. This chapter addresses itself to the latter of these efforts: namely, machine tool capability studies.

There are many reasons why machine capability studies are an important part of any well-run factory. Listed below are some of the reasons.
1. A capability study can answer these questions: Is the machine capable of holding the print or process tolerance? If not, what tolerances can the machine be expected to hold?
2. Annually most factories develop some type of capital equipment budget. The details of this budget usually reflect acquisition of equipment for one of several reasons.
    a. New equipment for capacity.
    b. New equipment for methods improvement.
    c. New equipment for replacement of old equipment.
Capability studies should be conducted in each case. To illustrate this point, we will use an example where new equipment is being considered to replace older equipment. One of three decisions can be made.
    a. Patch up the equipment and live with it for another season.
    b. Overhaul the equipment to make it like new.
    c. Purchase the new machine.
In each case cited above, a capability study is an important aspect of making an intelligent decision. To further illustrate this point, if a machine is required to hold a tolerance of $\pm$ .005 inches (0.13 mm) and has a capability of holding $\pm$ .006 inches (0.15 mm), perhaps something can be done to make it possible to live with it another season. However, if the machine's tolerance holding capability is $\pm$ .010 inches (0.25 mm), an entirely different decision might be made. In either event, before the decision is made, the magnitude of the problem must be measured.
3. Purchasing new equipment is like having Christmas in July, with many of its pleasant and sometimes not so pleasant surprises. It is somewhat akin to opening that gift you have been waiting for only to find it is a gaudy, green tie that can be worn only on St. Patrick's Day. With the cost of new equipment skyrocketing, it is good management not only to try a machine out on the builder's floor, but also to calculate what its capability is before you discover any surprises on your factory floor.

Many companies now purchasing new equipment are adopting the practice (in the purchase order by contract) that the new equipment must be able to produce equal to or less than five-eights of the blueprint tolerance. This contractual requirement represents an insurance policy for the purchaser to assure that the new machine will produce well within quality limits for a reasonable time.

Although there are differences between conducting a process capability study and conducting a machine capability study (different questions are used), the method of conducting the studies and methods of calculating the studies are the same.

Calculated by Hand

Presented on the next several pages is a machine capability study calculated by hand and then a computer program that does the same engineering job. Before we review those details, several comments should be mentioned about the ground rules for conducting a capability study. When conducting a machine capability study, at least 64 consecutive parts should be measured, thereby obtaining a sample large enough to create confidence in the results of the study. Smaller sample sizes tend to produce bias results that can be misleading. While there are ways to calculate the relationship of sample size to confidence limits (see Chapter Seven), it is generally acceptable in industry that a 64-piece consecutive sample is adequate. If the machine is producing more than one dimension, then the study should include a capability for each axis being used. This will necessitate measurement of more than one feature on the part under study. For example, if a machine is tooled to produce two lengths and two diameters on the part being machined, then the machine capability study should include at least one length and one diameter. The reader will recognize that measurement type gages must be used for capability studies and that go-not go gages, attribute gages and functional gages are not satisfactory. This raises an important question that could be the subject of an entire book: How should a part be gaged?

Another point for consideration is the number of spindles on a machine. A six-spindle automatic screw machine should be viewed as six different machines and a capability study should be made on each spindle. Sample studies often prove that poor quality on one of these machines can be traced to a single spindle.

Many factories still use the practice of controlling critical dimensions with the use of an average and range chart, or $\overline{X}$ & R chart. Data collected from these charts over a long period of time can be used to determine what quality level the machine has been producing. The engineer should recognize, however, that this quality record was developed with the operator making tool changes and adjustments and it does not reflect what the machine's capability is in a pure sense. While the $\overline{X}$ & R chart is an excellent operator's control tool, conducting a capability study from these data leaves many unanswered questions. One of the objectives of the capability study is to separate the machine and its performance from the operator's performance.

The way the question is presented is important. For example, "Is the machine capable of holding tolerance without undue operator attention for tool adjustment?" Or, "Is the machine capable of holding tolerance without regard to how much time the operator spends making adjustments?" For this reason, capability studies are conducted by using consecutive parts. There are two general math models used for calculation of sigma (σ). Both produce the same results but are used for different purposes. If a study is calculated by hand, it is easier to work with deviations from a number rather than use the number itself. This is called "coded numbers." The general math model for hand calculation is:

$$\sigma = i \sqrt{\frac{\Sigma f d^2}{\Sigma f} - \left(\frac{\Sigma f d}{\Sigma f}\right)^2}$$

Where:

σ = sigma or standard deviation
i = cell interval
Σfd^2 = sum of all frequency times the deviation squared
Σf = sum of all frequency
Σfd = sum of all frequency times the deviation

Where:

$$\overline{x} = A + \frac{\Sigma fd}{\Sigma f} i$$

Where:

$\overline{x}$ = average
A = estimated average
d = sum of all frequency times the deviation from A
Σf = sum of all frequency
i = cell interval

A hand calculated example is shown in *Table 4-1.* For the sample study used in this chapter, a form is used to assist the engineer in collecting and calculating data. *Figure 4-1* is called a "tally sheet" and represents the raw data as collected from the factory floor. The tally sheet

Machine Name:	Turret Lathe	Date:	4/12/81
Part Number:	12345	Part Name:	Cylinder
Dimension:	1.000	Tolerance:	± .005
Cell Interval:	.001	Length/Diameter:	Length

Measurement

.992		
.993		
.994	1	Lower Process Tolerance
.995	111	
.996	⊬⊬⊤ 1	
.997	⊬⊬⊤	
.998	⊬⊬⊤ 111	
.999	⊬⊬⊤ ⊬⊬⊤	
1.000	⊬⊬⊤ ⊬⊬⊤ ⊬⊬⊤ 1	
1.001	⊬⊬⊤ ⊬⊬⊤ 1	
1.002	⊬⊬⊤ ⊬⊬⊤	
1.003	⊬⊬⊤ 11	
1.004	⊬⊬⊤	
1.005	11	Upper Process Tolerance
1.006	1	
1.007		
1.008		

Figure 4-1. Machine Capability Study Tally Sheet. The number of recordings total 85.

Table 4-1
Frequency Distribution Data Chart

Machine Name:	Turret Lathe			Date:		4/16/81
Part Number:	12345			Part Name:		Cylinder
Dimension:	1.000			Tolerance:		± .005
Cell Interval	.001			Length/Diameter:		Length

Measurement (x)	Frequency (f)	Deviation	$f * d$	d^2	$f * d^2$
.994	1	-6	-6	36	36
.995	3	-5	-15	25	75
.996	6	-4	-24	16	96
.997	5	-3	-15	9	45
.998	8	-2	-16	4	32
.999	10	-1	-10	1	10
$A = 1.000$	16	0	0	0	0
1.001	11	1	11	1	11
1.002	10	2	20	4	40
1.003	7	3	21	9	63
1.004	5	4	20	16	80
1.005	2	5	10	25	50
1.006	1	6	6	36	36
	$\Sigma f = 85$		$\Sigma fd = 2$		$\Sigma fd^2 = 574$

$$\overline{x} = A + \frac{\Sigma fd}{\Sigma f} i = 1.000 + \frac{2}{85} * .001 = 1.000235 = 1.000$$

$$\sigma = i \sqrt{\frac{\Sigma fd^2}{\Sigma f} - \left(\frac{\Sigma fd}{\Sigma f}\right)^2} = .001\sqrt{\frac{574}{85} - \left(\frac{2}{85}\right)^2} = .00259 = .0026$$

$$\overline{x} + 3\sigma = 1.000 + (3 * .0026) = 1.0078$$

$$\overline{x} - 3\sigma = 1.000 - (3 * .0026) = .9922$$

Print Tolerance = $1.00 \pm .005$
Capability   = $1.000 \pm .0078$

Note: A = Estimated Average = 1.000

provides two functions. One, to collect the data and secondly, the histogram resulting from the tally can be viewed to determine its normality.

Notes on *Figure 4-2*

1. The print nominal dimension and the machine's actual average are the same. Therefore, it is not necessary to attempt to move the machine's actual working average. If, however, there were a major difference (as shown below), an effort should be made to adjust the machine's average to better conform to the nominal dimension because the machine would produce fewer defective parts. The $\overline{X}$ & R Chart is a useful tool in adjusting the machine's average.

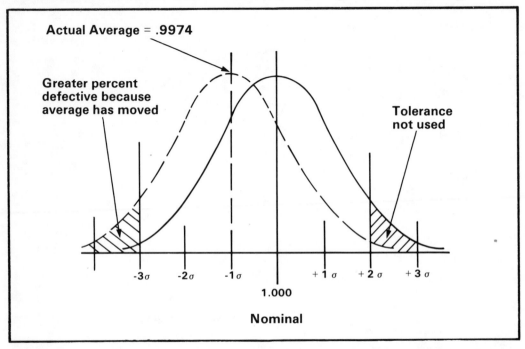

Figure 4-2. This bell curve shows the effect of moving the machine's average if the operator does not control the existing average.

2. A prediction of the percent defective parts can be made by the following calculation:

$$\frac{X-\overline{X}}{\sigma} = \text{units of sigma} = \frac{\text{Upper control limit} - \overline{X}}{\sigma}$$

$$\text{or} = \frac{\text{Lower control limit} - \overline{X}}{\sigma}$$

$$\frac{1.005 - 1.000}{.0026} = 1.92 \text{ units of sigma} = 48.6\% \text{ under the curve,}$$
or 1.4% defective parts over the high limit.

In this example, because the actual average and the nominal dimension are the same, a like relationship exists on the other end of the curve, i.e., 1.4% defective parts below low limit.

3. The sum of over the high limit and below the low limit equals 2.8% defective parts in the process.

4. Considering the normal variation expected in the actual average as a result of tool wear and the general shop practice of setting tools on or near low limit and letting the parts grow in size as the tool wears, the machine's actual average variation could be expected to vary $\pm$ one sigma. If this is true, while the machine's length capability on this part is $\pm$ .0078 inches (0.198 mm) it would not be unusual to find parts as large as 1.0104 inches (25.664 mm) or as small as .9896 inches (25.135 mm), if the average is not controlled.

5. The histogram produced in *Figure 4-1* looks normal; that is, it is not skewed or bimodal.

The microcomputer can be an asset to the engineer by rapidly calculating machine capability studies. A simple computer program is included in this chapter which performs most of the mundane tasks. However, before the program is examined, several of the standard deviation formulas should be reviewed.

The formula for standard deviation presented earlier in this chapter is a derivation of the formula presented below. The purpose of the previous formula is to suit the convenience of performing the calculations by hand. Some revision of the basic formula is required to facilitate easier programming.

The base formula for standard deviation is:

$$\sigma = \sqrt{\frac{\Sigma(x-\bar{x})^2}{N}}$$

The computer program named "STDEV" uses a math model derivation of this base equation. The printout shows the results of the calculations made by the computer, and is shown on page 110. The reader should note that the printout also provides a histrogram. Observing the shape of this histogram, it appears normal.

Program Name: "STDEV"

The memory required for this program is 1904 bytes.

Because this is a very common computer program, no attempt will be made to review each line of the program. Several comments will be made about the program itself. First, the length of time required to write this program was just under one hour. Secondly, if an engineer understands the principles of the bell curve and how it can be used to determine machine capability, it is not necessary to understand the math involved or, for that matter, how to write this program. The machine capability program can be executed by a user and not necessarily by the person who programmed it. This, of course, permits a less-skilled person to be responsible for the routine chores of conducting capability studies on a regular basis. In a well-organized engineering department, this type of data should be readily available for all processes in the plant.

Comments

In the following paragraphs, several comments will be made about individual program lines with which the reader may not be familiar.

Line 10 DIMX(25), F(25), N(25)

This line dimensions the array with a maximum number of entries that can be made. X is the variable for size, F is the variable for frequency and N is the variable for number of entries. Without this dimension statement, the computer would default after 10 such entries. The DIM statement reserves computer memory for entries greater than 10.

Line 130   INPUT "ENTER X, THEN THE FREQUENCY, F, SEPARATE BY A COMMA"; X(I), F(I)

X(I) and F(I) are called subscripted variables in the FOR-NEXT loop I. The purpose of using subscripted variables is to retain these variables in the computer memory. For example, the first time through the loop the computer will place the first X (.995) in a memory location coded X(1). The second time through the loop the second X (.996) will be placed in another memory location (mailbox) coded X(2), etc. The necessity for doing this is to have the ability to retrieve these values later in the program by recalling them from their mailbox locations, X(1), X(2).

Line 170   X1 = X1 + X(I)
Line 180   X2 = X2 + X(I)↑ * F(I)
Line 190   F1 = F1 + F(I): X3 = X3 + (X(I) * F(I))

The formula shown earlier which read:

$$\sigma = \sqrt{\frac{\Sigma\ (x-\bar{x})^2}{N}}$$

must be revised for easier programming. The average, or $\bar{x}$, is not known by the computer before all the data is entered. For this reason, the following lines are written:

Line 170 is an accumulation of all the X's (sum of all X's).
Line 180 squares X and multiplies it times that X's frequency.
Line 190 sums the frequency of that X and sums the X value times the frequency.
Line 220 S = SQR ((X2 - (((X3/ F1) ²) * F1))/ F1)

This line produces sigma and when translated back to our original formula it looks like this:

$$\sigma = \sqrt{\frac{\left(\Sigma x^2 f - \left(\left(\frac{\Sigma f x}{\Sigma n}\right)^2 * \Sigma n\right)\right)}{\Sigma n}}$$

Line 250 starts the histogram printout.

Lines 270 through 330. Lines 275 and 277 are tests to print out the specifications in lines 276 and 279. A nested FOR-NEXT loop is required to first print out the original data (the I loop) and the series of X's (the A loop) before starting the loop for a second time.

The computer program for machine capability studies which follows illustrates the computer's number crunching abilities and some of its graphics capabilities.

The reader may be interested at this point in a bit of history. Some years ago, one of the automotive companies developed what can be referred to as a poor man's capability study. The system was called SCAM, short for Systematic Capability Acceptance Method. The system was based on selecting 64 consecutive parts produced by a machine or process and measuring them in groups of 8, 16 and 32. This type of capability study, developed before the advent of the microcomputer, provided an easy way for engineers to evaluate capabilities. This approach to

108

SYSTEMATIC CAPABILITY ACCEPTANCE METHOD

Part Name _____ Number _____

Stage of completion of part _____

Operation _____ No. Stations, Die Cavities, etc. _____

Type Machine _____ Identification No. _____

Prod. Rate _____ Cycle Time _____ Speed _____

Operator _____ Dept. _____

Material _____ DHN _____

Specification _____ Tolerance _____ 0- _____

Provide any other desirable information on the reverse side of this sheet. Consider: Sketch of part showing dimension measured, mmeasuring method, tooling and fixtures on the machine, other available sets of tooling and fixtures, coolant, stock identification, or any disturbance affecting the operation during study.

Study request by _____ Date _____

Reason _____

Sample Group Number

	1	2	3		4	
1						
2						
3						
4						
5						
6						
7						
8						

Range

Multiply by 2.11 _____	R _____ x 2.11 _____ /T _____	Ave. Range of 4 Samples _____	Add 8 Ranges	Divide by 8 to obtain R _____
Divide by Tolerance _____		Multiply by 2.11 _____	_____	Multiply by 2.11 _____
Reject above 1.40 Accept below .33 for a confidence level of 99%	1.22 .44	Divide by Tolerance _____	_____ _____ _____ _____	Divide by Tolerance _____
		Reject above 1.07 Accept below .54	_____ _____	Reject above .97 Accept below .62

Calculated σ _____ 6 σ/Tolerance _____ Reject above .8; accept .8 or below

Analyst _____ Decision _____ Date _____

Figure 4-3. *A sample SCAM Data Sheet.*

109

```
1 REM PROGRAM NAME STDEV
2 REM WRITTEN BY J.E.NICKS
3 REM COMPUTER APPLICATIONS FOR THE MANUFACTURING ENGINEER
4 REM COPYRIGHT 1981 ALL RIGHTS RESERVED
10 DIMX(25),F(25),N(25)
15 CLS
20 PRINT"THIS PROGRAM CALCULATES STANDARD DEVIATION"
30 PRINT"FOR MACHINE CAPABILITY STUDIES"
40 PRINT"AND WILL ACCEPT UP TO 25 ENTRIES"
50 PRINT"ENTER THE DATA ASKED FOR BY THE COMPUTER"
60 PRINT
70 PRINT
71 PRINT"TYPE IN THE MACHINE NAME"
72 INPUTA$
73 PRINT"TYPE IN THE MACHINE NUMBER"
74 INPUTB$
75 PRINT"TYPE IN THE MAX AND MIN SPEC., SEPARATE BY A COMMA"
76 INPUTS1,S2
77 INPUT"TYPE IN THE UNIT OF MEASURE";U
78 CLS
80 PRINT"INPUT THE TOTAL NUMBER OF LINE ENTRIES"
90 PRINT"EACH LINE ENTRY IS MADE UP OF A FREQUENCY OF X"
100 PRINT"AND THE VALUE OF X"
105 PRINT"START WITH THE SMALLEST ENTRY FIRST"
110 INPUT"TOTAL LINE ENTRIES";N
120 FORI=1TON
130 INPUT"ENTER X , THEN THE FREQUENCY , F, SEPARATE BY A COMMA";X(I),F(I)
140 REM X1=SUM X
150 REM X2=SUM X SQR
160 REM F1=SUM F
170 X1=X1+X(I)
180 X2=X2+X(I)[2*F(I)
190 F1=F1+F(I):X3=X3+(X(I)*F(I))
200 NEXTI
210 REM S=STD DEV
220 S=SQR((X2-(((X3/F1)[2)*F1))/F1)
240 XB=X3/F1
241 LPRINTCHR$(27);CHR$(14);"MACHINE CAPABILITY STUDY"
242 LPRINTCHR$(138)
243 LPRINT"MACHINE NAME   ";A$
244 LPRINT"MACHINE NUMBER   ";B$
245 LPRINTCHR$(138)
246 LPRINTCHR$(138)
250 LPRINTTAB(5);"ITEM";TAB(10);"FREQ";TAB(15);"MEASUREMENT";TAB(30);"BAR CHART"
260 LPRINTCHR$(138)
265 S3=S1+U
270 FORI=1TON
275 IFS2=X(I)THEN276ELSE277
276 LPRINT"        -----------SPEC-----------";S2:GOTO277    ◄── Lines 270-330
277 IFX(I)=S3THEN279ELSE280                                       print out
279 LPRINT"        -----------SPEC-----------";S1:GOTO280         the histogram
280 LPRINTTAB(5);I;TAB(10);F(I);TAB(18);X(I);
290 FORA=1TOF(I)
300 LPRINTTAB(30);"X";
310 NEXTA
320 LPRINT""
330 NEXTI
340 LPRINTCHR$(138):LPRINTCHR$(138)
350 LPRINT"THE AVERAGE IS";XB;"AND THE STANDARD DEVIATION IS";S
390 SA=(S1+S2)/2
400 R1=S*3:C=S*6
410 LPRINT,"LOW","AVERAGE","HIGH"
420 LPRINT"SPEC",S2,SA,S1
430 LPRINT""
440 LPRINT"ACTUAL",XB-R1,XB,XB+R1
```

Printout 4-1

```
450 LPRINT""
460 IFC>S1-S2THEN470ELSE480
470 LPRINT"THE MACHINE IS NOT CAPABLE":GOTO510
480 LPRINT"THE MACHINE IS CAPABLE":GOTO510
490 LPRINT"THE MACHINE IS NOT CAPABLE":GOTO510
500 LPRINT"THE MACHINE IS CAPABLE"
510 LPRINT"THE MACHINE IS CAPABLE OF";C;"WHICH IS 6 SIGMA"
520 END
```

——————————————— **Printout 4-1 continued** ———————————————

```
MACHINE CAPABILITY STUDY

MACHINE NAME  LE BLOND N/C LATHE
MACHINE NUMBER   12345


    ITEM FREQ MEASUREMENT     BAR CHART

      1    3      .995        XXX
    ----------SPEC----------- .996
      2    6      .996        XXXXX
      3   10      .997        XXXXXXXXX
      4   14      .998        XXXXXXXXXXXXX
      5   16      .999        XXXXXXXXXXXXXXX
      6   20     1            XXXXXXXXXXXXXXXXXXX
      7   18     1.001        XXXXXXXXXXXXXXXXX
      8   15     1.002        XXXXXXXXXXXXXX
      9   10     1.003        XXXXXXXXX
     10    6     1.004        XXXXX
    ----------SPEC----------- 1.004
     11    1     1.005        X


THE AVERAGE IS .99995 AND THE STANDARD DEVIATION IS 2.23624E-03
              LOW           AVERAGE         HIGH
SPEC          .996          1               1.004
ACTUAL        .993241       .99995          1.00666
THE MACHINE IS NOT CAPABLE
THE MACHINE IS CAPABLE OF .0134175 WHICH IS 6 SIGMA
```

Printout 4-2

determine capability, however, had rather severe limitations. The results of this study concluded in a yes-no answer. A typical SCAM data sheet is provided for the reader in *Figure 4-3*.

It is the author's view that every machine and every process on the factory floor should have a capability study conducted at least once per year. As mentioned earlier, the value of supplying this vital data to Manufacturing Engineers who are doing the process planning function and to the maintenance department can well pay for a microcomputer. Having a clear understanding of what tolerances a machine is capable of holding is an important step in controlling scrap, rework and ultimately final quality and costs.

One final thought about vendor quality control. Small battery-operated microcomputers that fit compactly in a briefcase are now available for a modest investment. For most companies, quality control extends beyond the factory floor into vendor shops. Many companies now perform quality audits of supplying vendors. Coupling these audits with an easy way to calculate machine capabilities seems a natural next step.

Bibliography

Hansen, Bertrand L. *Quality Control Theory & Appliations*. Englewood Cliffs, NJ: Prentice-Hall, Inc., 1963.

Hayes, Glenn E. and Romig, Harry G., *Modern Quality Control*. Bruce—A Division of Benzinger Bruce & Glencoe, Inc., 1977.

Juran, J. M., Editor-in-Chief. *Quality Control Handbook*, 3rd Ed. New York: McGraw Hill Book Co., 1974.

Optional Lab Assignments

Lab Assignment 4-1 (least difficult)
Write a computer program that calculates the poisson expotential limit. The formula is:

$$P(c) = \frac{\mu'^c \; e-\mu'}{c!}$$

Where:

$\mu' = Np'$
N = Sample Size
p' = % Defective
e = 2.718 + Natural Logs
c = Number of Events
$!$ = Factorial

Lab Assignment 4-2 (moderate)

Write a computer program that calculates the points on an Operational Characteristic (O.C.) curve. (See: *Quality Control Handbook* for the details of construction.)

Lab Assignment 4-3 (difficult)

Change the "STDEV" program to include a calculation of area under the curve for data inputted into the program and then calculate the percent of parts out of specification, if such is the case. The area under the curve formula is shown below. A knowledge of calculus is required.

$$Y = \frac{1}{\sigma\sqrt{2\pi}} \; e - (x - \mu)^2/2\sigma^2$$

Where:

π = 3.1416
e = 2.718 + Natural Logs
μ = Population Average
σ = Population Standard Deviation

CHAPTER 5

Equipment Justification

As interest rates continue to soar to new heights, the competition for money becomes keener. In the "good old days" when a Manufacturing Engineer had a "good" idea and needed $25,000 for a new automatic assembly machine, he could go to his friendly controller and, if his story sounded convincing, he could get the needed money. But that was before the advent of money markets and other short-term investment schemes that bring high rates of return.

Today, the need for the Manufacturing Engineer to understand equipment justification principles is imperative. Productivity in the U.S. is at a standstill while inflation is rampant. One of the key elements needed to correct this national problem is new and modern equipment that produces product for less. But, production for less costs money, and money is tight in many companies.

The Manufacturing Engineer competes for money just as the banker, stockbroker, money market manager or the company treasurer. However, in terms of understanding the money parade, the Manufacturing Engineer is last on the list. This is not to say that with your new computer and a basic knowledge of money your problems will be over. Engineers must understand the questions before an attempt can be made to formulate the answers.

Most Manufacturing Engineers who have worked with accounting people find themselves ill-at-ease. The accountant's world is filled with numbers, profit or loss, depreciation, tax credits and investments, while the engineer's world is filled with mechanical devices, electronic devices and inventing ideas to reduce product cost. For these reasons (and more), this chapter discusses four subjects.

1. Money formulas.
2. Depreciation.
3. Popular methods of investment analysis.
4. Capital equipment budgeting.

The objective of this chapter is to show the Manufacturing Engineer that with a microcomputer and an expanded knowledge of money computation, the engineer is on a more-equal footing to compete for the money necessary for productivity improvement.

The first program in this chapter is named "MONEY". This program is designed to familiarize the Manufacturing Engineer with several money type formulas used to calculate initial values, future values and interest rates. While the Manufacturing Engineer may not be required to make such calculations on the job, this program is included here for educational purposes.

Program Name: "MONEY"

This program requires 3481 bytes and is divided into four modules.
1. Future value of an investment.
2. Initial value of an investment.
3. Effective interest rates.
4. Nominal interest rates.

A formula for each of the modules will be shown.

Future Value of an Investment

The future value of an investment is the future worth of X (dollars) invested at i (interest rate) compounded for a given number of years.

$$T = P (1 + i/N)^{N * Y}$$

Where:

T = total future value
P = initial investment
i = interest rate
N = number of compounding periods per year
Y = number of years

The TRS-80[1] calculates a correct number using the first formula for $N = 20$. For N greater than 20, natural logs should be used. This, however, develops a very slight error. When natural logs are used to calculate effective interest rate, the effect is the same as continuous compounding.

Initial Value of an Investment

The initial value of an investment is the inverse of future value. Stated another way, how much money must be invested to produce a future value?

$$P = T (1 + i/N)^{-N * Y}$$
$$\text{or}$$
$$P = T/(1 + i/N)^{N * Y}$$

If your computer will not accept negative exponents, the second formula must be used. All other variables remain the same, as in future value.

Effective Interest Rate

Effective interest rate is the interest rate produced by an investment of an initial value that generates a future value.

$$E = (1 + i/N)^{N}-1 \text{ or } E = EXP(i) -1$$

Where:

E = Effective Interest Rate

---

[1]*TRS-80 is a trademark of the Radio Shack Division of Tandy Corporation.*

It may be of some value for the engineer to determine at what point the computer defaults. The simple program below will determine this.

```
10  FOR N = 1 TO 100
20  E = ((1 + (.06/N))↑N)-1
30  LPRINT N,E
40  NEXT N
```

Nominal Interest Rate

The nominal interest rate is the inverse of effective interest rate.

$$i = N(T/P)^{\frac{1}{N-Y}} - N$$

On the next page is a typical printout from the "MONEY" program. The value of this program for the engineer lies in its usage for gathering facts quickly pertaining to the competition for money. This can give the engineer a "quick" feel for investment ideas. For example, in the first part of the printout, an expenditure of $10,000 must yield in excess of $17,000 in three years to compete with current money market rates.

Again, this program is included more for its educational value rather than everyday usage. Working with this program for a short period of time, the engineer can gain insight concerning the real value of money under various investment ideas.

Program Comments

This program is a good example of just how easy it is to use BASIC. The reader should note that there are six lines of program content that perform math operations. The remaining parts of the program consist of user instructions and LPRINT statements.

```
1 REM PROGRAM NAME MONEY
2 REM WRITTEN BY J.E.NICKS
3 REM COMPUTER APPLICATIONS FOR THE MANUFACTURING ENGINEER
4 REM COPYRIGHT 1981 ALL RIGHTS RESERVED
10 CLS
20 PRINT"THIS PROGRAM CALCULATES THE RELATIONSHIP"
30 PRINT"OF VERIOUS TYPES OF INVESTMENTS"
40 PRINT:PRINT:PRINT
50 PRINT"TYPE IN THE MODULE NUMBER YOU WISH TO WORK WITH"
60 PRINT:PRINT
70 PRINT"FUTURE VALUE OF AN INVESTMENT---------------1"
80 PRINT"INITIAL VALUE OF AN INVESTMENT-------------2"      ◄── Note the user menu
90 PRINT"EFFECTIVE INTEREST RATE--------------------3"
100 PRINT"NOMINAL INTEREST RATE---------------------4"
110 INPUTX
120 ONXGOTO130,300,470,620
130 CLS:REM FUTURE VALUE
131 PRINT"THIS MODULE CALCULATES THE FUTURE VALUE OF AN INVESTMENT"
132 PRINT"BY INPUTTING AN INITIAL INVESTMENT,INTEREST RATE AND"
133 PRINT"YEARS THE INVESTMENT IS OUTSTANDING"
```

Printout 5-1

```
134 PRINT:PRINT
140 INPUT"TYPE IN INITIAL INVESTMENT DOLLARS";P
150 INPUT"TYPE IN INTEREST RATE (AS A DECIMAL)";I
160 INPUT"TYPE IN NO. OF COMPOUNDING PERIODS";N
170 INPUT"TYPE IN NO. OF YEARS";Y
180 T=P*(1+(I/N))[(N*Y)
190 LPRINTTAB(20);CHR$(27);CHR$(14);"FUTURE VALUE"
200 LPRINTCHR$(138)
210 LPRINTTAB(10);"FOR AN INITIAL INVESTMENT OF $";P;"DOLLARS"
220 LPRINTTAB(10);"AT AN INTEREST RATE OF";I;"PERCENT"
230 LPRINTTAB(10);"COMPOUNDED ";N;"PERIODS PER YEAR"
240 LPRINTTAB(10);"FOR";Y;"YEARS"
250 LPRINTTAB(10);"THE FUTURE VALUE IS $";T;"DOLLARS"
255 LPRINTCHR$(138):LPRINTCHR$(138)
260 PRINT"TYPE 1 FOR MENU-----2 FOR ANOTHER CALCULATION"
270 PRINT"OR 3 TO EXIT"
280 INPUTX
290 ONXGOTO10,130,800
300 CLS:REM INITIAL VALUE
301 PRINT"THIS MODULE CALCULATES THE INITIAL VALUE OF AN INVESTMENT"
302 PRINT"BY INPUTTING THE FUTURE VALUE OF THE INVESTMENT,INTEREST"
303 PRINT"RATE AND YEARS OUTSTANDING FOR THE INVESTMENT"
304 PRINT:PRINT
310 INPUT"TYPE IN FUTURE INVESTMENT DOLLARS";T
320 INPUT"TYPE IN INTEREST RATE (AS A DECIMAL)";I
330 INPUT"TYPE IN NO. OF COMPOUNDING PERIODS";N
340 INPUT"TYPE IN NO. OF YEARS";Y
350 P=T/((1+(I/N))[(N*Y))
360 LPRINTTAB(20);CHR$(27);CHR$(14);"INITIAL VALUE"
370 LPRINTCHR$(138)
380 LPRINTTAB(10);"FOR A FUTURE INVESTMENT OF $";T;"DOLLARS"
390 LPRINTTAB(10);"AT AN INTEREST RATE OF";I;"PERCENT"
400 LPRINTTAB(10);"COMPOUNDED";N;"PERIODS PER YEAR"
410 LPRINTTAB(10);"FOR";Y;"YEARS"
420 LPRINTTAB(10);"THE INITIAL VALUE IS $";P;"DOLLARS"
425 LPRINTCHR$(138):LPRINTCHR$(138)
430 PRINT"TYPE 1 FOR MENU --------2 FOR ANOTHER CALCULATION"
440 PRINT"OR 3 TO ENIT"
450 INPUTX
460 ONXGOTO10,300,800
470 CLS:REM EFFECTIVE INTEREST RATE
471 PRINT"THIS MODULE CALCULATES EFFECTIVE INTEREST RATE"
472 PRINT"EFFECTIVE INTEREST RATE WILL VARY DEPENDING ON THE"
473 PRINT"NUMBER OF COMPOUNDING PERIODS"
474 PRINT:PRINT
480 INPUT"TYPE IN NOMINAL INTEREST RATE (AS A DECIMAL)";I
490 INPUT"TYPE IN NO. OF COMPOUNDING PERIODS";N
500 IFN>20THEN520ELSE510  ⟵  Note the IF-THEN test in Line 500
510 E=((1+(I/N))[N)-1:GOTO530
520 E=EXP(I)-1:GOTO530
530 LPRINTTAB(20);CHR$(27);CHR$(14);"EFFECTIVE INTEREST RATE"
540 LPRINTCHR$(138)
550 LPRINTTAB(10);"FOR A NOMINAL INTEREST RATE OF";I;"PERCENT"
560 LPRINTTAB(10);"AND FOR";N;"COMPOUNDING PERIODS"
570 LPRINTTAB(10);"THE EFFECTIVE INTEREST RATE IS";E;"PERCENT"
575 LPRINTCHR$(138):LPRINTCHR$(138)
580 PRINT"TYPE 1 FOR MENU ----------2 FOR ANOTHER CALCULATION"
590 PRINT"OR 3 TO EXIT"
600 INPUTX
610 ONXGOTO10,470,800
620 CLS:REM NOMINAL INTEREST RATE
621 PRINT"THIS MODULE CALCULATES BOTH EFFECTIVE AND NOMINAL"
```

Printout 5-1 continued

```
622 PRINT"INTEREST RATES BASED UPON AN INITIAL INVESTMENT AND"
623 PRINT"THE FUTURE VALUE OF THAT INVESTMENT"
624 PRINT:PRINT
630 INPUT"TYPE IN INITIAL INVESTMENT";P
640 INPUT"TYPE IN FUTURE VALUE";T
650 INPUT"TYPE IN NO. OF COMPOUNDING PERIODS";N
660 INPUT"TYPE IN NO. OF YEARS";Y
670 I=(N*((T/P)[(1/(N*Y))))-N
680 E=((T/P)[(1/Y))-1
690 LPRINTTAB(20);CHR$(27);CHR$(14);"NOMINAL INTEREST RATE"
700 LPRINTCHR$(138)
710 LPRINTTAB(10);"FOR AN INITIAL INVESTMENT OF $";P;"DOLLARS"
720 LPRINTTAB(10);"WITH A FUTURE VALUE OF $";T;"DOLLARS"
730 LPRINTTAB(10);"AND WITH";N;"COMPOUNDING PERIODS FOR";Y;"YEARS"
740 LPRINTTAB(10);"THE NOMINAL INTEREST RATE IS";I;"PERCENT"
750 LPRINTTAB(10);"AND THE EFFECTIVE INTEREST RATE IS";E;"PERCENT"
755 LPRINTCHR$(138):LPRINTCHR$(138)
760 PRINT"TYPE 1 FOR MENU ---------2 FOR ANOTHER CALCULATION"
770 PRINT"OR 3 TO ENIT"
780 INPUTX
790 ONXGOTO10,620,800
800 END
```

I = Nominal Rate

E = Effective Rate

FUTURE VALUE

```
FOR AN INITIAL INVESTMENT OF $ 10000 DOLLARS
AT AN INTEREST RATE OF .18 PERCENT
COMPOUNDED  360 PERIODS PER YEAR
FOR 3 YEARS
THE FUTURE VALUE IS $ 17158.4 DOLLARS
```

INITIAL VALUE

```
FOR A FUTURE INVESTMENT OF $ 20000 DOLLARS
AT AN INTEREST RATE OF .18 PERCENT
COMPOUNDED 12 PERIODS PER YEAR
FOR 5 YEARS
THE INITIAL VALUE IS $ 8185.98 DOLLARS
```

EFFECTIVE INTEREST RATE

```
FOR A NOMINAL INTEREST RATE OF .18 PERCENT
AND FOR 360 COMPOUNDING PERIODS
THE EFFECTIVE INTEREST RATE IS .197217 PERCENT
```

NOMINAL INTEREST RATE

```
FOR AN INITIAL INVESTMENT OF $ 20000 DOLLARS
WITH A FUTURE VALUE OF $ 25000 DOLLARS
AND WITH 360 COMPOUNDING PERIODS FOR 3 YEARS
THE NOMINAL INTEREST RATE IS .0743713 PERCENT
AND THE EFFECTIVE INTEREST RATE IS .0772175 PERCENT
```

Printout 5-1 continued

Depreciation

The government permits industry to depreciate equipment over the equipment's life span. While depreciation schedules are always an accounting function, it is sometimes necessary for the Manufacturing Engineer to calculate depreciation schedules as part of an equipment justification study. If the accounting department does not make this data available to the engineering department, the engineer then calculates it himself. Also, considering the impact depreciation can have on the early years of pay back of an investment, the engineer conducting the study may wish to see how the return on investment will alter when a different type of depreciation schedule is used. While the government will permit almost any scheme of depreciation as long as it is "reasonable" industry generally uses three types of depreciation.

The simplest type is straight line depreciation. The sum of digits and double declining balance methods are also very popular because they permit a capital asset to be depreciated faster during the early years of an investment. Standard accounting methods view depreciation as an expense to operations. When depreciation is viewed as an expense, it reduces gross profits and has the effect of reducing federal income taxes because it is subtracted from gross profits before taxes are calculated. If a company is in the 50% tax bracket, the original capital expense can be recovered faster if the depreciation (expense) is "written off" in larger amounts during the early years. Some of the capital equipment analysis models take this into consideration when calculating them while others do not.

While the decision in selection of a depreciation method is an accounting decision and not an engineering decision, it is important that the engineer working on a justification study has a knowledge of depreciation methods and what effect depreciation will have on the justification study.

Useful life of the equipment is a factor that the Manufacturing Engineer establishes, and this figure has an influence on how fast or slow an asset is depreciated.

The government now permits a tax credit to be used to speedup the recovery of an asset cost. In past years, the percentage allowed for tax credit has varied, and at this writing it currently is up to 10%. Up to 10% of the asset cost can be deducted in the first year in addition to the normal depreciation calculated for that year.

As stated earlier in this chapter, the three most popular methods of depreciation used in industry today are:
1. Straight line method.
2. Sum of digits method.
3. Double declining balance method.

Shown here is a brief example of each method.

Straight Line Method

In this example, there are three variables. Presume the Asset Life to be five years and the Asset Cost to be $1100. The Salvage Value is $100. Depreciation may be calculated with the following formula:

$$\text{Depreciation} = \frac{\text{Asset Value - Salvage Value}}{\text{Asset Life}}$$

Or, as in the case of the example:

$$\text{Depreciation} = \frac{1100 - 100}{5} = 200$$

Table 5-1
Straight Line Depreciation

Year	Beginning Value	Depreciation	Ending Value
1	$1100	$200	$900
2	900	200	700
3	700	200	500
4	500	200	300
5	300	200	100

Sum of Years Digits Method

The same variables as were used in the Straight Line Method will be used in this method, known as the Sum of Years Digits Method (S.O.D.). Observe that the depreciation in the early years recovers the investment faster. This method is presented in four parts.

1. Calculate the sum of the years digits (years life).
$$1 + 2 + 3 + 4 + 5 = 15$$

2. The Calculations for S.O.D. Depreciation in the first year follows this formula:
$$\text{Depreciation} = (\text{Asset Value} - \text{Salvage Value}) * \frac{\text{Year of Depreciation}}{\text{Total Years}}$$

Or, using our example:
$$\text{Depreciation} = (\$1100 - 100) * 5/15 = 333.33$$

The Ending Value at the conclusion of the first year is $766.67 as may be seen in *Table 5-2*.

3. In the second year, follow the formula established in the first year. More specifically, the calculations should appear as follows:
$$\text{Depreciation} = (1100 - 100) * 4/15 = 266.67$$

4. Calculations for the remaining years follow the formula using the fractions 3/15, 2/15 and 1/15.

Table 5-2
Sum of Years Digits Depreciation

Year	Beginning Value	S.O.D.	Depreciation	Ending Value
1	$1100.00	5/15	$333.33	$766.67
2	766.67	4/15	266.67	500.00
3	500.00	3/15	200.00	300.00
4	300.00	2/15	133.33	166.67
5	166.67	1/15	66.67	99.99

(Note: Observe the depreciation in the early years which recovers the investment faster.)

Double Declining Balance Method

Using this method of depreciation it is necessary to establish a Double Declining Balance (D.D.B.) factor of up to two. Using two, and recalling that the depreciation will occur for five years, the D.D.B. factor of .4 is established (two divided by five). The D.D.B. Method in the first year uses this formula:

$$\text{Depreciation} = \text{Asset Value} * \text{D.D.B. Factor}$$

Or, to carry-through our example:

$$\text{Depreciation} = 1100 * .4 = 440$$

A second step is necessary, that is, the calculation of the Beginning Value.

$$\text{Beginning Value} = \text{Asset Value} - \text{Depreciation}$$

So, the Beginning Value of the example is $660 for the second year. The Beginning Value for each will decrease each year as may be seen in *Table 5-3*. Calculations for D.D.B. depreciation in later years follows this formula:

$$\text{Depreciation} = \text{Beginning Value} * \text{D.D.B. Factor}$$

The Salvage Value is not used in this method. The Salvage Value is the Ending Value at the conclusion of the fifth year (or in the example $85.54).

The Internal Revenue Service permits other expense items to be depreciated in addition to the initial capital asset. These items can include freight, installation expense, tooling, design cost and engineering costs. The option provided here is to expense a cost element or to declare it a capital asset and depreciate it. The objective, of course, is to "write off" the cost element as soon as possible. There are, however, some tests that are usually evoked. Expendable tooling, for example, is never capitalized because it is expendable. Permanent tooling, on the other hand, might be capitalized, and depending on its life, might be a separate capital item. Another test is minimum cost. If an expense item costs $200, it may be expensed and not capitalized because of the record keeping necessary. Most companies establish a minimum amount for capitalizing an asset, assuming the asset passes the other tests mentioned.

One last element that should be considered is trade-in value applied to a new machine's cost. The accounting term used here is "cost basis". The cost basis for a new machine can be viewed as out-of-pocket expense. If there is a trade-in value, the original purchase cost is reduced to reflect this and the first year's beginning value is this adjusted figure. Of course, this figure must

Table 5-3
Double Declining Balance Depreciation

Year	Beginning Value	Depreciation	Ending Value
1	$1100.00	$440.00	$660.00
2	660.00	264.00	396.00
3	396.00	158.40	237.60
4	237.60	95.04	142.56
5	142.56	57.02	85.54

be reconciled with the value left "on the books," if any, for the machine being traded.

Program Name: "DEP"

The memory required is 3605 bytes.

The program named "DEP" is a depreciation program that calculates all three methods of depreciation covered in this chapter. The program gives the user the option of a printout for any one method or all three methods. This permits a quick comparison for justification purposes.

A sample printout from the "DEP" program is provided for the reader's review on the next two pages.

```
DEPRECIATION SCHEDULE

CAPITAL EXPENSE IS $ 50000
FREIGHT IS $ 1000
INSTALLATION EXPENSE IS $ 3000
TOOLING EXPENSE IS $ 6000
OTHER EXPENSE IS ENGINEERING
DOLLARS FOR ENGINEERING ARE $ 5000

THE TOTAL EXPENSE IS $ 65000

ASSET LIFE IS 8 YEARS

STRAIGHT LINE DEPRECIATION

PROJECT NAME          N/C LATHE

YEAR          BEGINNING VALUE DEPRECIATION     ENDING VALUE

1              65000              7250              57750
2              57750              7250              50500
3              50500              7250              43250
4              43250              7250              36000
5              36000              7250              28750
6              28750              7250              21500
7              21500              7250              14250
8              14250              7250              7000

DOUBLE DECLINING BALANCE

PROJECT NAME          N/C LATHE

YEAR          BEGINNING VALUE DEPRECIATION     ENDING VALUE

1              65000              16250             48750
2              48750              12187.5           36562.5
3              36562.5            9140.63           27421.9
4              27421.9            6855.47           20566.4
5              20566.4            5141.6            15424.8
6              15424.8            3856.2            11568.6
7              11568.6            2892.15           8676.45
8              8676.45            2169.11           6507.34

THE DDB FACTOR USED IS 2
```

Printout 5-2

```
1 REM PROGRAM NAME DEP
2 REM WRITTEN BY J.E.NICKS
3 REM COMPUTER APPLICATIONS FOR THE MANUFACTURING ENGINEER
4 REM COPYRIGHT 1981 ALL RIGHTS RESERVED
10 CLS:CLEAR100
20 PRINT"THIS PROGRAM CALCULATES DEPRECIATION SCHEDULES"
30 PRINT"FOR THREE DIFFERENT TYPES OF DEPRECIATION"
40 PRINT"TYPE IN THE MODULE NUMBER YOU WISH TO WORK WITH"
50 PRINT:PRINT
60 PRINT"STRAIGHT LINE DEPRECIATION------------1"
70 PRINT"DOUBLE DECLINING BALANCE--------------2"
80 PRINT"SUM OF YEAR DIGITS--------------------3"
90 INPUTX
100 CLS:ONXGOTO110,360,560
110 REM STRAIGHT LINE DEPRECIATION
120 GOSUB1000:GOSUB1500:GOSUB2520
130 LPRINTCHR$(27);CHR$(14);"STRAIGHT LINE DEPRECIATION"
131 GOSUB2010:GOSUB2520
190 T2=(T-S)
200 FORI=1TON
230 D=(T-S)/N
240 D2=D2+D
250 E=T-D2
260 LPRINTI,T-D1,D,E
270 D1=D1+D
280 NEXTI
290 LPRINTCHR$(138)
300 PRINT"TYPE 1 FOR A DOUBLE DECLINING BALANCE PRINT OUT"
310 PRINT"TYPE 2 FOR A SUM OF DIGITS PRINT OUT"
320 INPUT"OR TYPE 3 TO EXIT";X
330 ONXGOTO371,571,350
350 END
360 REM DDB
370 GOSUB1000:GOSUB1500:GOSUB2520
371 LPRINTCHR$(27)CHR$(14);"DOUBLE DECLINING BALANCE"
372 GOSUB2010:GOSUB2520
380 INPUT"TYPE IN THE DOUBLE DECLINING BALANCE FACTOR (UP TO 2)";F1
390 F=F1/N:E=T3
400 FORI=1TON
430 D=E*F
440 D2=D2+D
450 E=T3-D2
460 LPRINTI,T3-D1,D,E
470 D1=D1+D
480 NEXTI
481 LPRINTCHR$(138)
482 LPRINT"THE DDB FACTOR USED IS";F1
490 LPRINTCHR$(138)
500 PRINT"TYPE 1FOR A STRAIGHT LINE PRINT OUT"
510 PRINT"TYPE 2 FOR A SUM OF DIGITS PRINT OUT"
520 INPUT"OR TYPE 3 TO EXIT";X
530 ONXGOTO130,571,550
550 END
560 REM SUM OF DIGITS
570 GOSUB1000:GOSUB1500:GOSUB2520
571 LPRINTCHR$(27);CHR$(14);"SUM OF DIGITS"
572 GOSUB2010:GOSUB2520
580 FORI=1TON:N1=N1+I:NEXTI
590 T2=(T4-S)
600 FORI=NTO1STEP-1
630 D=T2*(I/N1)
640 D2=D2+D
650 E=T4-D2
660 LPRINT(N+1)-I,T4-D1,D,E
670 D1=D1+D
```

Note that GOSUB sets up print headings

Printout 5-2 continued

```
680 NEXTI
690 LPRINTCHR$(138)
700 PRINT"TYPE 1 FOR A STRAIGHT LINE PRINT OUT"
710 PRINT"TYPE 2 FOR A DOUBLE DECLINING BALANCE PRINT OUT"
720 INPUT"TYPE 3 TO EXIT";X
730 ONXGOTO130,371,750
750 END
1000 INPUT"TYPE IN THE PROJECT NAME";A$
1001 CLS
1010 PRINT"THE NEXT SERIES OF QUESTIONS RELATE TO CAPITAL EXPENDITURES"
1020 PRINT
1030 PRINT"CAPITAL EXPENSE, FREIGHT, INSTALLATION AND TOOLING"
1040 PRINT"ARE ALL INPUTTED SEPARATELY."
1050 PRINT"IF THERE ARE NO OTHER EXPENSES OTHER THEN THE"
1060 PRINT"INITIAL CAPITAL EXPENSE THEN TYPE 0 FOR THESE QUESTIONS"
1080 INPUT"TYPE IN THE CAPITAL EXPENSE DOLLARS";C
1081 CLS
1090 INPUT"TYPE IN THE FREIGHT DOLLARS";C1
1100 INPUT"TYPE IN INSTALLATION COSTS";C2
1110 INPUT"TYPE IN TOOLING EXPENSE";C3
1120 PRINT"ARE THERE ANY OTHER CAPITAL EXPENSES"
1130 INPUT"TYPE Y FOR YES OR N FOR NO";B$
1140 IFB$="Y"THEN1150ELSE1170
1150 INPUT"TYPE IN THE OTHER EXPENSES NAME";C$
1160 INPUT"THE DOLLARS FOR THIS EXPENSE IS";C4
1170 T=C+C1+C2+C3+C4

1220 INPUT"THE NUMBER OF YEARS OF THE ASSET LIFE IS";N
1230 PRINT:PRINT:PRINT"A SALVAGE VALUE IS USED ONLY FOR STRAIGHT LINE "
1240 PRINT"DEPRECIATION OR SUM OF DIGITS BUT NOT FOR"
1250 PRINT"DOUBLE DECLINING BALANCE (TYPE 0 IF NOT USED)"
1255 PRINT"OR TYPE IN A SALVAGE VALUE IF LATER YOU WISH OTHER PRINTOUTS"
1260 INPUT"TYPE IN THE SALVAGE VALUE";S
1265 GOSUB2500
1270 RETURN
1500 LPRINTCHR$(138)
1505 LPRINTCHR$(27);CHR$(14);"DEPRECIATION SCHEDULE"
1506 LPRINTCHR$(138)
1510 LPRINT"CAPITAL EXPENSE IS $";C
1520 LPRINT"FREIGHT IS $";C1
1530 LPRINT"INSTALLATION EXPENSE IS $";C2
1540 LPRINT"TOOLING EXPENSE IS $";C3
1550 IFB$="N"THEN1580ELSE1560
1560 LPRINT"OTHER EXPENSE IS ";C$
1570 LPRINT"DOLLARS FOR ";C$;" ARE $";C4
1580 LPRINTCHR$(138)
1590 LPRINT"THE TOTAL EXPENSE IS $";T
1600 LPRINTCHR$(138)
1630 LPRINT"ASSET LIFE IS";N;"YEARS"
1640 LPRINTCHR$(138)
1650 RETURN
2010 LPRINTCHR$(138)
2020 LPRINTCHR$(27);CHR$(14);"PROJECT NAME       ";A$
2030 LPRINTCHR$(138)
2040 LPRINT"YEAR","BEGINNING VALUE","DEPRECIATION","ENDING VALUE"
2050 LPRINTCHR$(138)
2060 RETURN
2500 REM T3=DDB TOT   T4=SOD TOT
2510 T3=T:T4=T:RETURN
2520 D=0:D1=0:D2=0:E=0:T2=0:RETURN
```

All variables are entered from the GOSUB 1000

Line 2520 sets all variables back to 0 and is also a GOSUB statement

Printout 5-2 continued

```
SUM  OF  DIGITS

PROJECT  NAME          N/C  LATHE

YEAR            BEGINNING VALUE DEPRECIATION    ENDING VALUE
1               65000           12888.9         52111.1
2               52111.1         11277.8         40833.3
3               40833.3         9666.67         31166.7
4               31166.7         8055.56         23111.1
5               23111.1         6444.44         16666.7
6               16666.7         4833.33         11833.3
7               11833.3         3222.22         8611.11
8               8611.11         1611.11         7000
```

Printout 5-2 continued

Program Notes for "DEP"

The programming approach used in this program is rather interesting; it defines how well the computer remembers. When the program is executed, a series of instructions appear coaching the user on what he is about to do. After the instructions, the user inputs answers to questions covering capital line items. The computer remembers these variables, then after the first printout for the depreciation method selected, the computer asks the user if he would like to have a second printout for one of the remaining two methods. If the user responds by pressing the proper key, the computer continues about the task of a second printout, remembering the variables and applying them to a new set of formulas.

Equipment Justification

If you were to pick up the classified section of a newspaper from any major city in the U.S. and look at how the ads for Manufacturing Engineers are written, one of the experience requirements you would find in many ads would be equipment justification. In manufacturing engineering, equipment justification is loosely defined, if at all. Most companies have some system to evaluate capital purchases. Generally, multiplant companies have some type of control or corporate staff function of Manufacturing Engineering that represents the plant counterpart. This is necessary (to some degree) so all capital equipment purchase requests and/or capital equipment budgets are evaluated on some common basis.

Most Manufacturing Engineers have a general grasp of the idea of justification but the details are often left to the accounting department. This is not all bad. However, most managers of Manufacturing Engineering would like the ability to analyze and perhaps screen budget requests long before they reach the final accounting stage. Again, the advent of the microcomputer has put this ability in the manager's hands. Some tutoring is necessary to fit the individual plant and/or corporation and some programming is necessary because even using the same methods of capital expenditure requests, there are many variations.

For the reasons stated earlier, the ability to analyze and re-analyze a capital budget request is becoming more important.

The program named "DISCOUNT" can assist in this effort. However, before this program is reviewed, several ground rules should be established. While most authors writing about the subject of equipment justification do not present the basic idea of justification in just this light, this author believes the subject is easier to understand if classified into three categories or levels. Each level can best be understood by example rather than name.

Level I

Level I is equipment justification in its simplest form. Take for example, the engineer wishes to interface an existing machine with a new automatic load and unload device that costs $3000. Justification for this device is in direct labor savings; the device will permit one man to operate two machines. The probability for success is high.

The impact of the new device on scrap or rework, maintenance, indirect labor, salary or management is almost nonexistent. The effect on cash flow and taxes are negligible.

The justification study required for approval of this idea is minimal. The department manager can practically answer this question by saying, "If we can recover the $3000 in less than six months and the idea has a 90% chance of working—do it!" The idea, of course, is that a computer analysis is not necessary. Some companies include a miscellaneous expense line item in their capital equipment budget to be used by the Manager of Manufacturing Engineering at his discretion. Another example of the Level I justification might be the purchase of a microcomputer to improve efficiency of the engineering department.

Level II

This level is more involved, requiring more thought and detailed analysis. For example, let's say the engineer is working on a proposal where one new CNC machine will replace two older less-productive pieces of equipment. The net effect or change on other tangible elements becomes important. The term net tangible change in this example means net plus or minus change. There may be less direct labor required for the new machine but more engineering support. Tangible means measurable and either in-pocket or out-of-pocket savings or costs. For example, the new machine will produce machined parts faster, therefore we should have less work in process. If we cannot measure the inventory reduction, it is not a savings. A second example: if additional engineering cost of $2000 per year is required but can be handled with existing people and an engineer does not have to be hired, it is not an expense.

A proposal such as the new CNC machine might cost $100,000 or more initial capital expense. Because of the amount of money required, the risk might be higher than the earlier example and the proposal should include a justification in much greater detail. Using direct labor savings as an example, the engineer must look at all costs and/or savings. FICA, retirement funds, medical insurance, vacation costs, holiday pay and shift premiums are examples of the necessary details that must be examined to determine in-pocket savings or out-of-pocket costs.

One important test is necessary to determine if this type of proposal fits into a classification of Level II. Will factory overhead, either fixed or variable, be substantially affected? If so, the proposal should be classified Level III. Level II proposals can become very involved without affecting the plant burden structure. Many companies develop their overhead percent factors based on a forecast of direct labor hours and costs for some future time period. This results in developing a ratio of all other costs to direct labor.

In a typical proposal, changes can be effected in many overhead type costs without materially affecting the plant's operating burden structure. The rule might be stated: When in doubt, ask the accounting department.

Level III

This level's proposals require an accounting study to determine the net effect on the factory's overhead rates and cash flow. For example, suppose there is a combination drilling and milling department that has twenty direct labor people in it and the proposal is to spend $2 million for a transfer line that will reduce the direct labor force to three. Evaluating this proposal is beyond the capability of the engineering department and must be done by the accounting department. However, the engineer's input is just as important for this type of justification study as in the previous example. The Manufacturing Engineer is the best authority to determine the net effects on direct labor, indirect labor, scrap and rework changes but is not equipped to determine the net effect of all these changes on plant burden.

Proposal Evaluation

The computer program named "DISCOUNT" can be of assistance in evaluating ideas for improvements. The program considers 14 different items for savings or costs and evaluates a proposal six different ways.

The two major advantages for computer assistance in justification studies are as follows:
1. Quick evaluation of alternatives.
2. Freeing up valuable engineering time.

In the sample printout from the "DISCOUNT" program, the reader will observe that one of the evaluation methods is "Discounted Cash Flow".

The computer here is a real asset. Those readers who have worked with discounted cash flow will realize that the computer can compute in half a minute what would take an engineer several hours to compute. Discount tables and interpolation are not necessary.

Naturally, each company has its own method of determining if a capital expenditure will pay for itself. Some companies use very simple methods while others use very complex methods. A recent study by the University of Michigan indicates that out of 342 companies surveyed, the most popular methods for justification are the following.

Pay Back Period I

$$PB1 = \sum_{y=0}^{\eta} FC/(NS/N)$$

Where:

FC = first costs or capitalized investment
NS = net savings after taxes
N = number of years

This method yields a figure in years—pay back. This approach in judging capital expenditures is by far the simplest and is very limited. It does not consider interest rates or the tax yield generated from depreciation, nor does it give favor for producing an early return on the investment.

Pay Back Period II

$$PB2 = \sum_{y=0}^{\eta} FC/((NS/N) + (D/N))$$

Where:

        D = depreciation

By including a factor for depreciation as part of the return on the investment, this method is better than Pay Back Period 1. You can see from the formula that the formula neither includes any interest nor gives favor to an investment that produces early return.

Pay Back Period III

$$PB3 = \sum_{y=0}^{\eta} FC/[(NS/N) + (D/N) + (((BV\text{-}D)i)/N)]$$

Where:

        BV = book value at the end of each year
         i = interest rate

Pay Back Period III is the best method of the three methods presented thus far for evaluation of a capital expenditure in terms of years return for that investment.

The example on page 133 which was generated by computer, involves a capital purchase of $65,000 and a return after taxes for the first five years of $136,360. The results:
1. Pay Back I: 2.38 years
2. Pay Back II: 1.75 years
3. Pay Back III: 1.47 years

One might ask, "Are we just playing with numbers?" Perhaps, but if a company wishes to analyze capital expenditure on the basis of years return, then Pay Back Period III is a more realistic prediction of when that investment will be recovered than Pay Back Period I. The major pitfall of all three methods is that no consideration is given to the value of those dollars in future years. Considering an inflation rate of 12% to 14% in recent years, and considering that money markets are producing a yield of 14% to 16%, the future value of dollars should be considered.

Some companies choose to evaluate an investment by using a rate of return on that investment as a criteria. The next two methods illustrate this idea.

Rate of Return on First Costs

$$RR = \sum_{y=0}^{\eta} (NS/N)/FC$$

Rate of return on first costs is just a rearrangement of the Pay Back I formula. Rate of return yields a percent return on investment and is subject to the same problems that pay back formulas generate.

Return on Average First Costs

$$RA = \sum_{y=0}^{\eta} (NS/N)/(BV/N)$$

The return on average first costs method also yields a percent return considering the average book value. Looking at the example printout again, these two figures are:
1. Rate Of Return: 41.95%
2. Return On Average First Costs: 83.91%

One might argue that any method used to evaluate a capital purchase is a good method if all proposals are evaluated using the same method. This argument is true as far as it goes, but consider the following. There are two distinctly different aspects of proposal evaluation:
1. Recovering the initial investment.
2. Establishing a priority because there are always more proposals than money available for investment.

Also, the competition for money from external sources is keen, as pointed out earlier. To illustrate this fact, the *Wall Street Journal* recently printed an article about a multi-million dollar company currently making in excess of 20% return on money market investments. In 1981, these investments should produce over $100 million for the company's coffers. An engineer working for this company may be hard-pressed to generate a proposal that competes with this track record.

Risk

Next, look at the risk involved. The money market return on investment could be considered a sure bet when compared to the engineer's proposal. This scenario suggests the engineer may never get approval for his idea, and for all of these reasons, namely:
1. Competition for money.
2. Risk.
3. Predicting capital investment recovery.
4. Cash flow.
5. Favor for investments that exhibit an early return.

The author favors discounted cash flow as the best method for capital purchase evaluation. Discounted cash flow is an evaluation method where future dollars (the return each year) are discounted by some interest rate and set equal to the original expense. The interest rate is then considered to be competitive or non-competitive. Another way discounted cash flow can be used is with a constant discount rate to determine if the investment pays for itself.

Discounted Cash Flow

$$DCF = \sum_{y=0}^{\eta} NS \, (1+i)^{-y}$$

Where:

DCF = discounted cash flow
N = number of years
NS = cost savings (each year)
i = interest rate
y = years

Example:

Capital expense = $10,000
Interest rate = 12%

The discount factor is calculated:

$$(1+i)^{-y} = (1 + .12)^{-5} = .5674$$

In the example shown in *Table 5-4,* the $4000 savings each is discounted by 12% or, stated another way, if the $4000 in five years will be equal to or greater than the original investment (at the stated discount rate), then the investment is a good one.

The second way discounted cash flow can be used is to set the two figures (original

Table 5-4
Cash Flow After Taxes

Year	Savings		Factor		Discounted Savings
1	$ 4000	*	.8978	=	$ 3571.42
2	$ 4000	*	.7972	=	$ 3188.76
3	$ 4000	*	.7118	=	$ 2847.12
4	$ 4000	*	.6355	=	$ 2542.07
5	$ 4000	*	.5674	=	$ 2269.70
	$20,000				$14,419.07

investment and the sum of all future dollars) equal to each other and then calculate what interest rate they produce. Here the computer is of real value because this can be done inside a loop and incremented either up or down by some fraction of a percent until the two sets of figures do equal each other. Companies work with discounted cash flow both ways. Some use the equal test to assist in setting priorities. The investment alternatives that have the highest discount factors should have the priority.

The discounted cash flow test also is useful as a test for money market alternatives, by comparing the percent to company yields. Other companies set some minimum discount rate and test alternative investments to that rate. If the sum of all discounted savings exceeds the original investment (as in the example), then it is a good investment.

The program on the following pages ("DISCOUNT") permits the user to input savings and/or expenses for 14 different items, calculates the after tax cash flow, then evaluates the proposal all six ways discussed in this chapter. A sample printout is shown on pages 133 and 134. This program is a real time saver. If an engineer had to do this analysis by hand, it would take hours. Each year most companies develop and submit a capital equipment budget for the next fiscal year. This is a very necessary activity, although very time consuming. The microcomputer is a must in performing much of the detailed analysis to choose good alternatives.

Program Name: "DISCOUNT"

The memory required is 10,835 bytes.

This program is written permitting the user to input savings and/or expenses over the first five years of the life of an investment. Attempting to estimate savings and expenses beyond a five-year period can be misleading. Most companies use some rather arbitrary maximum time period for investment recovery.

The program is very easy to work with because the engineer is required only to input figures. The computer organizes the data into table form and the final printout reflects this. Before an engineer can use the program, all of the information must be gathered from various sources.

The most difficult part of data gathering is probably associated with the direct and indirect labor savings or costs. Many companies shortcut the procedure by using a fringe rate (percent) to multiply the labor savings or costs by rather than trying to identify each separate cost element. The program does not require the user to have an input every time the computer asks for it. To illustrate the programming technique, observe line 1395.

IF D1 = 0 THEN . . . .

D1 is the summary of direct labor savings or expense produced by line 430. If D1 = 0, then the user has not entered any direct labor figures. The reason this is pointed out relates to an earlier comment about Level I justification. Recall that no formal justification was required. The second printout reflects the automated load and unload device. The "formal justification" took less than one minute for the computer to prepare.

Aside from organizing and evaluating data rapidly, the "DISCOUNT" program has many other values. As mentioned earlier in the chapter, companies use various ways to depreciate a capital asset and the depreciation model used has an effect on pay back methods of justification. Three computer runs were made of the N/C lathe proposal, each using a different depreciation model. The results are shown below in *Table 5-5*.

Table 5-5
NC Lathe Proposal Evaluated Using Three Depreciation Methods

	S.L. Dep.	S.O.D. Dep.	D.D.B. Dep.
Pay Back Period I	2.79 years	2.42 years	2.38 years
Pay Back Period II	2.13 years	1.78 years	1.75 years
Pay Back Period III	1.64 years	1.47 years	1.47 years
Rate of return	35.8%	41.4%	41.9%
Return on average first costs	71.6%	82.8%	83.9%
Discounted cash flow	24.1%	34.3%	37.5%

One last feature is included in the use of the "DISCOUNT" program. If the Manager of Manufacturing Engineering constructs the capital equipment budget by priority, he may wish to have each line item on the budget request subjected to an analysis for different time periods. The "DISCOUNT" program provides up to five years of input for savings or costs. By rerunning the program and inputting only the first three years figures, the manager can measure the affect of risk on each line item in the proposed budget.

EQUIPMENT JUSTIFICATION

PROJECT NAME N/C LATHE   YEARS LIFE 8

| | YEAR | | | | | |
ITEM	1	2	3	4	5	TOTAL
CAPITAL EXP	-65000	0	0	0	0	-65000
DIRECT LABOR	20000	20000	20000	20000	20000	100000
ENGINEERING	-2000	-2000	0	0	0	-4000
SCRAP	2000	2000	2000	2000	2000	10000
EXP TOOLING	1000	1000	1000	1000	1000	5000
DEPRECIATION	16250	12187	9140	6855	5141	49573
LINE TOTALS	-27750	33187	32140	29855	28141	95573

CASH FLOW BEFORE TAXES

	1	2	3	4	5
TOTALS NET	21000	21000	23000	23000	23000
LESS DEP	-16250	-12187	-9140	-6855	-5141
TAXABLE INCOME	4750	8813	13860	16145	17859
TAX	2375	4406.5	6930	8072.5	8929.5

CASH FLOW AFTER TAXES

	1	2	3	4	5
NET INCOME	34875	28780.5	25210	21782.5	19211.5
TAX CREDIT	6500				
NET ACCUM	41375	70155.5	95365.5	117148	136360

Note: Double Declining Balance Depreciation is from an earlier printout

ANALYSIS

TOTAL CAPITAL COSTS ARE $ -65000
TOTAL ACCUM SAVINGS AFTER TAXES ARE $ 136360

PAY BACK PERIOD 1
THE PROPOSAL WILL PAY IT SELF BACK IN 2.38341 YEARS
PAY BACK PERIOD 1 AVERAGES ALL YEARS SAVINGS

RATE OF RETURN ON FIRST COSTS
THIS PROPOSAL HAS A RETURN OF FIRST COSTS OF .419568 PERCENT FOR THE FIRST 5 YRS
.
RATE OF RETURN AVERAGES ALL YEARS SAVINGS

RETURN OF AVERAGE FIRST COSTS
THIS METHOD CONSIDERS THE AVERAGE BOOK VALUE OF THE INVESTMENT
AND ADDS THE TAX BENEFIT PART OF THIS TO SAVINGS
THIS PROPOSAL HAS A .839136 PERCENT RETURN ON FIRST COSTS FOR THE FIRST 5 YRS.

PAY BACK PERIOD 2
PAY BACK PERIOD 2 CONSIDERS THE EFFECT OF THE DEPRECIATION
AS PART OF THE CASH FLOW AND THE PAY BACK PERIOD IS LESS THEN PAY BACK PERIOD 1
THE PAY BACK PERIOD EQUALS 1.74795 YEARS

Printout 5-3

PAY BACK PERIOD 3
THIS METHOD CONSIDERS THE EFFECT OF DEPRECIATION AND
BOOK VALUE AT INTEREST RATE .18 FOR RE-INVESTMENT OF CASH FLOW ASSETS
USING THIS METHOD THE PAY BACK PERIOD IS 1.46643 YEARS

DISCOUNTED CASH FLOW
WHEN TOTAL SAVINGS ARE SET EQUAL TO THE TOTAL INVESTMENT
BY DISCOUNTING FUTURE SAVINGS BY SOME DISCOUNT RATE,THEN
THIS PROPOSAL HAS A DISCOUNT RATE OF .374999 PERCENT
THIS DISCOUNT RATE IS THE PERCENT RETURN
THE ORIGINAL INVESTMENT WOULD HAVE TO EARN
TO EQUAL THE SAVINGS OVER A 5 YEAR PERIOD

EQUIPMENT JUSTIFICATION

PROJECT NAME LOAD - UNLOAD DEVICE   YEARS LIFE 5

	YEAR					
ITEM	1	2	3	4	5	TOTAL
CAPITAL EXP	-3000	0	0	0	0	-3000
DIRECT LABOR	6000	6000	6000	6000	6000	30000
DEPRECIATION	600	600	600	600	600	3000
LINE TOTALS	3600	6600	6600	6600	6600	30000

CASH FLOW BEFORE TAXES

TOTALS					
NET	6000	6000	6000	6000	6000
LESS DEP	-600	-600	-600	-600	-600
TAXABLE INCOME	5400	5400	5400	5400	5400
TAX	2700	2700	2700	2700	2700

CASH FLOW AFTER TAXES

NET INCOME	3900	3900	3900	3900	3900
TAX CREDIT	99.99				
NET ACCUM	3999.99	7899.99	11800	15700	19600

ANALYSIS

TOTAL CAPITAL COSTS ARE $ -3000
TOTAL ACCUM SAVINGS AFTER TAXES ARE $ 19600

PAY BACK PERIOD 1
THE PROPOSAL WILL PAY IT SELF BACK IN .765307 YEARS
PAY BACK PERIOD 1 AVERAGES ALL YEARS SAVINGS

RATE OF RETURN ON FIRST COSTS
THIS PROPOSAL HAS A RETURN OF FIRST COSTS OF 1.30667 PERCENT FOR THE FIRST 5 YRS

RATE OF RETURN AVERAGES ALL YEARS SAVINGS

Printout 5-3 continued

RETURN OF AVERAGE FIRST COSTS

THIS METHOD CONSIDERS THE AVERAGE BOOK VALUE OF THE INVESTMENT
AND ADDS THE TAX BENEFIT PART OF THIS TO SAVINGS
THIS PROPOSAL HAS A 2.61333 PERCENT RETURN ON FIRST COSTS FOR THE FIRST 5 YRS.

PAY BACK PERIOD 2

PAY BACK PERIOD 2 CONSIDERS THE EFFECT OF THE DEPRECIATION
AS PART OF THE CASH FLOW AND THE PAY BACK PERIOD IS LESS THEN PAY BACK PERIOD 1
THE PAY BACK PERIOD EQUALS .663717 YEARS

PAY BACK PERIOD 3

THIS METHOD CONSIDERS THE EFFECT OF DEPRECIATION AND
BOOK VALUE AT INTEREST RATE .5 FOR RE-INVESTMENT OF CASH FLOW ASSETS
USING THIS METHOD THE PAY BACK PERIOD IS .553506 YEARS

DISCOUNTED CASH FLOW

WHEN TOTAL SAVINGS ARE SET EQUAL TO THE TOTAL INVESTMENT
BY DISCOUNTING FUTURE SAVINGS BY SOME DISCOUNT RATE,THEN
THIS PROPOSAL HAS A DISCOUNT RATE OF 1.25501 PERCENT
THIS DISCOUNT RATE IS THE PERCENT RETURN
THE ORIGINAL INVESTMENT WOULD HAVE TO EARN
TO EQUAL THE SAVINGS OVER A 5 YEAR PERIOD


```
1 REM PROGRAM NAME DISCOUNT
2 REM WRITTEN BY J.E.NICKS
3 REM COMPUTER APPLICATIONS FOR THE MANUFACTURING ENGINEER
4 REM COPYRIGHT 1981 ALL RIGHTS RESERVED
10 CLS:CLEAR400
20 PRINT"THIS PROGRAM ANALYZES CAPITAL EQUIPMENT INVESTMENTS"
30 PRINT"THE PROGRAM PROVIDES FOR THE PROPOSAL TO BE ANALYZED"
40 PRINT"SEVERAL WAYS, AMONG WHICH ARE RATE OF RETURN,"
50 PRINT"PAY BACK METHOD AND DISCOUNTED CASH FLOW."
60 PRINT"THE PROGRAM ALLOWS FOR THE ENTRY OF SAVINGS"
70 PRINT"AND EXPENSES FOR EACH OF THE FIRST FIVE YEARS OF THE"
80 PRINT"PROPOSAL OR AS A SINGLE ENTRY FOR A SINGLE YEAR"
90 PRINT"AND THE PRINT OUT WILL SHOW THE CASH FLOW FOR THE "
100 PRINT"FIRST FIVE YEARS"
110 PRINT:INPUT"TYPE IN THE PROPOSAL NAME";A$
115 INPUT"TYPE IN THE   YEARS OF LIFE";Y
120 CLS
130 PRINT"SAVINGS ARE TYPED IN AS POSITIVE NUMBERS"
140 PRINT"AND COSTS ARE TYPED IN AS NEGATIVE NUMBERS"
150 PRINT"TYPE IN THE NUMBER OF THE SAVINGS OR EXPENSE YOU WISH TO ENTER"
160 PRINT"IF A SAVINGS OR EXPENSE DOES NOT OCCUR IN A YEAR TYPE 0"
170 PRINT"TO INDEX TO THE YEAR IT SHOULD BE ENTERED AT"
180 PRINT"ALL SAVINGS OR EXPENSES MUST BE ON AN ANNUAL BASIS"
181 PRINT"PRESS ENTER TO CONTINUE"
182 INPUTINKEY:ONINKEYGOTO186
185 REM MENU
186 CLS
190 PRINT"CAPITAL EXPENSE------1     DIRECT LABOR---------2"
200 PRINT"INDIRECT LABOR-------3     MATERIAL-------------4"
210 PRINT"PROPERTY TAX--------5      INSURANCE------------6"
220 PRINT"SALARY & MGT. -------7     ENGINEERING----------8"
230 PRINT"MAINTENANCE----------9     SCRAP---------------10"
240 PRINT"SHOP SUPPLIES-------11     TOOLING-------------12"
250 PRINT"DEPRECIATION--------13     OTHER---------------14"
260 PRINT"         DATA ENTRY COMPLETE ---15"
270 INPUTN(I)
280 ONN(I)GOTO310,390,450,520,590
290 ONN(I)-5GOTO660,730,810,880,950
```

Printout 5-3 continued

135

```
300 ONN(I)-10GOTO1020,1090,1160,1230,1300
310 C$="CAPITAL EXP":CLS
320 PRINT"TYPE IN THE CAPITAL EXPENSE FOR EACH YEAR"
330 PRINT"REMINDER ! ! ! EXPENSE IS ENTERED AS A NEGATIVE NUMBER"
340 FORI=1TO5
350 INPUTC(I)
360 C1=C1+C(I)
370 NEXTI
375 GOSUB3000
380 GOTO185
390 D$="DIRECT LABOR":CLS
400 PRINT"ENTER DIRECT LABOR SAVINGS OR EXPENSE"
410 FOR I=1TO5
420 INPUTD(I)
430 D1=D1+D(I)
440 NEXTI
445 GOTO185
450 L$="INDIRECT LABOR":CLS
460 PRINT"INDIRECT LABOR SAVINGS OR EXPENSE"
470 FORI=1TO5
480 INPUTL(I)
490 L1=L1+L(I)
500 NEXTI
510 GOTO185
520 M$="MATERIAL":CLS
530 PRINT"MATERIAL SAVINGS OR EXPENSE"
540 FORI=1TO5
550 INPUTM(I)
560 M1=M1+M(I)
570 NEXTI
580 GOTO185
590 P$="PROPERTY TAX":CLS
600 PRINT"PROPERTY TAX SAVINGS OR EXPENSE"
610 FORI=1TO5
620 INPUTP(I)
630 P1=P1+P(I)
640 NEXTI
650 GOTO185
660 S$="INSURANCE":CLS
670 PRINT"INSURANCE SAVINGS OR EXPENSE"
680 FORI=1TO5
690 INPUTS(I)
700 S1=S1+S(I)
710 NEXTI
720 GOTO185
730 G$="SAL. $ MGT.":CLS
740 PRINT"SALARY AND MANAGEMENT SAVINGS OR EXPENSE"
750 FORI=1TO5
760 INPUTG(I)
770 G1=G1+G(I)
780 NEXTI
790 GOTO185
810 E$="ENGINEERING":CLS
820 PRINT"ENGINEERING SAVINGS OR EXPENSE"
830 FORI=1TO5
840 INPUTE(I)
850 E1=E1+E(I)
860 NEXT I
870 GOTO185
880 F$="MAINTENANCE":CLS
890 PRINT"MAINTENANCE SAVINGS OR EXPENSE"
900 FORI=1TO5
910 INPUTF(I)
920 F1=F1+F(I)
930 NEXTI
```

All savings or costs are entered in for next loops

Printout 5-3 continued

```
940 GOTO185
950 R$="SCRAP":CLS
960 PRINT"SCRAP SAVINGS OR EXPENSE"
970 FORI=1TO5
980 INPUTR(I)
990 R1=R1+R(I)
1000 NEXTI
1010 GOTO185
1020 W$="SHOP SUPP.":CLS
1030 PRINT"SHOP SUPPLIES EXPENSE OR SAVINGS"
1040 FORI=1TO5
1050 INPUTW(I)
1060 W1=W1+W(I)
1070 NEXTI
1080 GOTO185
1090 T$="EXP TOOLING":CLS
1100 PRINT"EXPENSED TOOLING SAVINGS OR COST"
1110 FORI=1TO5
1120 INPUTT(I)
1130 T1=T1+T(I)
1140 NEXTI
1150 GOTO185
1160 Z$="DEPRECIATION":CLS
1170 PRINT"NET DEPRECIATION EXPENSE"
1175 PRINT"INPUT DEPRECIATION AS A POSITIVE FIGURE"
1180 FORI=1TO5
1190 INPUTZ(I)
1200 Z1=Z1+Z(I)
1210 NEXTI
1220 GOTO185
1230 CLS:PRINT"OTHER EXPENSE OR SAVINGS "
1235 PRINT"LIMIT THE NAME TO 15 LETTERS"
1240 INPUT"TYPE IN THE NAME OF THE OTHER EXPENSE OR SAVINGS";O$
1245 PRINT"INPUT THE SAVINGS OR EXPENSE OF   " ;O$
1250 FORI=1TO5
1260 INPUTO(I)
1270 O1=O1+O(I)
1280 NEXTI
1290 GOTO185
1300 REM SUMMARY OF ALL EXPENSES AND SAVINGS
1310 FORI=1TO5
1320 X(I)=C(I)+D(I)+L(I)+M(I)+P(I)+S(I)+G(I)+E(I)+F(I)+R(I)+W(I)+T(I)+Z(I)+O(I)
1325 X1(I)=X(I)-C(I)
1330 X2=X2+X(I)
1340 NEXTI
1350 LPRINTCHR$(27);CHR$(14);"EQUIPMENT JUSTIFICATION"
1360 LPRINTCHR$(138)
1362 LPRINT"PROJECT NAME   ";A$;"                  YEARS LIFE";Y
1365 LPRINTCHR$(138):LPRINT"                        YEAR"
1370 LPRINT"ITEM";TAB(18);"1";TAB(28);"2";TAB(38);"3";TAB(48);"4";TAB(58);"5";TA
B(65);"TOTAL"
1380 LPRINTCHR$(138)
1390 LPRINTC$,C(1);TAB(25);C(2);TAB(35);C(3);TAB(45);C(4);TAB(55);C(5);TAB(65);C
1
1395 IFD1=0THEN1410ELSE1400
1400 LPRINTD$,D(1);TAB(25);D(2);TAB(35);D(3);TAB(45);D(4);TAB(55);D(5);TAB(65);D
1
1410 IFL1=0THEN1430ELSE1420
1420 LPRINTL$,L(1);TAB(25);L(2);TAB(35);L(3);TAB(45);L(4);TAB(55);L(5);TAB(65);L
1
1430 IFM1=0THEN1450ELSE1440
1440 LPRINTM$,M(1);TAB(25);M(2);TAB(35);M(3);TAB(45);M(4);TAB(55);M(5);TAB(65);M
1
1450 IFP1=0THEN1470ELSE1460
1460 LPRINTP$,P(1);TAB(25);P(2);TAB(35);P(3);TAB(45);P(4);TAB(55);P(5);TAB(65);P
```

Printout 5-3 continued

```
1
1470 IFS1=0THEN1490ELSE1480
1480 LPRINTS$,S(1);TAB(25);S(2);TAB(35);S(3);TAB(45);S(4);TAB(55);S(5);TAB(65);S
1
1490 IFG1=0THEN1510ELSE1500
1500 LPRINTG$,G(1);TAB(25);G(2);TAB(35);G(3);TAB(45);G(4);TAB(55);G(5);TAB(65);G
1
1510 IFE1=0THEN1530ELSE1520
1520 LPRINTE$,E(1);TAB(25);E(2);TAB(35);E(3);TAB(45);E(4);TAB(55);E(5);TAB(65);E
1
1530 IFF1=0THEN1550ELSE1540
1540 LPRINTF$,F(1);TAB(25);F(2);TAB(35);F(3);TAB(45);F(4);TAB(55);F(5);TAB(65);F
1
1550 IFR1=0THEN1570ELSE1560
1560 LPRINTR$,R(1);TAB(25);R(2);TAB(35);R(3);TAB(45);R(4);TAB(55);R(5);TAB(65);R
1
1570 IFW1=0THEN1590ELSE1580
1580 LPRINTW$,W(1);TAB(25);W(2);TAB(35);W(3);TAB(45);W(4);TAB(55);W(5);TAB(65);W
1
1590 IFT1=0THEN1610ELSE1600
1600 LPRINTT$,T(1);TAB(25);T(2);TAB(35);T(3);TAB(45);T(4);TAB(55);T(5);TAB(65);T
1
1610 IFZ1=0THEN1630ELSE1620
1620 LPRINTZ$,Z(1);TAB(25);Z(2);TAB(35);Z(3);TAB(45);Z(4);TAB(55);Z(5);TAB(65);Z
1
1630 IFO1=0THEN1650ELSE1640
1640 LPRINTO$,O(1);TAB(25);O(2);TAB(35);O(3);TAB(45);O(4);TAB(55);O(5);TAB(65);O
1
1650 LPRINTCHR$(138):LPRINTCHR$(138)
1660 LPRINT"LINE TOTALS",X(1);TAB(25);X(2);TAB(35);X(3);TAB(45);X(4);TAB(55);X(5
);TAB(65);X2
1670 LPRINTCHR$(138)
1680 LPRINT"                    CASH FLOW BEFORE TAXES"
1690 LPRINTCHR$(138)
1700 LPRINT"TOTALS"
1710 FORI=1TO5
1720 X1(I)=D(I)+L(I)+M(I)+P(I)+S(I)+G(I)+E(I)+F(I)+R(I)+W(I)+T(I)+(-Z(I))+O(I)
1730 X3(I)=D(I)+L(I)+M(I)+P(I)+S(I)+G(I)+E(I)+F(I)+R(I)+W(I)+T(I)+O(I)
1740 NEXTI
1750 LPRINT"NET",X3(1);TAB(25);X3(2);TAB(35);X3(3);TAB(45);X3(4);TAB(55);X3(5)
1760 LPRINTCHR$(138)
1770 LPRINT"LESS DEP",-Z(1);TAB(25);-Z(2);TAB(35);-Z(3);TAB(45);-Z(4);TAB(55);-Z
(5)
1780 LPRINTCHR$(138)
1790 LPRINT"TAXABLE INCOME",X1(1);TAB(25);X1(2);TAB(35);X1(3);TAB(45);X1(4);TAB(
55);X1(5)
1800 LPRINTCHR$(138)
1810 FORI=1TO5
1820 IFX1(I)<1THEN1840ELSE1830
1830 X4(I)=X1(I)/2:GOTO1850
1840 X4(I)=0:GOTO1850
1850 X5(I)=X3(I)-X4(I)+Z(I)
1870 NEXTI
1875 X6(1)=X5(1)+ABS(Y1):X6(2)=X6(1)+X5(2):X6(3)=X6(2)+X5(3):X6(4)=X6(3)+X5(4):X
6(5)=X6(4)+X5(5)
1880 LPRINT"TAX",X4(1);TAB(25);X4(2);TAB(35);X4(3);TAB(45);X4(4);TAB(55);X4(5)
1890 LPRINTCHR$(138)
1900 LPRINT"                    CASH FLOW AFTER TAXES"
1910 LPRINTCHR$(138)
1920 LPRINT"NET INCOME",X5(1);TAB(25);X5(2);TAB(35);X5(3);TAB(45);X5(4);TAB(55);
X5(5)
1925 LPRINT"TAX CREDIT",ABS(Y1)
1930 LPRINT"NET ACCUM",X6(1);TAB(25);X6(2);TAB(35);X6(3);TAB(45);X6(4);TAB(55);X
6(5)
1940 LPRINTCHR$(138):LPRINTCHR$(138):CLS:PRINT"THIS IS A PROGRAMED STOP TO PERMI
T PRINTER PAPER TO BE INDEXED"
```

Printout 5-3 continued

```
1941 PRINT"WHEN THIS IS COMPLETE , TYPE CONT AND ENTER."
1942 STOP
1950 LPRINTCHR$(27);CHR$(14);"ANALYSIS"
1980 REM PAY BACK PERIOD 1
1990 P1=ABS(C1)/(X6(5)/5)
2000 LPRINTCHR$(138):LPRINTCHR$(138)
2005 LPRINT"TOTAL CAPITAL COSTS ARE $ ";C1
2006 LPRINT"TOTAL ACCUM SAVINGS AFTER TAXES ARE $ ";X6(5)
2007 FORI=1TO3:LPRINTCHR$(138):NEXTI
2010 LPRINTCHR$(27);CHR$(14);"PAY BACK PERIOD 1"
2020 LPRINT"THE PROPOSAL WILL PAY IT SELF BACK IN";P1;"YEARS"
2030 LPRINT"PAY BACK PERIOD 1 AVERAGES ALL YEARS SAVINGS"
2040 REM RETURN ON FIRST COSTS
2050 P2=(X6(5)/5)/ABS(C1)
2060 LPRINTCHR$(138):LPRINTCHR$(138)
2070 LPRINTCHR$(27);CHR$(14);"RATE OF RETURN ON FIRST COSTS"
2080 LPRINT"THIS PROPOSAL HAS A RETURN OF FIRST COSTS OF";P2;"PERCENT FOR THE FI
RST 5 YRS."
2090 LPRINT"RATE OF RETURN AVERAGES ALL YEARS SAVINGS"
2100 LPRINTCHR$(138):LPRINTCHR$(138)
2110 P3=(X6(5)/5)/(ABS(C1)*.5)
2120 LPRINTCHR$(27);CHR$(14);"RETURN OF AVERAGE FIRST COSTS"
2130 LPRINT"THIS METHOD CONSIDERS THE AVERAGE BOOK VALUE OF THE INVESTMENT"
2135 LPRINT"AND ADDS THE TAX BENEFIT PART OF THIS TO SAVINGS"
2140 LPRINT"THIS PROPOSAL HAS A ";P3;"PERCENT RETURN ON FIRST COSTS FOR THE FIRS
T 5 YRS."
2150 LPRINTCHR$(138):LPRINTCHR$(138)
2160 REM PAY BACK PERIOD 2
2170 LPRINTCHR$(27);CHR$(14);"PAY BACK PERIOD 2"
2180 P4=ABS(C1)/((X6(5)/5)+(ABS(Z1)/5))
2190 LPRINT"PAY BACK PERIOD 2 CONSIDERS THE EFFECT OF THE DEPRECIATION"
2200 LPRINT"AS PART OF THE CASH FLOW AND THE PAY BACK PERIOD IS LESS THEN PAY BA
CK PERIOD 1"
2205 LPRINT"THE PAY BACK PERIOD EQUALS";P4;"YEARS"
2206 LPRINTCHR$(138):LPRINTCHR$(138)
2210 REM PAY BACK PERIOD 3
2220 PRINT"PAY BACK PERIOD 3 CONSIDERS AN INTEREST RATE FOR"
2230 PRINT"RE-INVERSTMENT OF CASH FLOW ASSETS"
2235 INPUT"TYPE IN THE INTEREST RATE (DECIMAL) YOU WISH TO USE";A
2240 REM H=BOOK VALUE:A=INTEREST RATE:A1=INTEREST
2250 H1=ABS(C1):A1=H1*A
2260 H2=(H1-ABS(Z(1))):A2=H2*A
2270 H3=(H2-ABS(Z(2))):A3=H3*A
2280 H4=(H3-ABS(Z(3))):A4=H4*A
2290 H5=(H4-ABS(Z(4))):A5=H5*A
2300 A6=(A1+A2+A3+A4+A5)/5
2310 P5=ABS(C1)/((X6(5)/5)+(ABS(Z1)/5)+A6)
2320 LPRINTCHR$(27);CHR$(14);"PAY BACK PERIOD 3"
2330 LPRINT"THIS METHOD CONSIDERS THE EFFECT OF DEPRECIATION AND"
2340 LPRINT"BOOK VALUE AT INTEREST RATE";A;"FOR RE-INVESTMENT OF CASH FLOW ASSET
S"
2350 LPRINT"USING THIS METHOD THE PAY BACK PERIOD IS";P5;"YEARS"
2360 LPRINTCHR$(138):LPRINTCHR$(138)
2365 CLS:PRINT"THE COMPUTER IS CALCULATING"
2366 PRINT"DISCOUNTED CASH FLOW MAY TAKE A FEW MOMENTS TO CALCULATE"
2370 REM DISCOUNTED CASH FLOW
2380 REM INTEREST =A: CAP EXP =C1:SAVINGS=X5(I)
2385 IFABS(C1)>X6(5)THEN2570
2386 X5(1)=X5(1)+ABS(Y1)
2390 X8=0
2400 FORI=1TO5
2410 X7=X5(I)*((1+A)[-I)
2420 X8=X8+X7
2430 NEXTI
2440 IFX8>ABS(C1)-100ANDX8<ABS(C1)+100THEN2490ELSE2450
2450 IFX8>ABS(C1)THEN2460ELSE2470
```

Printout 5-3 continued

```
2460  A=A+.001:GOTO2390
2470  IFX8<ABS(C1)THEN2480
2480  A=A-.001:GOTO2390
2490  REM DISCOUNTED PERCENT CALCULATED
2500  LPRINTCHR$(27);CHR$(14);"DISCOUNTED CASH FLOW"
2510  LPRINT"WHEN TOTAL SAVINGS ARE SET EQUAL TO THE TOTAL INVESTMENT"
2520  LPRINT"BY DISCOUNTING FUTURE SAVINGS BY SOME DISCOUNT RATE,THEN"
2530  LPRINT"THIS PROPOSAL HAS A DISCOUNT RATE OF";A;"PERCENT"
2540  LPRINT"THIS DISCOUNT RATE IS THE PERCENT RETURN"
2550  LPRINT"THE ORIGINAL INVESTMENT WOULD HAVE TO EARN"
2560  LPRINT"TO EQUAL THE SAVINGS OVER A 5 YEAR PERIOD"
2565  END
2570  LPRINT"THIS PROPOSAL CANNOT BE EVALUATED BY DISCOUNTED CASH FLOW"
2580  LPRINT"THE SAVINGS OVER A 5 YEAR PERIOD
2590  LPRINT"DOES NOT EQUAL THE ORIGINAL INVESTMENT"
2600  END
3000  REM Y=YEARS,Y1=TAX CREDIT
3010  IFY<3THEN3070ELSE3020
3020  IFY<5.01THEN3030ELSE3040
3030  Y1=(C1*.3333)*.1:RETURN
3040  IFY<7.01THEN3050ELSE3060
3050  Y1=(C1*.6666)*.1:RETURN
3060  IFY>7.01THENY1=C1*.1:RETURN
3070  Y1=0:RETURN
```

Lines 3000 to 3070 calculate the tax credit based on years life of the asset

Printout 5-3 continued

Bibliography

Bolten, Steven E. *Managerial Finance, Principles and Practice.* Boston: Houghton Mifflin Co., 1976.

Steffy, Wilbert; Smith, Donald N. and Sovter, Donald. *Economic Guidelines for Justifying Capital Purchases.* Ann Arbor, MI: Industrial Development Division, Institute of Science and Technology, University of Michigan, 1973.

White, John A.; Agee, Marvin H., and Case, Kenneth. *Principles of Engineering Economic Analysis.* New York: John Wiley & Sons, 1977.

Optional Lab Assignments

Lab Assignment 5-1 (least difficult)
Write a computer program that calculates the savings and costs of direct labor. The user input should be limited to direct labor hours savings per year and a direct labor rate. The computer program should contain data statements for other elements of direct labor. These other elements should include FICA, insurance, shift premium and vacation, to mention a few.

Lab Assignment 5-2 (moderate)
Write a GOSUB module to the "DISCOUNT" program that considers the cash flow produced by the program versus leasing the item. Once leasing elements have been inputted and the tax effect calculated, a discounted cash flow factor should be calculated to compare to the one already produced earlier in the program.

Lab Assignment 5-3 (most difficult)
Write a computer program that evaluates capital equipment budget requests using the alternative method of discounted cash flow discussed in this chapter. The program should include input of up to five capital equipment line items and evaluate these against three different interest rates. The program output should be in table form as shown in *Table 5-6*.

Table 5-6
Capital Equipment Budget Analysis

	Cash Outlay	Discounted Cash Flow 12%	15%	18%
Line item 1	$10,000	$ 8000	$10,000	$15,000
Line item 2	10,000	10,000	15,000	20,000
Line item 3	15,000	20,000	23,000	26,000
Line item 4	18,000	25,000	30,000	35,000
Line item 5	20,000	12,000	15,000	18,000

(Note: Figures in this table are illustrative only.)

CHAPTER 6

Regression Analysis

Regression analysis is a useful statistical tool designed to assist the engineer in evaluating rather complicated conditions found on the shop floor.

Before proceeding with this chapter, let's explore a use for regression analysis for the reader who may not be familiar with the subject. To do this we will take a typical shop floor problem. Assume the Manufacturing Engineer is working with a new material in the drilling department. This material does not behave the same as other materials the engineer has worked with in the past. The problem lies in producing oversized holes by drilling, and after careful measurement of the drill size and the holes produced, the engineer concludes that further study is required. Holes being produced with standard-sized drills are outside the tolerance range of acceptable parts. With additional measurement, and after consulting several handbooks that contain data on expected hole size, the engineer concludes that this material is not reacting in a normal way.

Objective

The objective of regression analysis is to mathematically predict the behavior of the dependent variable (hole size) from the independent variable (drill size).

The drilling example is not complex. The example is used only to illustrate the concept of regression analysis, although this type of problem is certainly typical. With an understanding of the various regression models presented in this chapter, the engineer would have one of several tools at his disposal to solve the problem. While regression analysis may not be an everyday occurrence in the life of the engineer, the ideas presented in this chapter are worth study.

This chapter contains four computer programs which perform regression analysis. Each program works with a different math model. The format of this chapter is as follows.

First, the math formulas are presented. Then the computer program is presented with editorial comments and, after each program, at least one sample printout of a typical problem is included.

The four regression models presented are:
1. Simple Regression (straight line correlation).
2. Multiple Regression (straight line correlation for two independent variables).
3. Log-linear Regression.
4. Curvilinear Regression.

Before we review simple regression, a comment should be made about forecasting from regression models. The opinions of authors differ as to the mathematical correctness of forecasting using regression analysis. Some authors say there is no evidence that regression analysis can be used for forecasting, while others say regression analysis can be used for forecasting in a limited way. This author's opinion is that regression analysis is a powerful tool and can be used for forecasting, although some caution must be exercised.

It is important to understand that regression analysis is a math-oriented tool and can be used to make predictions of behavior within the limits of good judgment. This may sound vague to the reader, however, reflect for a minute on the words "good judgment". Manufacturing Engineering is a blend of science, technology and judgment. Arguments can be offered as to what portion of this skill is judgment, but no practicing Manufacturing Engineer can say that good judgment is not a vital part of his day-to-day activities.

Simple Regression or Least Squares Fit

If data collected for the independent variable (x) and for the dependent variable (y) has a distribution of values where y is linear to x, then x and y relate to the equation:

$$y = a + bx$$

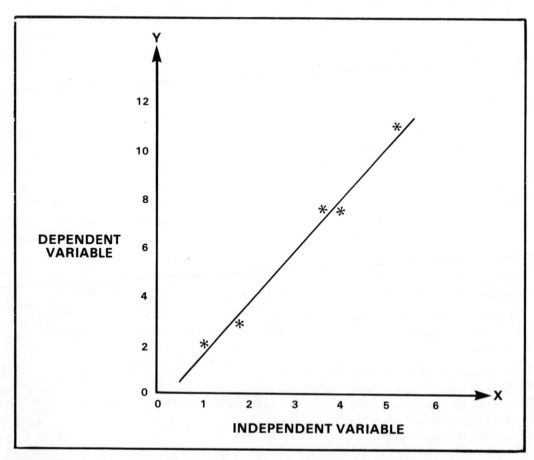

Figure 6-1. Data is collected in chart form. The straight line shows the line of best fit.

144

These data, when plotted on graph paper, may appear to conform to a straight line (more or less). See *Figure 6-1* and *Table 6-1*.

Table 6-1
Data Collected for the Independent and Dependent Variables

Sample	Independent Variable X	Dependent Variable Y
1	1	2
2	2	3
3	3	7
4	4	7
5	5	11

Using our equation we should be able to derive an estimate of y for a value of $x = 3.5$. The data is arranged in table form in *Table 6-2*.

Table 6-2
Summation array

Sample	X	Y	XY	X^2	Y^2
1	1	2	2	1	4
2	2	3	6	4	9
3	3	7	21	9	49
4	4	7	28	16	49
5	5	11	55	25	121
$\Sigma a = 5$	$\Sigma x = 15$	$\Sigma y = 30$	$\Sigma xy = 112$	$\Sigma x^2 = 55$	$\Sigma y^2 = 232$

Solving the above equations by substitution yields:

$$\Sigma y = \Sigma a + \Sigma xb = 30 = 5a + 15b$$
$$\Sigma xy = \Sigma xa + \Sigma x^2 b = 112 = 15a + 55b$$
$$a = -.6$$
$$b = +2.2$$
$$y = a + bx \text{ now becomes } ye = a + bx$$

Where:
ye = corrected y, or forecasted y
The corrections can be seen in *Table 6-3*.

Table 6-3
Original Values of X and Y and Corrected Values of Ye

Sample	X	Ye	Y
1	1	1.6	2
2	2	3.8	3
3	3	6.0	7
4	4	8.2	7
5	5	10.4	11

Where:

$$y = a + bx \text{ therefore } y = -.6 + 2.2(x)$$

The data originally gathered has been "made" to fit a straight line by a least squares method. The next step is to determine how well the data fits a straight line or to determine what the correlation is between the gathered data and calculated data.

The formula for the correlation coefficient is shown below:

$$R = \frac{\frac{1}{n}\Sigma\,(x-\bar{x})\,(y-\bar{y})}{\sigma x \ \sigma y}$$

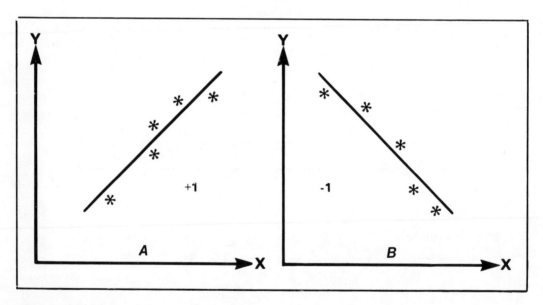

Figure 6-2. *Figure 6-2a and 6-2b, notice that the correlation coefficient values are positive (6-2a) and negative (6-2b) depending on the original size.*

The correlation coefficient is defined as a test to determine how well the data fits a straight line. Values range from 0 to +1 and 0 to –1. The closer to 1 (+1 or –1) the R factor is, the better the fit.

As shown in *Figures 6-2a* and *6-2b,* a positive one (+1) is used for data that has a positive attitude, while a negative one (–1) is used for data that has a negative attitude.

Table 6-4
Summation Table for Correlation Coefficient

Sample	X	Y	$(X-\bar{X})^2$	$(Y-\bar{Y})^2$	$(X-\bar{X})(Y-\bar{Y})$
1	1	2	4	16	8
2	2	3	1	9	3
3	3	7	0	1	0
4	4	7	1	1	1
5	5	11	4	25	10

$$n=5 \quad \frac{\Sigma X}{n}=\frac{15}{5} \quad \frac{\Sigma Y}{n}=\frac{30}{5} \quad \Sigma=10 \quad \Sigma=52 \quad \Sigma=22$$

$$\bar{x}=3 \quad \bar{y}=6 \quad \sigma x=\sqrt{\frac{10}{5}} \quad \sigma y=\sqrt{\frac{52}{5}}$$

$$R=\frac{\frac{1}{5}(22)}{\left(\sqrt{\frac{10}{5}}\right)\left(\sqrt{\frac{52}{5}}\right)} = \frac{4.4}{(1.414)(3.225)} = .9647$$

The hand-calculated example above serves to illustrate the mechanics of a simple regression. However, the formulas must be rearranged to write a computer program because the formula first presented permits only entry of data.

The original formula: $y = a + bx$ becomes $y = Bo + B1\ x + e$

Where:

Bo = Intercept
B1 = Slope
e = Random error = $R = 1 - R2$

And where:

$Ye = a + bx$

Now becomes:

$Ye = bo + b1x$

Where:

$$Ye = \overline{y} \left[\frac{\Sigma\ (x\text{-}\overline{x})\ (y\text{-}\overline{y})}{\Sigma\ (x\text{-}\overline{x})^2} \right] \overline{x} + \left[\frac{\Sigma\ (x\text{-}\overline{x})\ (y\text{-}\overline{y})}{(x\text{-}\overline{x})^2} \right] x$$

Then the following formulas apply.

$$b1 = \frac{\Sigma\ (x\text{-}\overline{x})\ (y\text{-}\overline{y})}{\Sigma(x\text{-}\overline{x})^2}$$

$$bo = \overline{y} - b1\overline{x}$$

$$R2 = \frac{b1\ \Sigma\ (x\text{-}\overline{x})\ (y\text{-}\overline{y})}{\Sigma\ (y\text{-}\overline{y})^2}$$

Where:

$R2$ explains the variation in percent of y.

$$R1 = \frac{\Sigma\ (x\text{-}\overline{x})\ (y\text{-}\overline{y})}{\sqrt{\dfrac{\Sigma\ (x\text{-}\overline{x})^2}{n}\ \dfrac{\Sigma\ (y\text{-}\overline{y})^2}{n}}}$$

$R1$ is the correlation coefficient.

Many shop floor conditions have been found to lend themselves to regression analysis. Shown in *Table 6-5* are several such examples.

Table 6-5
Typical Uses of Regression Analysis

Independent Variable	Dependent Variable
1. Drill size	1. Hole produced
2. Heat-treat temperature	2. Straightness
3. Depth of cut	3. Deflection
4. Weld bead size	4. Heat affected zone
5. Feed	5. RMS

For any of the typical examples listed in *Table 6-5*, there are many other contributing factors which could be represented as independent variables, each having a specific influence on the outcome of the problem. One of the major objectives in conducting a regression analysis study is to hold all other variables constant.

Program Name: "REG I"

The memory required for this program is 1912 bytes.

Lines 20 through 91 are user instructions. The computer permits as many as 10 individual entries to be made without a DIM or dimension statement. Line 95 is for user convenience by permitting as many as 25 entries of X and Y. If more than 25 entries are required, line 95 must be changed to reflect that number. As is, the computer will set aside memory for 25 inputs of X, Y and Z.

By inputting variables as X(I) or subscripted variables in the FOR-NEXT loop, the computer has the ability to recall each variable as an individual for later use, such as to calculate the average.

Lines 175 through 285. If the user were calculating the model longhand, he would establish a data table to keep track of each dependent and independent variable. The program logic does this in summing X and Y, calculating the average, then completing the required calculations. Line 275 calculates the new Y, or corrected Y, as variable name Z(I) and line 280 prints out the original data X(I), Y(I) and the corrected Y as Z(I).

Lines 300 and 310 calculate the R1 and R2 factors mentioned earlier. Lines 380 through 490 form the second module of the program that permits the user to input new values of X and calculate corrected values of Y. The computer still has all of the original input values in memory. Line 430 rearranges the formula to read Y = B2 + (B1X). The B1 and B2 factors were calculated earlier in the program using the original input data of X and Y.

```
1 REM PROGRAM NAME REG1
2 REM WRITTEN BY J.E.NICKS
3 REM COMPUTER APPLICATIONS FOR THE MANUFACTURING ENGINEER
4 REM COPYRIGHT 1981 ALL RIGHTS RESERVED
10 CLS
20 PRINT"THIS PROGRAM CALCULATES REGRESSION LINES"
30 PRINT"FOR ONE UNKNOWN"
40 PRINT"THE PROLGRAM IS DEVELOPED IN 2 PARTS"
50 PRINT"THE FIRST PART THE USER INPUTS X AND Y DATA"
60 PRINT"THEN THE COMPUTER CALCULATES A CORRECTED Y"
65 PRINT
70 PRINT"THE USER THEN HAS THE OPTION OF TYPING IN A"
80 PRINT"SINGLE ENTRY FOR A FORECAST OF Y"
85 PRINT
90 PRINT"X VALUES ARE INDEPENDENT DATA"
91 PRINT"Y VALUES ARE DEPENDENT DATA"
92 FORI=1TO3:PRINT:NEXT
93 INPUT"ENTER THE NAME OF THE X VALUES";X$
94 INPUT"ENTER THE NAME OF THE Y VALUES";Y$
95 DIMX(25),Y(25),Z(25)
96 CLS
100 INPUT"ENTER THE TOTAL NO. OF X & Y DATA POINTS";N
110 FORI=1TON
120 PRINT"TYPE IN X & Y VALUES SEPARATED BY A COMMA"
130 INPUTX(I),Y(I)
135 REMX1=SUM X,X2=SUM X SQ
140 X1=X1+X(I):X2=X2+X(I)[2
150 Y1=Y1+Y(I):Y2=Y2+Y(I)[2
```

Printout 6-1

```
155 REM X3=SUM X* SUM Y
160 X3=X3+(X(I)*Y(I))
170 NEXTI
175 REMX4=X BAR
180 X4=X1/N:Y4=Y1/N
185 REM X5=SUM A-X BAR SQ
190 X5=X2-((X1[2)/N)
200 Y5=Y2-((Y1[2)/N)
205 REM X6=SUM X-X BAR * SUM Y-Y BAR
210 X6=X3-((X1)*(Y1))/N
220 B1=X6/X5
230 B2=Y4-(B1*X4)
240 REM Z(I)=CORRECTED Y
260 LPRINTCHR$(27);CHR$(14);"REGRESSION ANALYSIS"
261 LPRINT"  "
265 LPRINT"SAMPLE";TAB(15);"X";TAB(29);"Y";TAB(43);"CORRECTED Y"
266 LPRINT TAB(15);X$;TAB(29);Y$
267 LPRINT"  "
270 FORI=1TON
275 Z(I)=B2+(B1*X(I))
280 LPRINTI,X(I),Y(I),Z(I)
285 NEXT
289 LPRINT"  "
290 LPRINT"B1 =";B1,"B2 =";B2
300 R2=(B1*(X3-((X1*Y1)/N)))/(Y2-((Y1)[2)/N)
310 R1=(X3-((X1*Y1)/N))/SQR((Y2-((Y1)[2)/N)*(X2-((X1)[2)/N))
320 LPRINT"THE CORRELATION COEFFICIENT IS";R1
330 LPRINT"THE CLOSER TO 1 THE BETTER THE DATA FITS Y=A+BX"
340 LPRINT"  "
350 LPRINT"THE PREDICTION Y EXPLAINS";R2;"% OF THE"
360 LPRINT"VARIATION OF THE DATA INPUTTED AS Y"
370 CLS
380 PRINT"TO INPUT A SINGLE VALUE TYPE 1 OR TYPE 2 TO EXIT"
400 INPUTP
410 ONPGOTO420,500
420 INPUT"THE VALUE OF X IS";X
430 Y=B2+(B1*X)
440 LPRINT"FOR A VALUE OF";X;"Y EQUALS";Y
450 CLS:PRINT"FOR A VALUE OF";X;"Y EQUALS";Y
460 PRINT"FOR ANOTHER VALUE TYPE 1 OR 2 TO EXIT"
470 INPUTP
480 ONPGOTO420,500
500 END
```

Printout 6-1 continued

REGRESSION ANALYSIS

SAMPLE	X DRILL SIZE	Y HOLE PRODUCED	CORRECTED Y
1	.257	.2608	.26101
2	.375	.3796	.37933
3	.5	.5048	.504669
4	.6875	.6925	.692677
5	.7812	.7864	.78663
6	.875	.8809	.880684

B1 = 1.00271   B2 = 3.31438E-03
THE CORRELATION COEFFICIENT IS .999999
THE CLOSER TO 1 THE BETTER THE DATA FITS Y=A+BX

THE PREDICTION Y EXPLAINS .999998 % OF THE
VARIATION OF THE DATA INPUTTED AS Y

FOR A VALUE OF .125 Y EQUALS .128653
FOR A VALUE OF .25 Y EQUALS .253991
FOR A VALUE OF .625 Y EQUALS .630007
FOR A VALUE OF 1 Y EQUALS 1.00602
FOR A VALUE OF 1.25 Y EQUALS 1.2567
FOR A VALUE OF 1.5 Y EQUALS 1.50738
FOR A VALUE OF 1.75 Y EQUALS 1.75805

—————————————— **Printout 6-2** ——————————————

REGRESSION ANALYSIS

SAMPLE	X BORE DIA.	Y CHIP CLEARANCE	CORRECTED Y
1	1.25	.183	.183283
2	1.625	.238	.238174
3	1.875	.275	.274769
4	2.25	.33	.32966
5	2.75	.403	.402849
6	3.25	.476	.476038
7	3.75	.549	.549227

B1 = .146378   B2 = 3.10361E-04
THE CORRELATION COEFFICIENT IS .999998
THE CLOSER TO 1 THE BETTER THE DATA FITS Y=A+BX

THE PREDICTION Y EXPLAINS .999995 % OF THE
VARIATION OF THE DATA INPUTTED AS Y

FOR A VALUE OF 1 Y EQUALS .146688
FOR A VALUE OF 1.5 Y EQUALS .219877
FOR A VALUE OF 1.75 Y EQUALS .256471
FOR A VALUE OF 2 Y EQUALS .293066
FOR A VALUE OF 2.5 Y EQUALS .366255
FOR A VALUE OF 3 Y EQUALS .439444
FOR A VALUE OF 3.5 Y EQUALS .512633
FOR A VALUE OF 4 Y EQUALS .585821
FOR A VALUE OF 5 Y EQUALS .732199

Printout 6-3

Comments on Sample Printouts

Printout Number 1. The reader should immediately recognize the data on drill size and resulting hole size is taken directly from the Handbook. The reader also should observe that there is a good correlation. This is staged data, but serves to demonstrate the program.

Printout Number 2. The question here is, "How much chip clearance should there be for a boring bar of a given size?" The answer is produced from a table which has several data points. However, the table was not complete.

Multiple Regression

The next example of regression analysis to be reviewed is multiple regression. As the name implies, multiple regression uses more than one independent variable.

"REG 2"

"REG 2" is a computer program that calculates this model and is designed for two inputs of X as independent variables and one input of Y as the dependent variable. No attempt will be made to calculate a sample by hand: the formulas are much like simple regression, except more involved. For a more detailed example of the hand calculations, any good statistics book will suffice.

The programming formulas used for this computer program were taken from the *Quality Control Handbook*.

There are many examples in industry where two separate yet controllable factors generate a third dependent factor. Typical examples of multiple regression are shown in *Table 6-6*.

Table 6-6
Typical uses for Multiple Regression Analysis

	Controllable Factors Independent Variables		Controlled Factors Dependent Variable
	$X1$	$X2$	Y
1. Time		Temperature	Case depth
2. Material hardness		Feed	Tool life
3. Carbon content		Cross Section	Core

The general math model is:

$$Y = Bo + B1x1 + B2x2...Bkxk + e$$

Where:

The B's are the unknown parameters of the x's and e is the random error

Then:

$$\hat{Y} = bo + b1x1 + b2x2...bkxk$$

Where:

$\hat{y}$ = The predicted values of y

$bo, b1...bk$ = The unkown paramters of $Bo, B1...Bk$

The general equation can be written in matrix form:

$$\overset{S}{\begin{bmatrix} \Sigma\ X1^2\ \Sigma\ X1\ X2...\ \Sigma\ X1\ X\ K \\ \Sigma\ X2\ X1\ \Sigma\ X2^2...\ \Sigma\ X2\ X\ K \\ \Sigma\ X\ K\ X1\ \Sigma\ X\ K\ X2...\ \Sigma\ X\ K^2 \end{bmatrix}} \overset{b}{\begin{bmatrix} b1 \\ b2 \\ bk \end{bmatrix}} = \overset{a}{\begin{bmatrix} \Sigma\ X\ 1\ Y \\ \Sigma\ X\ 2\ Y \\ \Sigma\ X\ K\ Y \end{bmatrix}}$$

Where $Sb = a$

Writing a computer program for this math model can be somewhat involved. A method of handling the equation is referred to as the Forward Doolittle Technique. The interested reader is directed to the first and second reference in the bibliography of this chapter.

The basic concept of this text is to provide the Manufacturing Engineer with useful tools to assist in engineering calculations and not to provide an exercise in mathematics. For this reason, the "REG 2" program for multiple regression has been written by taking the general math model and breaking it down into its component parts.

There is one major restriction in writing the program in this manner that should be pointed out. The reader's attention is directed to the general math model. XK can be defined as any number of independent variables. For example, if there were six independent variables, XK would be the sixth set of independent variables. The program ("REG 2") that follows, allows for two sets of independent variables; i.e., $X1$ and $X2$. When MAT statements are part of the programming language, parts of the program could be written simpler. After the program has performed its calculations, new sets of data for $X1$ and $X2$ can be entered from the keyboard.

The general model for this is:
$$\hat{y} = \bar{y} + b1(x1 - \bar{x}1) + b2(x2 - \bar{x}2)$$

Where $X1$ and $X2$ are new values of the independent variables and $\bar{Y}, \bar{X}1$ and $\bar{X}2$ are the averages (X bar) of the original sets of data. $b1$ and $b2$ are the calculated coefficients to $X1$ and $X2$.

At the end of the program an identity matrix is printed out. The general idea of the identity matrix is like that of the coefficient of correlation in simple regression; i.e., to provide a way for the user to determine how well the data fits a straight line curve. A perfect fit would result in the identity matrix producing the numeral 1's along the principal diagonal of the matrix with 0's elsewhere as shown in *Figure 6-3 and Figure 6-4*.

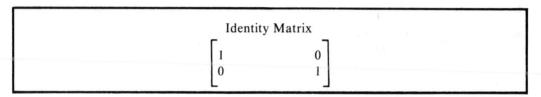

Identity Matrix

$$\begin{bmatrix} 1 & 0 \\ 0 & 1 \end{bmatrix}$$

Figure 6-3. A sample Indentity Matrix.

The original data may be charted (see *Figure 6-5*).

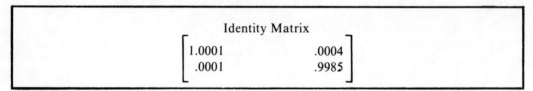

Identity Matrix

$$\begin{bmatrix} 1.0001 & .0004 \\ .0001 & .9985 \end{bmatrix}$$

Figure 6-4. *Note on this typical Identity Matrix that a perfect fit would result in all ones and zeros. This chart displays typical data plotted for X1, X2 and Y values.*

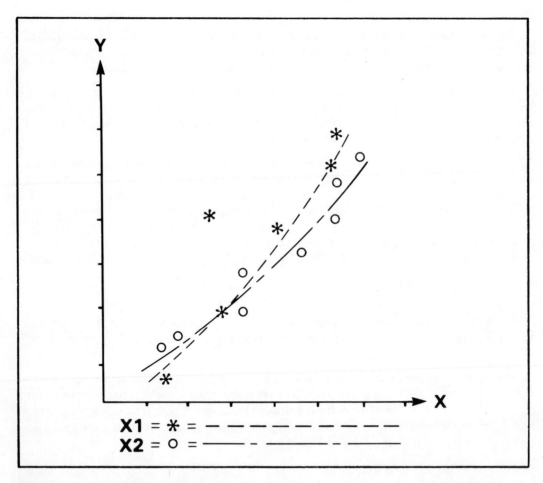

Figure 6-5. *Charted data may appear to be skewed when plotted. The Identity Matrix will determine how well the data fits a straight line.*

Program Name: "REG 2"

The memory required for this program is 3252 bytes.

Lines 1 through 290. The program format follows the same structure as "REG 1". The REM statements provide the user or programmer with a description of what is being done in the program. For example:

Line 180 REM XE = Sum X1 + Y.

If presented in table form, the data inputted and calculated thus far in the program can be seen in *Table 6-7*.

Table 6-7
REG 2 Program Variables

Data Item No.	$X1 = X1(I)$	$X2 = X2(I)$	$Y = Y(I)$
1	$X\,1,1$	$X\,2,1$	$Y1$
2	$X\,1,2$	$X\,2,2$	$Y2$
3	$X\,1,3$	$X\,2,3$	$Y3$
$\vdots$	$\vdots$	$\vdots$	$\vdots$
n	$X\,1,n$	$X\,2,n$	$Y\,n$
	$XA = \Sigma\,X1$	$XB = \Sigma\,X2$	$Y1 = Y$
	$XC = \Sigma\,X1^2$	$XD = \Sigma\,X2^2$	$Y2 = \Sigma\,Y^2$
	$XE = \Sigma\,X1\,Y$	$XF = \Sigma\,X2\,Y$	
		$XG = \Sigma\,X1X2$	
	$XH = \overline{X}1$	$XJ = \overline{X}2$	$Y3 = \overline{y}$

$$S1 = \Sigma\,X1^2 - ((\Sigma\,X1)^2/n)$$
$$S2 = \Sigma\,X2^2 - ((\Sigma\,X2)^2/n)$$

Often it is necessary that equations be rearranged to provide an easy way to calculate data inside and/or outside the FOR-NEXT loops.

Lines 300 through 480. The term - matrix - is used only to indicate a table is being constructed and should not be interpreted as a matrix in a mathematical sense.

Lines 490 through 560. This section of the program permits the user to input individual entries of X1 and X2 for a calculated Y value; where X1 and X2 are not part of the original input values, in other words, the forecasting section of the program.

Lines 490 through 710. The identity matrix is calculated just as the R1 factor in simple regression.

One academic footnote—there have been many scholarly books, articles and treatises written on the subject of regression analysis, some of which are presented in the Bibliography to this work. The purpose of this chapter is to present the Manufacturing Engineer with the fundamentals of microcomputer usage and statistical models that can be programmed to assist him in his function. Understandably, the sample programs presented in this work are base programs.

The astute reader will recognize that some of the statistical tests; i.e., ANOVA tests, have been omitted from this work. Also, some measure of "statistical awareness" is necessary on the user's part to acknowledge this fact.

On the user's behalf, an analogy might be drawn. If an engineer on the shop floor is studying a problem concerning scrap and rework, and the unit of measure being used is .001 inch (.03 mm), there would be little value in an engineering approach to solve the problem using measurement values of .00001 (.0003 mm). While there may be some pedagorical value in this approach, it tends to defeat the purpose. Illustratively, the statistical error in the difference between $\Sigma xm^2 - (\Sigma xm)^2/n$ and $\Sigma(xm-\bar{x})^2$ for the most part is academic in nature when viewed in the overall perspective.

```
1 REM PROGRAM NAME REG2
2 REM COMPUTER APPLICATIONS FOR THE MANUFACTURING ENGINEER
3 REM WRITTEN BY J.E.NICKS
4 REM COPY RIGHT ALL RIGHTS RESERVED
10 CLS
20 PRINT"THIS PROGRAM CALCULATES REGRESSION LINES"
30 PRINT"FOR 2 UNKNOWNS"
40 PRINT"THE PROGRAM IS DEVELOPED IN 2 PARTS"
50 PRINT"FOR THE FIRST PART, THE USER INPUTS X1, X2 AND Y DATA"
60 PRINT"AND THE COMPUTER CALCULATES A CORRECTED Y OR (YE)"
70 PRINT"THEN THE USER INPUTS SINGLE ENTRIES OF X1 AND X2"
80 PRINT"FOR A SINGLE CORRECTED VALUE OF Y OR (YE)"
90 DIMX1(20),X2(20),Y(20),Z(20)
91 DIMRE(20)
95 FORX=1TO4:PRINT:NEXTX
96 INPUT"ENTER THE NAME OF X1";N1$
97 INPUT"ENTER THE NAME OF X2";N2$
98 INPUT"ENTER THE NAME OF Y";N3$
100 INPUT"ENTER THE TOTAL NUMBER OF Y DATA POINTS";N
110 FORI=1TON
120 PRINT"ENTER THE DATA X1,X2,Y (SEPARATE BY COMMAS)"
130 INPUT X1(I),X2(I),Y(I)
140 REM XA=SUM X1,XB=SUM X2,Y1=SUM Y
150 XA=XA+X1(I):XB=XB+X2(I):Y1=Y1+Y(I)
160 REM XC=SUM X1 SQR,XD=SUM X2 SQR,Y2=SUM Y SQR
170 XC=XC+X1(I)[2:XD=XD+X2(I)[2:Y2=Y2+Y(I)[2
180 REM XE=SUM X1*Y:XF=SUM X2*Y:XG=SUM X1*X2
190 XE=XE+(X1(I)*Y(I)):XF=XF+(X2(I)*Y(I)):XG=XG+(X1(I)*X2(I))
200 NEXTI
210 REM XH=X1 BAR:XJ=X2 BAR: Y3=Y BAR
220 XH=XA/N:XJ=XB/N:Y3=Y1/N
230 REM START MATRIX
240 S1=XC-((XA[2)/N)
250 S2=XD-((XB[2)/N)
260 A1=XE-(((XA)*(Y1))/N)
270 A2=XF-(((XB)*(Y1))/N)
```

Printout 6-4

```
280 S3=XG-(((XA)*(XB))/N)
290 S4=S3
300 REM MATRIX CONSTRUCTION NEW CONTINUES AS P
310 P1=0:P8=0:P2=S1:P3=S3:A3=A1
320 P4=1:P5=S3/S1:A4=A3/S1
330 P6=S2-(P5*S3)
340 A5=A2-(P5*A3)
350 P7=1
360 A6=A5/P6
370 B2=A6
380 B1=A4-(P5*B2)
390 REM B3=B0
400 B3=Y3-(B1*XH)-(B2*XJ)
410   LPRINT CHR$(27);CHR$(14);"MULTIPLE REGRESSION"
420 LPRINT "ITEM",N1$,N2$,N3$,"FORECAST"
425 LPRINT " "
430 LPRINT " ",;"X1";,;"X2";,;"Y";,;"YE"
440 FORI=1TON
450 YE=Y3+(B1*(X1(I)-XH))+(B2*(X2(I)-XJ))
460 LPRINT I,X1(I),X2(I),Y(I),YE
461 RE(I)=Y(I)-YE:SR=SR+RE(I)
470 NEXT I
471 LPRINT "ITEM","RESIDUAL"
472 FORI=1TON
473 LPRINT I,RE(I)
474 NEXTI
475 LPRINT "SUM RESIDUAL";SR
480 LPRINT " "
490 PRINT"FOR A SINGLE ENTRY OF X1,X2 TYPE 1"
491 PRINT"OR TYPE 2 TO EXIT"
500 INPUTT
510 ONTGOTO520,570
520 INPUT"TYPE IN THE VALUE OF X1,X2";L,M
530 YE=B3+((B1*L)+(B2*M))
540 LPRINT "FOR A VALUE OF ";L;"AND";M;"THE EXPECTED Y OR YE IS";YE
550 INPUT "FOR ANOTHER SINGLE ENTRY TYPE 1 OR 2 TO EXIT";T
560 ONTGOTO520,570
570 REM IDENTITY MATRIX
573 LPRINT RE,SR
580 C2=1/P6:C3=-(C2*P5):C1=1/P2-(C3*P5):C4=C3
590 I1=(C1*S1)+(C3*S4)
600 I3=(C1*S3)+(C3*S2)
610 I4=(C4*S1)+(C2*S4)
620 I2=(C4*S3)+(C2*S2)
630 LPRINT " "
640 LPRINT CHR$(1);"THE IDENTITY MATRIX"
660 LPRINT I1,I3
665 LPRINT " "
670 LPRINT I4,I2
680 LPRINT " "
690 LPRINT "IN THE IDENTITY MATRIX, THE CLOSER THE VALUES ARE"
700 LPRINT "TO 1 AND 0 THE BETTER THE DATA FITS"
710 END
```

Printout 6-4 continued

```
MULTIPLE REGRESSION
ITEM            PRESSURE          ACID              STRENGTH          FORECAST

                X1                X2                Y                 YE
 1              110               116               665               672.343
 2              119               104               618               636.181
 3              138               94                620               624.101
 4              130               86                574               578.012
 5              143               110               682               699.009
 6              133               87                594               586.913
 7              147               114               722               722.054
 8              142               106               700               680.675
 9              125               107               681               658.175
10              135               106               695               669.684
11              152               98                664               662.847
12              118               86                548               559.171
13              155               87                620               621.455
14              128               96                595               616.783
15              146               120               740               745.63
16              132               108               670               673.356
17              130               104               640               653.452
18              112               91                590               570.706
19              113               92                570               576.467
20              120               100               640               620.987
ITEM            RESIDUAL
 1              -7.34332
 2              -18.1808
 3              -4.10132
 4              -4.01196
 5              -17.0092
 6              7.08667
 7              -.053833
 8              19.3253
 9              22.8254
10              25.3158
11              1.15332
12              -11.1711
13              -1.45496
14              -21.7828
15              -5.63031
16              -3.3562
17              -13.4516
18              19.2939
19              -6.46729
20              19.0134
SUM RESIDUAL-8.54492E-04


FOR A VALUE OF   121 AND 98 THE EXPECTED Y OR YE IS 614.175
FOR A VALUE OF   122 AND 98 THE EXPECTED Y OR YE IS 615.745
FOR A VALUE OF   123 AND 98 THE EXPECTED Y OR YE IS 617.315
 0                 -8.54492E-04

THE IDENTITY MATRIX
 1               0

 0               1

IN THE IDENTITY MATRIX, THE CLOSER THE VALUES ARE
TO 1 AND 0 THE BETTER THE DATA FITS
```

Printout 6-5

Non-Linear Regression Models

Most Manufacturing Engineers have used Log-Log or Semi-Log graph paper. Learning curves, for example, can be charted using Log-Log graph paper. Often when data is plotted on simple graph paper it becomes apparent that such data does not fit a straight line model. Two additional regression models are presented in this chapter, supported with computer programs.

Log-Linear Regression

The first model discussed is called Log-Linear and has a semi-log relationship. Semi-log means one axis is linear and the other is log.

The general math model for this relationship is derived from the straight line equation:

$$Y = a + bx$$

The semi-log relationship is then transposed:

$$lny = lna + bx$$

using natural logs. Then:

$$b = \frac{n \Sigma xy - \Sigma x \Sigma y}{n \Sigma x^2 - (\Sigma x)^2}$$

And:

$$a = 1/n \, (\Sigma y - b \Sigma x)$$

The coefficient of correlation is:

$$R = \frac{n \Sigma xy - \Sigma x \Sigma y}{\sqrt{\left[n \Sigma x^2 - (\Sigma x)^2\right] \left[n \Sigma y^2 - (\Sigma y)^2\right]}}$$

Typical data plotted showing this relationship is shown in *Figure 6-6*.

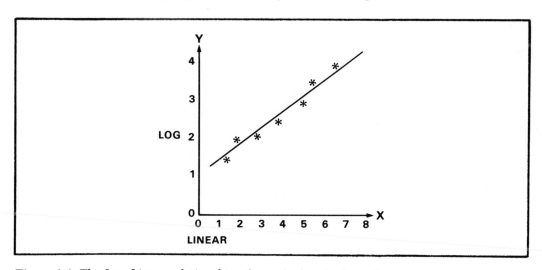

Figure 6-6. *The Log-Linear relationship of sample data is charted.*

Program Name: "REG 3"

The memory required for this program is 1726 bytes.

A word of advice is in order when using regression analysis other than straight line models. When working on an engineering problem, data can sometimes be misleading, or perhaps the analysis of data can be misleading, or both.

The point is, before using this or any other regression model, the engineer must assure himself that the data collected fits the regression model used.

A case in point can be made here by reviewing the sample printout from the "REG 3" program. Note that the corrected Y values do not have a good correlation to the sample Y data figures. This could be for one of two reasons.
1. The range of Y values as they deviate from the X values is too great, or:
2. The collected values (X, Y) do not fit the regression model.

A good case can be made for the latter. Observe now that the correlation is .9839%. This is an indication that this data does not fit a linear-log relationship very well.

Curvilinear Regression

The last regression model to be reviewed in this chapter is curvilinear regression. Curvilinear regression can be defined as one axis, X, being linear while the second axis, Y, is some exponential function of X.

This program is written to the second order, and resembles an exponential curve. The general math model is:

$$Y = bo + b1 \, x \, 1 + b2 \, x \, 1^2 + e$$

This model is expanded and solved by substitution:

$$\Sigma \, y = nbo + b1 \, \Sigma \, x + b2 \, \Sigma x^2$$
$$\Sigma \, xy = bo \, \Sigma \, x + b1 \, \Sigma \, x^2 + b2 \, \Sigma \, x^3$$
$$\Sigma \, y \, x^2 = bo \, \Sigma \, x^2 + b1 \, \Sigma \, x^3 + b2 \, \Sigma \, x^4$$

The program and typical printout follows.

Program Name: "REG 4"

The memory required for this program is 1338 bytes.

The curvilinear regression program is patterned after a parabola in that if several points on the curve are known the entire curve can be regressed. Note the sample printout and *Figure 6-6*.

Our original input data was six points on the curve. The program was reworked to printout the plot points as shown.

Before we leave the subject of regression analysis, one final reminder: have a good idea of the shape of the curve before selecting a regression model.

General Comments

The basic format for each of the programs in this chapter is the same. Data are inputted by

```
1 REM PROGRAM NAME REG3
2 REM WRITTEN BY J.E.NICKS
3 REM COMPUTER APPLICATIONS FOR THE MANUFACTURING ENGINEER
4 REM COPYRIGHT 1981 ALL RIGHTS RESERVED
10 CLS
20 PRINT"THIS REGRESSION MODEL IS USED WHEN"
30 PRINT"X IS LINEAR AND Y IS (LOG)"
40 PRINT"X IS INDEPENDENT AND Y IS THE DEPENDENT VARIABLE"
50 PRINT"FOR THE FUNCTION  INY=INA + BX INE"
60 PRINT"THE PROGRAM IS CALCULATED IN NATURAL OR E BASE LOGS"
90 PRINT"AND THE PROGRAM IS DEVELOPED IN 2 PARTS"
100 PRINT"THE FIRST PART IS CALCULATING THE MODEL AND THE SECOND"
110 PRINT"PART IS ENTERING SINGLE VALUES OF X FOR FORECASTING"
111 INPUT"TYPE IN THE NAME OF X";X$
112 INPUT"TYPE IN THE NAME OF Y";Y$
120 INPUT"TYPE IN THE NUMBER OF DATA POINTS FOR X";N
130 FORI=1TON
140 INPUT"TYPE IN X & Y VALUES, SEPARATE BY A COMMA";X(I),Y(I)
150 REM A=SUMX:B=SUMY:C=X*Y:D=X SQR:E=Y SQR
160 A=A+X(I):Y1(I)=LOG(Y(I)):B=B+Y1(I)
170 D=D+X(I)[2:E=E+Y1(I)[2:C=C+(X(I)*Y1(I))
180 NEXTI
190 B1=((N*C)-(A*B))/(N*D-(A[2))
200 A1=((1/N)*(B-(B1*A)))
210 LPRINT CHR$(27);CHR$(14);"SEMI - LOG REGRESSION"
220 LPRINT" "
230 LPRINT"SAMPLE",X$,Y$,"CORRECTED Y"
240 FORI=1TON:YE=A1+(B1*X(I)):YE=EXP(YE)
260 LPRINTI,X(I),Y(I),YE:NEXTI:LPRINT" "
270 R=((N*C)-(A*B))/SQR(((N*D)-(A[2))*((N*E)-(B[2)))
275 LPRINT"THE CORRELATION IS ";R
280 LPRINT"THE CLOSER TO +1 OR -1 , THE BETTER THE DATA FITS"
290 LPRINT"THE MODEL INY=INA+BX"
310 INPUT"FOR A SINGLE ENTRY TYPE 1 OR 2 TO EXIT";P
320 ONPGOTO330,380
330 INPUT"TYPE IN THE X VALUE";X
340 Y=EXP(B1*X)*EXP (A1)
350 LPRINT"FOR A VALUE OF ";X;"YE EQUALS";YE
360 INPUT"FOR ANOTHER SINGLE ENTRY TYPE 1 OR 2 TO EXIT";P
370 ONPGOTO330,380
380 END
```

SEMI — LOG REGRESSION

SAMPLE	SAMPLE X	SAMPLE Y	CORRECTED Y
1	1	1.25	1.41346
2	2	1.85	1.65029
3	3	2	1.92678
4	4	2.19	2.24961
5	5	2.66	2.62652
6	6	3.17	3.06659
7	7	3.55	3.58038
8	8	4.02	4.18026

THE CORRELATION IS .983959
THE CLOSER TO +1 OR -1 , THE BETTER THE DATA FITS
THE MODEL INY=INA+BX

Printout 6-6

the user, programming statements are next written to accomplish the following:
1. Perform calculations inside the first FOR-NEXT loop.
2. Retain the identity of each input data subscripted variables.
3. Calculate the average once all data is inputted.
4. Write a second loop to perform additional calculations. The reader should note that all data are inputted before the second loop starts.
5. A last loop then produces the forecasted or corrected figure YE. As mentioned earlier, the user will encounter problems using regression analysis in determining which model to "fit" the data to. Notice the approach is to fit the model to the data and not fit the data to the model. Data, unless staged, will rarely fit a regression model perfectly. For literary purposes, of course, this is easy in the real world, although it does not happen. It should be recognized that the four programs included in this chapter are a first step and that an entire book of computer programs could be written on the subject.

Data Fit Problems

The problems of data fit can be handled in one of three ways:
1. Charting.
2. Standard error testing.
3. Orthogonal polynomials.

Charting

The first method of testing, charting, should be considered by the novice. Charting sample test data on a simple graph will give the engineer a feel for what type of data has been gathered.

If both X and Y data are linear in nature, a chart will usually highlight this. Occasionally, it may be necessary to rework the data for charting purposes to produce the straight line more convenient for the chart; i.e., divide by 10 or 100 or multiply both sets of data by 10 or 100, or even 1000.

Other data plots may be necessary. Plotting data on semi-log or log-log graph paper can be useful in determining the character of the data. Data plotted on this type of graph paper produces a straight line.

Standard Error Testing

A second method of determining the data fit is to test the data using standard error formulas. This method is called Standard Error Testing. For example, two such formulas are shown below:

1. Standard error for simple regression.

$$\sigma\, xy = \sqrt{\frac{\Sigma\, y^2 - b1\, \Sigma\, y - b2\, \Sigma\, xy}{n - df}}$$

2. Standard error for curvilinear regression.

$$\sigma\, xy = \sqrt{\frac{\Sigma\, y - ye}{n - df}}$$

The answers each of these formulas produce are then subjected to F distribution testing. This branch of statisticals is called statistical inference or hypothesis testing.

Orthogonal Polynomials

A third method of testing to determine the best fit for raw data is called orthogonal polynomials. In this test, a table is established to produce key numbers that determine the best fit. Orthogonal polynomials can be developed to produce these key numbers where the X's are evenly spaced and other methods are used where the X or independent variable are of unequal intervals. This method, however, is advised only for the person who has had some experience in statistics.

```
1 REM PROGRAM NAME REG 4
2 REM COMPUTER APPLICATIONS FOR THE MFG ENG
3 REM WRITTEN BY J.E.NICKS
4 REM COPY RIGHT 1981 ALL RIGHTS RESERVED
10 FORX=0TO32:PRINT:NEXTX
20 PRINT"THIS REGRESSION MODEL IS USED FOR"
30 PRINT"CURVILINEAR DATA"
40 PRINT"WHEN X IS LINEAR AND Y IS CURVED"
50 PRINT"THE PROGRAM IS DEVELOPED IN 2 PARTS"
60 PRINT"THE FIRST PART IS INPUTTING X AND Y DATA"
70 PRINT"AND THE SECOND PART IS FOR SINGLE ENTRIES FOR FORECASTING"
71 INPUT"TYPE IN THE NAME OF X";X$
72 INPUT"TYPE IN THE NAME OF Y";Y$
80 INPUT"INPUT THE NUMBER OF DATA POINTS";N
90 REM X(I)=X,Y(I)=Y,A=SUM X, B=SUM Y
100 FORI=1TON
110 INPUT"ENTER X AND Y DATA, SEPARATE BY A COMMA";X(I),Y(I)
120 A=A+X(I):B=B+Y(I)
130 NEXT I
140 REM XB=X BAR
150 XB=A/N
160 FORI=1TON
170 X1(I)=X(I)-XB:C=C+(X1(I)*Y(I)):D(I)=X1(I)[2
180 E=E+(D(I)*Y(I)):F=F+D(I):G=G+(X1(I)[4)
190 NEXTI
200 B1=C/F
210 B2=(E-((B/N)*F))/(G-((F/N)*F))
220 B0=(B-(B2*F))/N
221 LPRINT "B1","B2","B0"
222 LPRINT B1,B2,B0
230 LPRINT CHR$(27);CHR$(14);"CURVILINEAR REGRESSION"
240 LPRINT CHR$(2);
250 LPRINT "ITEM",X$,Y$,"FORECASTED Y"
260 LPRINT "X","Y","YE"
265 LPRINT " "
270 FORI=1TON
280 YE=B0+(B1*X1(I))+(B2*D(I))
290 LPRINT I,X(I),Y(I),YE
300 NEXTI
310 LPRINT " "
320 PRINT"FOR A SINGLE ENTRY TYPE 1 OR 2 TO EXIT"
330 INPUTQ
331 ONQGOTO340,400
340 INPUT"THE VALUE OF X IS";X
350 YE=B0+(B1*(X-XB))+(B2*((X-XB)[2))
360 LPRINT "FOR A VALUE OF";X;"YE EQUALS";YE
370 PRINT"FOR ANOTHER ENTRY TYPE 1 OR 2 TO EXIT"
380 INPUTQ
390 ONQGOTO340,400
400 END
```

Printout 6-7

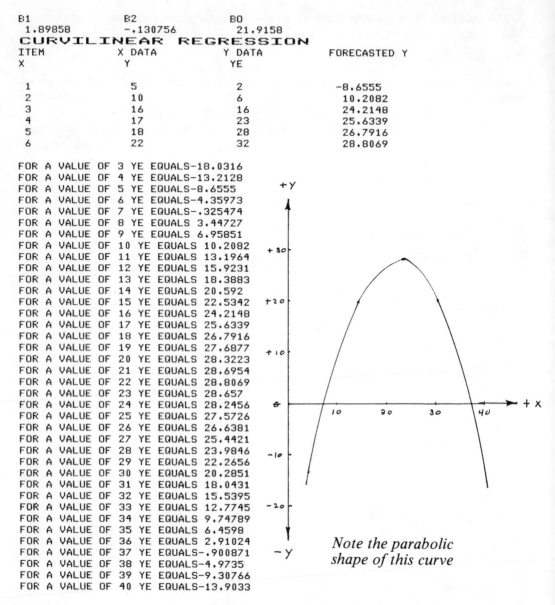

```
B1                  B2                  B0
 1.89858            -.130756            21.9158
CURVILINEAR  REGRESSION
ITEM                X DATA              Y DATA           FORECASTED Y
X                   Y                   YE

1                   5                   2                -8.6555
2                   10                  6                10.2082
3                   16                  16               24.2148
4                   17                  23               25.6339
5                   18                  28               26.7916
6                   22                  32               28.8069
```

```
FOR A VALUE OF 3 YE EQUALS-18.0316
FOR A VALUE OF 4 YE EQUALS-13.2128
FOR A VALUE OF 5 YE EQUALS-8.6555
FOR A VALUE OF 6 YE EQUALS-4.35973
FOR A VALUE OF 7 YE EQUALS-.325474
FOR A VALUE OF 8 YE EQUALS 3.44727
FOR A VALUE OF 9 YE EQUALS 6.95851
FOR A VALUE OF 10 YE EQUALS 10.2082
FOR A VALUE OF 11 YE EQUALS 13.1964
FOR A VALUE OF 12 YE EQUALS 15.9231
FOR A VALUE OF 13 YE EQUALS 18.3883
FOR A VALUE OF 14 YE EQUALS 20.592
FOR A VALUE OF 15 YE EQUALS 22.5342
FOR A VALUE OF 16 YE EQUALS 24.2148
FOR A VALUE OF 17 YE EQUALS 25.6339
FOR A VALUE OF 18 YE EQUALS 26.7916
FOR A VALUE OF 19 YE EQUALS 27.6877
FOR A VALUE OF 20 YE EQUALS 28.3223
FOR A VALUE OF 21 YE EQUALS 28.6954
FOR A VALUE OF 22 YE EQUALS 28.8069
FOR A VALUE OF 23 YE EQUALS 28.657
FOR A VALUE OF 24 YE EQUALS 28.2456
FOR A VALUE OF 25 YE EQUALS 27.5726
FOR A VALUE OF 26 YE EQUALS 26.6381
FOR A VALUE OF 27 YE EQUALS 25.4421
FOR A VALUE OF 28 YE EQUALS 23.9846
FOR A VALUE OF 29 YE EQUALS 22.2656
FOR A VALUE OF 30 YE EQUALS 20.2851
FOR A VALUE OF 31 YE EQUALS 18.0431
FOR A VALUE OF 32 YE EQUALS 15.5395
FOR A VALUE OF 33 YE EQUALS 12.7745
FOR A VALUE OF 34 YE EQUALS 9.74789
FOR A VALUE OF 35 YE EQUALS 6.4598
FOR A VALUE OF 36 YE EQUALS 2.91024
FOR A VALUE OF 37 YE EQUALS-.900871
FOR A VALUE OF 38 YE EQUALS-4.9735
FOR A VALUE OF 39 YE EQUALS-9.30766
FOR A VALUE OF 40 YE EQUALS-13.9033
```

Note the parabolic shape of this curve

Printout 6-7 continued

Bibliography

Hansen, Bertrand L. *Quality Control Theory & Applications*. Englewood Cliffs, NJ: Prentice-Hall, Inc., 1963.

Mann, Lawrence Jr. *Applied Engineering Statistics for Practicing Engineers*. New York: Barnes & Noble, 1970.

Mendanhall, Reinmuth. *Statistics for Management & Economics*, 2nd Ed. Duxbury, 1974.

Stockton, John R. and Clark, Charles T. *Introduction to Business and Economic Statistics*, 5th Ed. South-Western Publishing Company, 1975.

Optional Lab Assignments

Lab Assignment 6-1 (least difficult)

Write a computer program that calculates permutations and combinations. This is an easy program to write and will determine when your computer defaults calculating factorials. The formulas and definitions are as follows:

Permutations: The number of ways of ordering n objects selected r at a time and expressed as:

$$P^n_r = \frac{n!}{(n-r)!}$$

Where:

P = permutations
n = number of objects
r = objects taken at a time
$!$ = factorial where $0! = 1$ by definition

Example:

There are 10 parts in a box selected three at a time.

How many permutations are there?

$$P^{10}_3 \frac{10!}{(10-3)!} = \frac{10 \times 9 \times 8 \times 7 \times 6 \times 5 \times 4 \times 3 \times 2 \times 1}{7 \times 6 \times 5 \times 4 \times 3 \times 2 \times 1}$$

$$P^{10}_3 = \frac{10!}{(10-3)!} = \frac{10 \times 9 \times 8 \times 7!}{7!} = 720$$

Combinations: The number of combinations of n objects selected r at a time and expressed as:

$$C^n_r = \frac{n!}{r!\,(n-r)!}$$

Using the same example above, how many combinations are there for 10 parts selected three at a time?

$$C^{10}_3 = \frac{10!}{3!\,(10-3)} = \frac{10 \times 9 \times 8 \times 7!}{3 \times 2 \times 1 \times 7!} = 120$$

Lab Assignment 6-2 (moderate)

Rewrite "REG 1" to include the standard error formula included in the text.

Lab Assignment 6-3 (difficult)

Write a computer program for multiple regression to include three independent variables for x and one dependent variable y.

CHAPTER 7

Manpower
Analysis

Traditionally, time study has been considered an Industrial Engineering tool. Time study embodies both the art and science of many early pioneers in American management. The most notable of these being Fredrick W. Taylor, Frank and Lillian Gilbreath, and more recently the renowned author, Ralph Barnes.

Time Study

Over the last decade, as colleges and universities have developed curricula specifically designed to train the Manufacturing Engineer, many traditionally accepted Industrial Engineering subjects have been borrowed for the training of the Manufacturing Engineer. As the duties of the Manufacturing Engineer broaden, many educational institutions have found it necessary to develop course work in such subjects as motion and time study, work sampling and plant layout as well as material handling, to name a few.

Colleges and Universities

While the two disciplines, as taught in colleges and universities remain distinctly different, there are pressures from industry to share some of these common skills. While the Manufacturing Engineer will not claim to be an expert in the field of time study, there is some justification for this industry pressure. Time study is just one of the many different subjects studied by the Industrial Engineer, and time study engineering is usually considered an entry level position in industry reserved for the young engineer just graduating from college. Many companies feel a tour of duty on the shop floor is an excellent way to introduce the young engineer to production activity. This tour of duty usually embraces an element of establishing work standards by time study.

Another reason institutions include this subject in their Manufacturing Engineering coursework is to impart what the author refers to as a "concept of time". This concept of time is an essential ingredient in the engineer's training and serves to establish a foundation for later work in the field of cost estimating.

The dilemma faced by most institutions of higher learning that teach Manufacturing Engineering subjects is one of trying to provide training for the young engineer to serve both functions mentioned while not severely encroaching on what has been considered traditional Industrial Engineering discipline. In facing this problem and other internal pressures, the typical curriculum usually includes only one course in which the subject of time study is covered. Further, in this one course, many other subjects are touched upon. The problem provokes this question: Can a Manufacturing Engineer be trained to conduct watch time studies accurately as part of one course in college?

The answer is no.

While there have been many advances in recent years in Industrial Engineering education, one element which has lagged behind in the author's opinion, is watch time study. The purpose of recounting and commenting on this history of the academic aspects is to introduce the contents of this chapter.

Two programs are presented in this chapter; the first, named "TIME", is a program that permits watch-type time studies to be conducted and calculated by a microcomputer. The second program presented is named "RATIO" and uses the microcomputer to assist the engineer in conducting work sampling studies.

The first program to be discussed is the "TIME" program. To understand how the computer can be converted to a stop watch requires some knowledge of a computer's internal workings. The microcomputer has, in effect, two internal clocks. One is a real time clock which can be accessed and set to tick just as any other clock. This real time clock ticks in seconds and is, therefore, too slow to act as a time study watch. The second clock inside the computer is a FOR-NEXT loop. The FOR-NEXT loop can be set to tick at almost any rate, depending on what is being done inside the loop. The FOR-NEXT loop is the device chosen to act as a stop watch in the program presented in this chapter. The microcomputer could be interfaced to either a digital or analog device to act as a timer. Because of the cost of interfacing, this use is not practical. Before reviewing a printout from the "TIME" program, an overview of how the program works is necessary. As in a conventional time study, the engineer records data such as operation number, name, speeds and feeds. The user then enters an element description for up to eight elements. Once the internal stop watch is started (a FOR-NEXT loop), all the engineer is required to do is press a number key to record the termination of that element. The computer then jumps out of the loop, records the time value, jumps back into the loop and starts timing the next element. How much time is lost jumping out of and back into the loop? The answer is less than 20 microseconds. While the internal stop watch is running, the keyboard is being strobed for the termination of the element, and the instant a key is depressed, the computer terminates the loop. Anyone who has read a stop watch while conducting a conventional time study will realize that most of the watch reading skill is eliminated by not having to record numbers on a time study form. Computer time studies permit more time for the observer to concentrate on what the operator is doing, and they eliminate all of the watch reading skills required.

At the conclusion of the time study, the engineer can review the time values recorded and cross out any time values not desired in the study, just as in the conventional way. This cross out review is completed on the CRT.

Limitations

One limitation of the computer's ability to record a time study in this manner is apparent. Using a conventional method to conduct a time study, the observer is taught to record symbols for future cross outs; such as, T for talk, F for fumble, etc. While the computer has the ability to do this, it interrupts the clock cycle for that element and this leads to an inaccurate time value being recorded. This is a minor problem considering what is being accomplished by the computer.

Another minor problem was transport of the computer to the work site. This problem was solved by setting the entire computer with disk drive, printer and CRT on a 20″ x 35″ cart. One caution about the shop floor environment: with electric motors, magnetic fields and static electricity present, it is advisable to have a filter and surge supressor for all electrical plugs of the computer. With a surge supressor, all that is required is one 115-volt electrical outlet. After the time study is completed and cross outs are made, the engineer then inputs rating factors and allowances. The computer calculates the time study and prints out the results.

The only chore the microcomputer cannot do is produce a sketch of the work place layout. The author is hesitant to say "cannot" and perhaps should say the next step is to produce a work place layout. Without an enormous amount of additional programming, this might be accomplished with the aid of a digitizer or light pen.

Program Overview

Using this method to conduct a time study, as stated earlier, is more accurate than reading a conventional watch. The program overview for computer assisted time studies is:
1. The program will accept up to eight elements in the time study.
2. Each element will accept up to 25 records. (Note: This can be modified by changing the DIM statements in line 20.)
3. The computer clock is activated after element descriptions are entered.
4. Once the timing is completed, rating factors are entered for each element and cross outs can be made.
5. Allowances are entered.
6. Prorations are entered for any of the elements that are prorated.
7. A summary of the time study is printed out on hard copy.

Program Name: "TIME"

The memory required for this program is 12,308 bytes.

Review of Lines

Lines 10 through 500. The first 50 lines of the program are dedicated to user instructions and input of the various data items that normally appear on a conventional time study form. In lines 360 and 370, the user is coached to use abbreviations for element descriptions when possible.

Lines 510 through 605. This is the never-ending FOR-NEXT loop that actually does the timing. The INKEY$ statement allows the key pad to be strobed until a number key is depressed. Once a numbered key between 1 and 8 is depressed, the computer is directed to jump out of the loop and go to one of the line numbers from 610 to 680.

Lines 610 through 680. These lines are mock FOR-NEXT loops.

Example:

> Line 610 A = A+1: A(A) = I/925: N1 = N1+1: PRINT "Element 1", A,A(A): GOTO510

A = A+1 is a counter for the subscript A(A) = I/925. The first time element 1 is terminated, A(1) subscript is recorded for that element time. In line 610, 925 is constant. One minute is divided into 925 equal parts. This constant will vary depending on how the program is written. N1 = N1+1 is a counter of the number of recordings. The screen shows "Element 1", the cycle number and the correct time value in decimal minutes, A(A). The computer is then instructed to GOTO 510 and start the strobing process over. Comments earlier about the never-ending FOR-NEXT loop are explained this way. Line 520 reads for 1 = 1 to 3000—the computer never reads line 605 NEXT. The computer is terminated by the INKEY$ function. The longest time that any one element can take before reaching line 605 NEXT is 3000/925 = 3.24 minutes.

Cross outs. After recording phase of the time study is complete, the engineer then makes cross outs. Note lines 940 through 2970. The raw data recordings are shown on the upper part of the CRT and each recording in turn is displayed at the bottom of the screen along with the statement "TYPE 1 IF OK OR 2 FOR CROSS OUTS". The engineer can review the recordings and average before any cross outs are made. After this review, the engineer makes a decision to accept the recordings or cross it out of the study.

Foreign element. Element 8 has a dual purpose. It can be used in the regular way or be reserved as a place to capture foreign elements. If element 8 is used for foreign elements, the user must type in 1000 when asked what the rating for element 8 is. This permits the computer to know element 8 is be eliminated.

A foreign element is defined as an element·that is not included in the study. During a conventional watch study the engineer would be required to observe the foreign element, record the time for it and later disallow its time. Element 8 performs the same task.

Time Study Comments

Because this is a long program, no attempt was made to compress any of the lines and, at first glance, the program may seem confusing. There are 41 FOR-NEXT loops with over 60 variables used. For the reader reviewing the program, however, there is a thread of consistency in the use of the variables. A, A(A), N1, R1, A2, A3 are all variables devoted to the first element. B, B(B), N2, R2, B2, B3 are variables for the second element, and so forth.

A sample time study is presented on the following pages. The operation studied was a drilling and reaming operation on a gang drill. By referring to the printout, the reader will note several cross outs were made by the engineer at the conclusion of the study. The reader also should observe that the operator stopped production and talked to his supervisor during the study. This time was captured in element 8 and was disallowed as a foreign element.

The sample time study is marked up to assist the reader in following what was crossed out in the study. One last important item to remember about this program: the entire study, which included time recordings, cross outs, ratings and final calculations with printout, was completed on the shop floor in less than 15 minutes.

Before moving on to the next subject, we will examine several thoughts briefly. To do this, a scenario is necessary. The idea of time studies conducted by computer may not have any serious influence on quelling labor unrest over work standards in this country, but nevertheless could have a positive affect on labor's attitude. Today, almost every industrial task is conducted by—or at least assisted by—computers. In American industry, there still seems to be an aura connected to computer usage. The general theme is: if the computer said it, it must be correct. While other elements of conducting a time study need a fresh look, such as the judgment necessary in establishing a rating factor, the use of a computer to conduct time studies certainly has its advantages. The chief advantages that come to mind are:

1. More accurate recordings.
2. Less timing skill required by the engineer.

Whether or not people will have more faith in work standards established by a computer remains to be seen.

Another scenario also could develop. Suppose computer time studies do not catch on in industry. Many companies still employ the practice of permitting a union time study engineer to conduct a time study to assist in resolving jobs under dispute. Suppose also that the company still uses the stop watch and the union uses a computer. What then?

```
END
TIME STUDY FOR  12345   OPER NO  20
PART NAME   HOUSING
DATE  01/01/81   ENGINEER   JEN
OPERATION DESCRIPTION   DRILL & REAM 1 - .5 INCH HOLE
NO OF MACHINES   1   NO OF OPERATIONS   1

RPM OR SPM   RPM DRILL 350 - REAM 200
SFPM 65
FEED PER   FPR DRILL .007 - REAM .012
CUT: DEPTH: WIDTH   LENGTH DRILL & REAM 1.125
CUTTING TOOL   HSS
```

Note: Those cycles circled in the raw data section have been crossed out of the study

```
ELEMENT 1
RH REACH 18 IN.-GRASP PART-TRANS TO JIG-LOCATE-LH HOLD-CLAMP-MOVE TO SPIN 1
RAW DATA
 1  .0897297  (2  .132973) 3  .111351  4  .0854054  5  .0994595  (6  .147027) 7  .
092973  8  .102703  9  .0951352  10  .105946  11
 .092973  12  .124324  13  .103784  14  .101622  15  .0972973

SUM 1.5827 AVERAGE .105514
CORRECTED AND RATED DATA
RATING FOR THIS ELEMENT .9
 1  .0897297  (2  0) 3  .111351  4  .0854054  5  .0994595  (6  0) 7  .092973  8  .
102703  9  .0951352  10  .105946  11  .092973  12
 .124324  13  .103784  14  .101622  15  .0972973

SUM 1.3027 RATED AVERAGE .0901871


ELEMENT 2
SPIN TO WORK-DRILL 1-.5 DIA HOLE-SPIN UP-SWING BUSHING PLATE UP
RAW DATA
 1  .08  2  .100541  3  .0789189  4  .109189  5  .118919  (6  .0627027) 7  .10918
9  8  .0886486  (9  .12973) 10  .112432  11  .112432
 12  .0832433  13  .0918919  14  .100541  15  .0983784

SUM 1.47676 AVERAGE .0984505
CORRECTED AND RATED DATA
RATING FOR THIS ELEMENT 1
 1  .08  2  .100541  3  .0789189  4  .109189  5  .118919  (6  0) 7  .109189  8  .
0886486  (9  0) 10  .112432  11  .112432  12
 .0832433  13  .0918919  14  .100541  15  .0983784

SUM 1.28432 RATED AVERAGE .0987942


ELEMENT 3
LH MOVE JIG TO SPIN 2

RAW DATA
 1  .0367568  2  .0389189  3  .052973  4  .0324324  5  .0518919  6  .0518919  7
 .0356757  8  .0508108  (9  .0627027) 10  .0443243
 11  .0356757  (12  .0918919) 13  .04  14  .0356757  15  .0367568
```

Printout 7-1

SUM .698379 AVERAGE .0465586
CORRECTED AND RATED DATA
RATING FOR THIS ELEMENT .85
1 .0367568 2 .0389189 3 .052973 4 .0324324 5 .0518919 6 .0518919 7
.0356757 8 .0508108 (9 0) 10 .0443243 11
.0356757 (12 0) 13 .04 14 .0356757 15 .0367568

SUM .543784 RATED AVERAGE .0355551

ELEMENT 4
SPIN TO WORK—REAM 1—.5 HOLE—SPIN UP—MOVE TO UNLOAD
RAW DATA
1 .103784 2 .124324 3 .114595 4 .104865 5 .0918919 (6 .163243) (7 .07)
78378 8 .0908108 9 .0940541 10 .11027 11
.0994595 12 .0972973 13 .0886486 14 .11027 (15 .0778378)

SUM 1.54919 AVERAGE .103279
CORRECTED AND RATED DATA
RATING FOR THIS ELEMENT .95
1 .103784 2 .124324 3 .114595 4 .104865 5 .0918919 (6 0) (7 0) 8 .09
08108 9 .0940541 10 .11027 11 .0994595 12
.0972973 13 .0886486 14 .11027 (15 0)

SUM 1.23027 RATED AVERAGE .0973964

ELEMENT 5
LH HOLD—RH LOOSE CLAMP—RH REMOVE PART—DISP 18 IN TO REAR
RAW DATA
1 .0940541 2 .0810811 3 .118919 4 .0908108 (5 .145946) 6 .0886486 7
.113514 8 .0994595 9 .112432 10 .0864865 11
.0821622 12 .114595 13 .113514 14 .0854054 15 .108108

SUM 1.53514 AVERAGE .102342
CORRECTED AND RATED DATA
RATING FOR THIS ELEMENT 1
1 .0940541 2 .0810811 3 .118919 4 .0908108 (5 0) 6 .0886486 7 .11351
4 8 .0994595 9 .112432 10 .0864865 11
.0821622 12 .114595 13 .113514 14 .0854054 15 .108108

SUM 1.38919 AVERAGE .0992278
ELEMENT6
INSPECT PART WITH PLUG GAGE—EVERY 10 PARTS
RAW DATA
1 .219459 2 .232432

SUM .451892 AVERAGE .225946
CORRECTED AND RATED DATA
RATING FOR THIS ELEMENT 1
1 .219459 2 .232432

SUM .451892 AVERAGE .225946

ELEMENT 8
RAW DATA
1 .555676

SUM .555676 AVERAGE .555676 ◄——————— *Operator talked to supervisor*
FOREIGN ELEMENT NOT ALLOWED

Printout 7-1 continued

```
FOREIGN ELEMENT NOT ALLOWED
ELEMENT 6 IS PRORATED BY 10

TOTAL ALLOWED TIME FOR ALL ELEMENTS IS .443755
ALLOWANCES
PERSONAL TIME    24
TOOLING ALLOWANCE                    35
MATERIAL HANDLING                    15
CLEAN UP         5
NET PRODUCTION PER SHIFT IS 903.652
TOTAL ALLOWED TIME .443755
TOTAL PERSONAL TIME .0265589
TOTAL OTHER ALLOWANCES .0608642
TOTAL ALLOWED WITH ALLOWANCES .531178
NET PER HR. 112.956
ATTAINABLE PER HR. 135.21
STANDARD HOURS PER PC. 8.85297E-03


RECAP

ELEMENT 1  RH REACH 18 IN.-GRASP PART-TRANS TO JIG-LOCATE-LH HOLD-CLAMP-MOVE TO
SPIN 1
RATING .9 ALLOWED TIME .0901871
ELEMENT 2  SPIN TO WORK-DRILL 1-.5 DIA HOLE-SPIN UP-SWING BUSHING PLATE UP
RATING 1 ALLOWED TIME .0987942
ELEMENT 3  LH MOVE JIG TO SPIN 2
RATING .85 ALLOWED TIME .0355551
ELEMENT 4  SPIN TO WORK-REAM 1-.5 HOLE-SPIN UP-MOVE TO UNLOAD
RATING .95 ALLOWED TIME .0973964
ELEMENT 5  LH HOLD-RH LOOSE CLAMP-RH REMOVE PART-DISP 18 IN TO REAR
RATING 1 ALLOWED TIME .0992278
ELEMENT 6  INSPECT PART WITH PLUG GAGE-EVERY 10 PARTS
RATING 1 ALLOWED TIME .225946
PRORATED BY 10 PRORATED TIME .0225946
ELEMENT 8
FOREIGN ELEMENT NOT ALLOWED
RATING 1000 ALLOWED TIME 0


1 REM PROGRAM NAME TIME
2 REM WRITTEN BY J.E.NICKS
3 REM COPYRIGHT 1981 ALL RIGHTS RESERVED
4 REM COMPUTER APPLICATIONS FOR THE MANUFACTURING ENGINEER
10 CLEAR1000
20 DIMA(25),B(25),C(25),D(25),E(25),F(25),G(25),H(25)
30 CLS
40 PRINT"THIS PROGRAM IS DESIGNED FOR THE ENGINEER"
50 PRINT"TO TAKE TIME STUDIES ON THE MICROCOMPUTER"
60 PRINT"THE PROGRAM WILL ACCEPT UP TO 7 TOTAL ELEMENTS"
65 PRINT"ELEMENT 8  CAN BE USED FOR A FOREIGN ELEMENT REGISTER"
66 PRINT"OR AS A REGULAR ELEMENT -----BUT NOT BOTH-----"
70 PRINT"AND 25 RECORDINGS FOR EACH ELEMENT."
80 PRINT"AFTER THE STUDY HAS BEEN TAKEN, RATING FACTORS ARE INPUTTED"
100 PRINT"THEN A RATE OF PRODUCTION WILL BE CALCULATED."
110 PRINT:PRINT:PRINT
120 INPUT "TYPE IN THE PART NUMBER";A$
130 INPUT"TYPE IN THE PART NAME";B$
140 INPUT"TYPE IN THE DATE 00/00/00";C$
150 INPUT"TYPE IN THE ENGINEER'S NAME";D$
170 INPUT"TYPE IN THE OPERATION DESCRIPTION";E$
180 INPUT"TYPE IN THE OPERATION NUMBER";F$
190 CLS
200 PRINT"OTHER INFORMATION"
210 INPUT"NUMBER OF MACHINES";G$
```

Printout 7-1 continued

```
220 INPUT"NUMBER OF OPERATIONS";H$
270 INPUT"RPM OR STROKES PER MINUTE";J$
280 INPUT"SFPM";K$
290 INPUT"FEED PER MINUTE: REV : PER TOOTH";L$
300 INPUT"CUT: DEPTH: WIDTH: LENGTH";M$
310 INPUT"CUTTING TOOL TYPE";N$
330 CLS
340 PRINT"TYPE IN AN ELEMENT DESCRIPTION FOR EACH ELEMENT"
350 PRINT"AND LIMIT THE DESCRIPTION TO 80 CHARACTERS."
360 PRINT"USE ABBREVIATIONS WHEN POSSIBLE."
370 PRINT"EX: R.H. REACH 18: P.U. STK & LOC TO FIX"
380 INPUT"TYPE IN THE NUMBER OF ELEMENTS";N
390 FORI=1TON
395 PRINT"TYPE IN THE ELEMENT DESCRIPTION"
400 INPUTP$(I)
410 NEXTI
420 CLS:PRINT"ONCE YOU START THE TIME STUDY,"
430 PRINT"DEPRESS THE NUMBER KEY THAT COINCIDES WITH"
440 PRINT"THE COMPLETION OR BREAKPOINT OF EACH ELEMENT."
450 PRINT"EXAMPLE: 1,2,3,4,5,6,7,8"
455 PRINT"TO END THE STUDY TYPE 9."
456 PRINT"NOTE:ELEMENT 8 CAN BE USED FOR A FOREIGN ELEMENT"
457 PRINT"IF SOMETHING OCCURS DURING THE STUDY THAT LATER SHOULD"
458 PRINT"CROSSED OUT (I.E. GET DRINK-TALK-LEAVE ETC)"
459 PRINT"TYPE IN 8 . THEN LATER ENTER 1000 AS A RATING FACTOR"
460 INPUT"TO START THE INTERNAL CLOCK TYPE 1 AND ENTER WHEN READY";A
470 ONAGOTO480
480 A=0:B=0:C=0:D=0:E=0:F=0:G=0:H=0
500 CLS
510 FORI=1TO3000
520 Q$=INKEY$:IFQ$="1"THEN610
530 IFQ$="2"THEN620
540 IFQ$="3"THEN630
550 IFQ$="4"THEN640
560 IFQ$="5"THEN650
570 IFQ$="6"THEN660
580 IFQ$="7"THEN670
590 IFQ$="8"THEN680
600 IFQ$="9"THEN690
605 NEXT
610 A=A+1:A(A)=I/925:N1=N1+1:PRINT"ELEMENT 1",A,A(A):GOTO510
620 B=B+1:B(B)=I/925:N2=N2+1:PRINT"ELEMENT 2",B,B(B):GOTO510
630 C=C+1:C(C)=I/925:N3=N3+1:PRINT"ELEMENT 3",C,C(C):GOTO510
640 D=D+1:D(D)=I/925:N4=N4+1:PRINT"ELEMENT 4",D,D(D):GOTO510
650 E=E+1:E(E)=I/925:N5=N5+1:PRINT"ELEMENT 5",E,E(E):GOTO510
660 F=F+1:F(F)=I/925:N6=N6+1:PRINT"ELEMENT 6",F,F(F):GOTO510
670 G=G+1:G(G)=I/925:N7=N7+1:PRINT"ELEMENT 7",G,G(G):GOTO510
680 H=H+1:H(H)=I/925:N8=N8+1:PRINT"ELEMENT 8",H,H(H):GOTO510
690 GOTO700
700 LPRINT"END"
830 LPRINT"TIME STUDY FOR   ";A$;"    OPER NO   ";F$
840 LPRINT"PART NAME     ";B$
850 LPRINT"DATE   ";C$;"    ENGINEER    ";D$
860 LPRINT"OPERATION DESCRIPTION    ";E$
870 LPRINT"NO OF MACHINES   ";G$;"    NO OF OPERATIONS    ";H$
880 LPRINTCHR$(138)
890 LPRINT"RPM OR SPM    ";J$
895 LPRINT"SFPM ";K$
900 LPRINT"FEED PER    ";L$
910 LPRINT"CUT: DEPTH: WIDTH    ";M$
920 LPRINT"CUTTING TOOL   ";N$
930 LPRINTCHR$(138)
940 CLS:PRINT"THE NEXT SECTION IS WHERE CROSSOUTS CAN BE MADE."
950 PRINT"THE RAW DATA WILL APPEAR AT THE TOP OF THE SCREEN"
960 PRINT"AND EACH CYCLE (ONE AT A TIME) AT THE BOTTOM."
```

Printout 7-1 continued

```
975 PRINT"IF IT IS TO BE CROSSED OUT, TYPE 2."
980 PRINT"THE RATING FACTOR IS ALSO INPUTTED IN THIS SECTION."
990 PRINT"INPUT THE RATING FACTOR AS A DECIMAL, I.E. .90%."
1000 INPUT"TYPE 1 TO CONTINUE";Z
1010 ONZGOTO1020
1020 CLS
1030 LPRINT"ELEMENT 1"
1040 LPRINTP$(1)
1050 PRINT"ELEMENT 1"
1060 PRINTP$(1)
1070 INPUT"RATING FACTOR FOR THIS ELEMENT";R1
1080 LPRINT"RAW DATA"
1090 FORA=1TON1:A1=A1+A(A):PRINTA,A(A),:LPRINTA;A(A);:NEXTA
1095 LPRINTCHR$(138)
1100 A2=A1/N1:PRINT"SUM";A1;"AVERAGE";A2
1110 LPRINT"SUM";A1;"AVERAGE";A2
1120 FORA=1TON1
1130 PRINT@850,A,A(A)
1140 INPUT"TYPE 1 IF OK OR 2 FOR CROSSOUT";Y
1150 ONYGOTO1160,1180
1160 NEXTA
1170 GOTO1190
1180 A(A)=0:X=X+1:NEXTA
1190 A1=0:A2=0
1200 FORA=1TON1:A1=A1+A(A):NEXTA
1210 A2=(A1/(N1-X))*R1
1220 LPRINT"CORRECTED AND RATED DATA"
1230 LPRINT"RATING FOR THIS ELEMENT";R1
1240 FORA=1TON1:LPRINTA;A(A);:NEXTA
1245 LPRINTCHR$(138)
1250 LPRINT"SUM";A1;"RATED AVERAGE";A2
1255 FORI=1TO2:LPRINTCHR$(138):NEXTI
1265 IFB=0THEN1520ELSE1270
1270 CLS
1280 LPRINT"ELEMENT 2"
1290 LPRINTP$(2)
1300 PRINT"ELEMENT 2"
1310 PRINTP$(2)
1320 INPUT"RATING FOR THIS ELEMENT";R2
1330 LPRINT"RAW DATA"
1340 FORB=1TON2:B1=B1+B(B):PRINTB,B(B),:LPRINTB;B(B);:NEXTB
1345 LPRINTCHR$(138)
1350 B2=B1/N2:PRINT"SUM";B1;"AVERAGE";B2
1360 LPRINT"SUM";B1;"AVERAGE";B2
1370 FORB=1TON2
1380 PRINT@850,B,B(B)
1390 INPUT"TYPE 1 IF OK OR 2 FOR CROSSOUT";Y
1400 ONYGOTO1410,1430
1410 NEXTB
1420 GOTO1440
1430 B(B)=0:X1=X1+1:NEXTB
1440 B1=0:B2=0
1450 FORB=1TON2:B1=B1+B(B):NEXTB
1460 B2=(B1/(N2-X1))*R2
1470 LPRINT"CORRECTED AND RATED DATA"
1480 LPRINT"RATING FOR THIS ELEMENT";R2
1490 FORB=1TON2:LPRINTB;B(B);:NEXTB
1495 LPRINTCHR$(138)
1500 LPRINT"SUM";B1;"RATED AVERAGE";B2
1510 FORI=1TO2:LPRINTCHR$(138):NEXTI
1520 IFC=0THEN1780ELSE1530
1530 CLS
1540 LPRINT"ELEMENT 3"
1550 LPRINTP$(3)
1560 PRINT"ELEMENT 3"
```

Printout 7-1 continued

```
1570 PRINTF$(3)
1580 INPUT"RATING FOR THIS ELEMENT";R3
1590 LPRINT"RAW DATA"
1600 FORC=1TON3:C1=C1+C(C):PRINTC,C(C),:LPRINTC;C(C);:NEXTC
1610 C2=C1/N3:PRINT"SUM";C1;"AVERAGE";C2
1615 LPRINTCHR$(138)
1620 LPRINT"SUM";C1;"AVERAGE";C2
1630 FORC=1TON3
1640 PRINT@850,C,C(C)
1650 INPUT"TYPE 1 IF OK OR 2 FOR CROSSOUT";Y
1660 ONYGOTO1670,1690
1670 NEXTC
1680 GOTO1700
1690 C(C)=0:X2=X2+1:NEXTC
1700 C1=0:C2=0
1710 FORC=1TON3:C1=C1+C(C):NEXTC
1720 C2=(C1/(N3-X2))*R3
1730 LPRINT"CORRECTED AND RATED DATA"
1740 LPRINT"RATING FOR THIS ELEMENT";R3
1750 FORC=1TON3:LPRINTC;C(C);:NEXTC
1755 LPRINTCHR$(138)
1760 LPRINT"SUM";C1;"RATED AVERAGE";C2
1770 FORI=1TO2:LPRINTCHR$(138):NEXTI
1780 IFD=0THEN2040ELSE1790
1790 CLS
1800 LPRINT"ELEMENT 4"
1810 LPRINTF$(4)
1820 PRINT"ELEMENT 4"
1830 PRINTF$(4)
1840 INPUT"RATING FOR THIS ELEMENT";R4
1850 LPRINT"RAW DATA"
1860 FORD=1TON4:D1=D1+D(D):PRINTD,D(D),:LPRINTD;D(D);:NEXTD
1865 LPRINTCHR$(138)
1870 D2=D1/N4:PRINT"SUM";D1;"AVERAGE";D2
1875 LPRINTCHR$(138)
1880 LPRINT"SUM";D1;"AVERAGE";D2
1890 FORD=1TON4
1900 PRINT@850,D,D(D)
1910 INPUT"TYPE 1 IF OK OR 2 FOR CROSSOUT";Y
1920 ONYGOTO1930,1950
1930 NEXTD
1940 GOTO1960
1950 D(D)=0:X3=X3+1:NEXTD
1960 D1=0:D2=0
1970 FORD=1TON4:D1=D1+D(D):NEXTD
1980 D2=(D1/(N4-X3))*R4
1990 LPRINT"CORRECTED AND RATED DATA"
2000 LPRINT"RATING FOR THIS ELEMENT";R4
2010 FORD=1TON4:LPRINTD;D(D);:NEXTD
2015 LPRINTCHR$(138)
2020 LPRINT"SUM";D1;"RATED AVERAGE";D2
2030 FORI=1TO2:LPRINTCHR$(138):NEXTI
2040 IFE=0THEN2300ELSE2050
2050 CLS
2060 LPRINT"ELEMENT 5"
2070 LPRINTF$(5)
2080 PRINT"ELEMENT 5"
2090 PRINTF$(5)
2100 INPUT"RATING FOR THIS ELEMENT";R5
2110 LPRINT"RAW DATA"
2120 FORE=1TON5:E1=E1+E(E):PRINTE,E(E),:LPRINTE;E(E);:NEXTE
2130 E2=E1/N5:PRINT"SUM";E1;"AVERAGE";E2
2135 LPRINTCHR$(138)
2140 LPRINT"SUM";E1;"AVERAGE";E2
2150 FORE=1TON5
```

Printout 7-1 continued

```
2160 PRINT@850,E,E(E)
2170 INPUT"TYPE 1 IF OK OR 2 FOR CROSSOUT";Y
2180 ONYGOTO2190,2210
2190 NEXTE
2200 GOTO2220
2210 E(E)=0:X4=X4+1:NEXTE
2220 E1=0:E2=0
2230 FORE=1TON5:E1=E1+E(E):NEXTE
2240 E2=(E1/(N5-X4))*R5
2250 LPRINT"CORRECTED AND RATED DATA"
2260 LPRINT"RATING FOR THIS ELEMENT";R5
2270 FORE=1TON5:LPRINTE;E(E);:NEXTE
2275 LPRINTCHR$(138)
2280 LPRINT"SUM";E1;"AVERAGE";E2
2300 IFF=0THEN2560ELSE2310
2310 CLS
2320 LPRINT"ELEMENT6"
2330 LPRINTF$(6)
2340 PRINT"ELEMENT 6"
2350 PRINTF$(6)
2360 INPUT"RATING FOR THIS ELEMENT";R6
2370 LPRINT"RAW DATA"
2380 FORF=1TON6:F1=F1+F(F):PRINTF,F(F),:LPRINTF;F(F);:NEXTF
2390 F2=F1/N6:PRINT"SUM";F1;"AVERAGE";F2
2395 LPRINTCHR$(138)
2400 LPRINT"SUM";F1;"AVERAGE";F2
2410 FORF=1TON6
2420 PRINT@850,F,F(F)
2430 INPUT"TYPE 1 IF OK OR 2 FOR CROSSOUT";Y
2440 ONYGOTO2450,2470
2450 NEXTF
2460 GOTO2480
2470 F(F)=0:X5=X5+1:NEXTF
2480 F1=0:F2=0
2490 FORF=1TON6:F1=F1+F(F):NEXTF
2500 F2=(F1/(N6-X5))*R6
2510 LPRINT"CORRECTED AND RATED DATA"
2520 LPRINT"RATING FOR THIS ELEMENT";R6
2530 FORF=1TON6:LPRINTF;F(F);:NEXTF
2535 LPRINTCHR$(138)
2540 LPRINT"SUM";F1;"AVERAGE";F2
2550 FORI=1TO2:LPRINTCHR$(138):NEXTI
2560 IFG=0THEN2820ELSE2570
2570 CLS
2580 LPRINT"ELEMENT 7"
2590 LPRINTF$(7)
2600 PRINT"ELEMENT 7"
2610 PRINTF$(7)
2620 INPUT"RATING FOR THIS ELEMENT";R7
2630 LPRINT"RAW DATA"
2640 FORG=1TON7:G1=G1+G(G):PRINTG,G(G),:LPRINTG;G(G);:NEXTG
2650 G2=G1/N7:PRINT"SUM";G1;"AVERAGE";G2
2660 LPRINT"SUM";G1;"AVERAGE";G2
2665 LPRINTCHR$(138)
2670 FORG=1TON7
2680 PRINT@850,G,G(G)
2690 INPUT"TYPE 1 IF OK OR 2 FOR CROSSOUT";Y
2700 ONYGOTO2710,2730
2710 NEXTG
2720 GOTO2740
2730 G(G)=0:X6=X6+1:NEXTG
2740 G1=0:G2=0
2750 FORG=1TON7:G1=G1+G(G):NEXTG
2760 G2=(G1/(N7-X6))*R7
2770 LPRINT"CORRECTED .AND RATED DATA"
```

Printout 7-1 continued

```
2780 LPRINT"RATING FOR THIS ELEMENT";R7
2790 FORG=1TON7:LPRINTG;G(G);:NEXTG
2795 LPRINTCHR$(138)
2800 LPRINT"SUM";G1;"AVERAGE";G2
2810 FORI=1TO2:LPRINTCHR$(138):NEXTI
2820 IFH=0THEN3080ELSE2830
2830 CLS
2840 LPRINT"ELEMENT 8"
2850 LPRINTP$(8)
2860 PRINT"ELEMENT 8"
2870 PRINTP$(8)
2880 INPUT"RATING FOR THIS ELEMENT";R8
2890 LPRINT"RAW DATA"
2900 FORH=1TON8:H1=H1+H(H):PRINTH,H(H),:LPRINTH;H(H);:NEXTH
2910 H2=H1/N8:PRINT"SUM";H1;"AVERAGE";H2
2915 LPRINTCHR$(138)
2920 LPRINT"SUM";H1;"AVERAGE";H2
2930 FORH=1TON8
2940 PRINT@850,H,H(H)
2950 INPUT"TYPE 1 IF OK OR 2 FOR CROSSOUT";Y
2960 ONYGOTO2970,2990
2970 NEXTH
2980 GOTO3000
2990 H(H)=0:X7=X7+1:NEXTH
3000 H1=0:H2=0
3005 IFR8=1000THEN3006ELSE3010
3006 LPRINT"FOREIGN ELEMENT NOT ALLOWED":H1=0:H2=0:H3=0:GOSUB5000
3007 GOTO3070
3010 FORH=1TON8:H1=H1+H(H):NEXTH
3020 H2=(H1/(N8-X7))*R8
3030 LPRINT"CORRECTED AND RATED DATA"
3040 LPRINT"RATING FOR THIS ELEMENT";R8
3050 FORH=1TON8:LPRINTH;H(H);:NEXTH
3055 LPRINTCHR$(138)
3060 LPRINT"SUM";H1;"AVERAGE";H2
3070 FORI=1TO2:LPRINTCHR$(138):NEXTI
3080 CLS
3081 IFR8=1000THEN3082ELSE3090
3082 LPRINT"FOREIGN ELEMENT NOT ALLOWED"
3090 PRINT"PRORATING"
3100 PRINT"THE NEXT STEP IS TO PRORATE ANY OF THE ELEMENTS."
3110 PRINT"A PRORATED ELEMENT MIGHT BE LIKE AND INSPECTION ELEMENT"
3120 PRINT"WHERE THE AVERAGE ELEMENT TIME IS DIVIDED BY THE PRORATED FACTOR"
3130 PRINT"EXAMPLE: INSPECTION OF EVERY 10TH PART"
3140 PRINT
3150 PRINT"IF ANY ELEMENT IS TO BE PRORATED , TYPE IN THE ELEMENT NO."
3160 PRINT"OR IF NO ELEMENT IS PRORATED TYPE 9"
3170 PRINT"OR IF YOU ARE COMPLETED TYPE 9"
3180 INPUTW
3190 ONWGOTO3210,3230,3250,3270,3290
3200 ON W -5 GOTO 3310,3330,3350,3370
3210 INPUT"ELEMENT 1 IS PRORATED OR DIVIDED BY";Q(1)
3220 A3=A2/Q(1):GOTO3140
3230 INPUT"ELEMENT 2 IS PRORATED OR DIVIDED BY";Q(2)
3240 B3=B2/Q(2):GOTO3140
3250 INPUT"ELEMENT 3 IS PRORATED OR DIVIDED BY";Q(3)
3260 C3=C2/Q(3):GOTO3140
3270 INPUT"ELEMENT 4 IS PRORRATE OR DIVIDED BY";Q(4)
3280 D3=D2/Q(4):GOTO3140
3290 INPUT"ELEMENT 5 IS PRORATED OR DIVIDED BY";Q(5)
3300 E3=E2/Q(5):GOTO3140
3310 INPUT"ELEMENT 6 IS PRORATED OR DIVIDED BY";Q(6)
3320 F3=F2/Q(6):GOTO3140
3330 INPUT"ELEMENT 7 IS PRORATED OR DIVIDED BY";Q(7)
3340 G3=G2/Q(7):GOTO3140
```

Printout 7-1 continued

```
3350 INPUT"ELEMENT 8 IS PRORATED OR DIVIDED BY";Q(8)
3360 H3=H2/Q(8):GOTO3140
3370 REM PRORATION COMPLETE
3380 REM ALLOWANCES:CLS
3390 PRINT"THIS SECTION OF THE PROGRAM IS WHERE ALLOWANCES ARE INPUTTED"
3400 PRINT"TO INPUT ALLOWANCES, TYPE THE NUMBER NEXT TO THE ALLOWANCE"
3410 PRINT"PERSONAL TIME ---------------1"
3420 PRINT"TOOLING ALLOWANCE ----------2"
3430 PRINT"MATERIAL HANDLING ----------3"
3440 PRINT"OTHER ----------------------4"
3445 PRINT"COMPLETED--------5"
3450 INPUTW
3460 ONWGOTO3470,3500,3530,3560,3590
3470 S$="PERSONAL TIME"
3480 PRINT"ENTER PERSONAL TIME IN MIN. PER 8 HR. SHIFT"
3490 INPUTS1:GOTO3380
3500 T$="TOOLING ALLOWANCE"
3510 PRINT"ENTER TOOLING ALLOWANCE IN MIN. PER 8 HR. SHIFT"
3520 INPUTT1:GOTO3380
3530 U$="MATERIAL HANDLING"
3540 PRINT"ENTER MATERIAL HANDLING ALLOWANCE IN MIN. PER 8 HR. SHIFT"
3550 INPUTU1:GOTO3380
3560 INPUT"TYPE IN THE NAME OF THE OTHER ALLOWANCE";V$
3570 PRINT"ENTER ";V$;" ALLOWANCE IN MIN. PER 8 HR. SHIFT"
3580 INPUTV1:GOTO3380
3590 REM END OF ALLOWANCES
3600 REM SUMMARY
3610 REM TOTAL TIME
3620 IFQ(1)=0THENZ1=Z1+A2ELSEZ1=Z1+A3
3630 IFQ(2)=0THENZ1=Z1+B2ELSEZ1=Z1+B3
3640 IFQ(3)=0THENZ1=Z1+C2ELSEZ1=Z1+C3
3650 IFQ(4)=0THENZ1=Z1+D2ELSEZ1=Z1+D3
3660 IFQ(5)=0THENZ1=Z1+E2ELSEZ1=Z1+E3
3670 IFQ(6)=0THENZ1=Z1+F2ELSEZ1=Z1+F3
3680 IFQ(7)=0THENZ1=Z1+G2ELSEZ1=Z1+G3
3690 IFQ(8)=0THENZ1=Z1+H2ELSEZ1=Z1+H3
3700 FORQ=1TO8
3710 IFQ(Q)=0THEN3730ELSE3720
3720 LPRINT"ELEMENT";Q;"IS PRORATED BY";Q(Q)
3730 NEXTQ
3740 LPRINTCHR$(138)
3750 LPRINT"TOTAL ALLOWED TIME FOR ALL ELEMENTS IS";Z1
3760 LPRINT"ALLOWANCES"
3770 LPRINTS$,S1
3780 IFT1=0THEN3800ELSE3790
3790 LPRINTT$,T1
3800 IFU1=0THEN3820ELSE3810
3810 LPRINTU$,U1
3820 IFV1=0THEN3840ELSE3830
3830 LPRINTV$,V1
3840 Z2=(480-(S1+T1+U1+V1))/Z1
3850 LPRINT"NET PRODUCTION PER SHIFT IS";Z2
3860 Z3=480-(S1+T1+U1+V1):REM NET PROD MIN
3870 Z4=(S1/Z3)*Z1:REM PERS TIME
3880 Z5=((T1+U1+V1)/Z3)*Z1:REM OTHER ALLOW
3890 Z6=Z1+Z4+Z5:REM TOTAL ALLOWED TIME
3900 Z7=60/Z6:REM NET PER HR
3910 Z8=60/Z1:REM ATTAINABLE PER HR
3920 Z9=Z6/60:REM STD HR
3930 LPRINT"TOTAL ALLOWED TIME";Z1
3940 LPRINT"TOTAL PERSONAL TIME";Z4
3950 LPRINT"TOTAL OTHER ALLOWANCES";Z5
3960 LPRINT"TOTAL ALLOWED WITH ALLOWANCES";Z6
3970 LPRINT"NET PER HR.";Z7
3980 LPRINT"ATTAINABLE PER HR.";Z8
```

Printout 7-1 continued

```
3990 LPRINT"STANDARD HOURS PER PC.";Z9
4000 FORI=1TO2:LPRINTCHR$(138):NEXTI
4010 LPRINT"RECAP"
4020 LPRINTCHR$(138)
4030 LPRINT"ELEMENT 1   ";P$(1)
4040 LPRINT"RATING";R1;"ALLOWED TIME";A2
4050 IFQ(1)=0THEN4070ELSE4060
4060 LPRINT"PRORATED BY";Q(1);"PRORATED TIME";A3
4070 IFB=0THEN4120ELSE4080
4080 LPRINT"ELEMENT 2   ";P$(2)
4090 LPRINT"RATING";R2;"ALLOWED TIME";B2
4100 IFQ(2)=0THEN4120ELSE4110
4110 LPRINT"PRORATED BY";Q(2);"PRORATED TIME";B3
4120 IFC=0THEN4170ELSE4130
4130 LPRINT"ELEMENT 3   ";P$(3)
4140 LPRINT"RATING";R3;"ALLOWED TIME";C2
4150 IFQ(3)=0THEN4170ELSE4160
4160 LPRINT"PRORATED BY";Q(3);"PRORATED TIME";C3
4170 IFD=0THEN4220ELSE4180
4180 LPRINT"ELEMENT 4   ";P$(4)
4190 LPRINT"RATING";R4;"ALLOWED TIME";D2
4200 IFQ(4)=0THEN4220ELSE4210
4210 LPRINT"PRORATED BY";Q(4);"PRORATED TIME";D3
4220 IFE=0THEN4270ELSE4230
4230 LPRINT"ELEMENT 5   ";P$(5)
4240 LPRINT"RATING";R5;"ALLOWED TIME";E2
4250 IFQ(5)=0THEN4270ELSE4260
4260 LPRINT"PRORATED BY";Q(5);"PRORATED TIME";E3
4270 IFF=0THEN4320ELSE4280
4280 LPRINT"ELEMENT 6   ";P$(6)
4290 LPRINT"RATING";R6;"ALLOWED TIME";F2
4300 IFQ(6)=0THEN4320ELSE4310
4310 LPRINT"PRORATED BY";Q(6);"PRORATED TIME";F3
4320 IFG=0THEN4370ELSE4330
4330 LPRINT"ELEMENT 7   ";P$(7)
4340 LPRINT"RATING";R7;"ALLOWED TIME";G2
4350 IFQ(7)=0THEN4370ELSE4360
4360 LPRINT"PRORATED BY";Q(7);"PRORATED TIME";G3
4370 IFH=0THEN4420ELSE4380
4380 LPRINT"ELEMENT 8   ";P$(8)
4381 IFR8=1000THEN4382ELSE4390
4382 LPRINT"FOREIGN ELEMENT NOT ALLOWED"
4390 LPRINT"RATING";R8;"ALLOWED TIME";H2
4400 IFQ(8)=0THEN4420ELSE4410
4410 LPRINT"PRORATED BY";Q(8);"PRORATED TIME";H3
4420 END
```

Printout 7-1 continued

Work Sampling

Work sampling is a problem-solving tool first developed in the early 1940's. When initially developed, work sampling was called "ration delay". The concept of work sampling or ratio delay is to determine the relationship between work and/or non-work (idle) elements to each other. The assumption is that if we can accurately determine this relationship, we can set about to correct the situation by improvement in what the work group does. Over the years, the original concept of "delay" has been expanded to other use purposes.

For example, suppose there is a Turning Department in the plant and piece part inspection is performed externally by the production operator. The questions might be:
1. How much time is spent in the department inspecting parts?
2. If this amount of time is substantial, what can be done to reduce it?

The first question is a natural for work sampling. The engineer assigned to this task might determine that most of the work performed in the department can be classified by the elements shown below:
1. Loading.
2. Processing (cutting).
3. Unloading.
4. Material handling.
5. Inspection.
6. Idle (or away from the machine).
7. Miscellaneous.

A work sampling study conducted over a period of time would yield how much time (in percent) each of the people in the work group spend performing each of these work elements. Once the study is completed, then management can determine if the overall work effort could be improved by designing a methods program to reduce the amount of operator inspection time, thereby increasing the amount of processing time.

The scope of work sampling is broad. Work sampling is used in a variety of other useful applications. Shown below is a list of some of its uses:
1. Determining the ratios of typing, filing, writing, etc., for clerical people to assist in determining salary scales appropriate to the tasks being performed.
2. Determining an efficiency index for people working in a shipping department. This index could be based on what percent of their time is spent doing various shipping chores versus the number of outgoing cartons or packages.
3. Determining the number of typewriters necessary in student dorms based on typewriter usage.

The examples given above are just a sampling of uses. In fact, work sampling is one of the most powerful tools management has for gathering accurate data about workers, equipment and situations used today. There are many good texts on the subject of work sampling for the reader who is not familiar with the subject. Several are listed in the Bibliography at the end of this chapter.

Microcomputers and Work Sampling

Some math formula review is appropriate before we examine what the microcomputer can do for us in assisting the with work sampling studies. A determination is needed to find the level of accuracy desired in the study. Accuracy can be expressed two ways—relative accuracy and absolute accuracy.

As an example, if an occurrence happens 25% of the time, then a relative accuracy of ±10% produces an absolute accuracy of (.25)(.10) = ±.025. Or expressed another way, the occurrence will happen from 22.5% to 27.5% of the time with an average occurrence of 25%. The next question is: What is the level of confidence in these figures? Confidence is expressed in units of sigma which is related to a percent under the bell curve.

For example, if we wish 90% confidence in the results, this is equal to ±1.64 sigma. *Table 7-1* shows the relationship of units of sigma or standard deviation in respect to the confidence level or percent under the curve.

Table 7-1
Standard Deviation

Units of Sigma	Percent Confidence = C
± 1	68%
± 1.64	90%
± 2	95.45%
± 3	99.73%

Observe that accuracy and confidence are a result of the number of recordings in the study. The greater the number of recordings, the smaller the error factor and the greater the confidence level. There is a trade-off between the cost required to gather a large number of recordings versus a small improvement in accuracy and confidence. This must be determined, before the study is started, by asking the question: How accurate does the data need to be?

Work Sampling Math

Where:

R = relative accuracy
A = desired absolute accuracy
P = percent of the occurrence (decimal)
C = confidence level desired
S = standard deviation
N = number of recordings
US = units of sigma (see *Table 7-1*)

Then:

$$S = \sqrt{\frac{P(1-P)}{N}}$$

$$A = US\sqrt{\frac{P(1-P)}{N}}$$

Example: From the first 100 recordings, idle time is 25%.

$$S = \sqrt{\frac{(.25)(.75)}{100}} = .0433$$

$$A = 2\sqrt{\frac{(.25)(.75)}{100}} = .0866$$

Therefore, with confidence of 95.45%, idle time is 25% ± 8.66%.

Assume we require a relative accuracy of ± 2.5% with a confidence of 95.45%, or 2 sigma units then:

$$N = \left(\frac{US}{R}\right)^2 * \left(\frac{1-P}{P}\right) = \left(\frac{2}{.025}\right)^2 * \left(\frac{.75}{.25}\right) = 19,200 \text{ recordings}$$

A work sampling study can be conducted over a long period of time to assure the recordings are representative and therefore random. There are two ways a computer program can be written to assist the engineer. One way is to develop a "filing system" using either a random or sequential filing routine. This approach permits each day's recording to be inputted into the computer and then placed on disk file. If the filing routine program is to be flexible enough to cover a wide range of typical work sampling studies, much thought will be spent in devising a coding system to handle the filing. (See Chapter Nine for filing examples.)

Another way a computer program can be written is by using DATA statements. DATA statements may be more awkward to input, but serve the same purpose as filing, without the extra programming effort. To illustrate this, the computer program named "RATIO" uses DATA statements for the input of each day's recordings. Updating the program necessitates changing one line of the program each day and adding one line each day. Once this is accomplished, the sum of all the days' results are printed out and analyzed to determine the accuracy and number of recordings necessary to complete the study.

Another very time consuming problem in conducting a work sampling study is the development of a daily schedule to determine the times at which each observation will be made. There are several standard ways this task is accomplished. One way is by selecting numbers from a random number table. Another method is to use the local phone book and select phone numbers in sequence. The phone numbers are then arranged into a table that becomes the next day's observation schedule. The program "RATIO" has a feature programmed into it that generates random times and also prints out the next day observation schedule on a pre-printed observation form.

Program Name: "RATIO"

The memory required for this program is 5,377 bytes.

The program is constructed in three modules:
1. Headings for the work sampling study.
2. Updating for each day's activities.
3. Printout of the results.

The easiest way to review the accomplishments of this program is by reviewing the printouts.

Case Study

Four clerks working in an office are the subject of the study. Daily routines for the clerks are:
1. Typing.
2. Phoning.
3. Filing.
4. Writing.
5. Away (out of the office area).
6. Idle.

Let's assume the study is already underway and this is the end of the fourth day. The results for the fourth day are illustrated in *Table 7-2*.

Table 7-2

A result of a work sampling study conducted of four clerks.

Item	Number of Occurrences
1. Typing	56
2. Phoning	35
3. Filing	28
4. Writing	24
5. Away	15
6. Idle	21

This occurrence data is entered in the program as a data statement.

Line 2110 Data 56, 35, 28, 24, 15, 21.

Also, line 2070 is updated. It is changed from:

Line 2070 Data 3

and now reads:

Line 2070 Data 4

After the data is entered, the engineer enters RUN 600 ENTER and the computer prints out the summary dated 01/01/81. This summary shows the percent occurrence for each item, the absolute accuracy and the number of recordings necessary to achieve an accuracy of ± 3.5% at a 3 sigma level of confidence.

Note that in reviewing the summary, the number of recordings to date is 759. Also note the typing item needs 1616 recordings to achieve the desired accuracy level.

At the beginning of Day 5, the engineer conducting the study boots the program up and the computer prepares today's worksheet. (See Day 5 worksheet.) The worksheet contains all of the random times for the Day 5 schedule. After the observations for Day 5 have been collected and again entered in the program, another summary is produced. (See summary dated 01/02/81.) At this point, the engineer has collected 939 observations and there are some slight differences in the summary data. The study continues until its completion.

OFFICE STUDY 4 CLERKS

SUMMARY

01/01/81

ITEM TYPE
PERCENT FOR THIS ELEMENT IS .326746
ABSOLUTE ACCURACY NOW IS .0510734 OR THE RANGE IS .326746 + OR - .0510734
THE NUMBER OF RECORDINGS TO ACHIEVE .035 PERCENT ACCURACY AT 3 SIGMA IS 1616

ITEM PHONE
PERCENT FOR THIS ELEMENT IS .225296
ABSOLUTE ACCURACY NOW IS .0454931 OR THE RANGE IS .225296 + OR - .0454931
THE NUMBER OF RECORDINGS TO ACHIEVE .035 PERCENT ACCURACY AT 3 SIGMA IS 1282

ITEM FILE
PERCENT FOR THIS ELEMENT IS .131752
ABSOLUTE ACCURACY NOW IS .03683 OR THE RANGE IS .131752 + OR - .03683
THE NUMBER OF RECORDINGS TO ACHIEVE .035 PERCENT ACCURACY AT 3 SIGMA IS 840

ITEM WRITE
PERCENT FOR THIS ELEMENT IS .105402
ABSOLUTE ACCURACY NOW IS .0334379 OR THE RANGE IS .105402 + OR - .0334379
THE NUMBER OF RECORDINGS TO ACHIEVE .035 PERCENT ACCURACY AT 3 SIGMA IS 692

ITEM AWAY
PERCENT FOR THIS ELEMENT IS .0724638
ABSOLUTE ACCURACY NOW IS .028231 OR THE RANGE IS .0724638 + OR - .028231
THE NUMBER OF RECORDINGS TO ACHIEVE .035 PERCENT ACCURACY AT 3 SIGMA IS 493

ITEM IDLE
PERCENT FOR THIS ELEMENT IS .13834
ABSOLUTE ACCURACY NOW IS .037596 OR THE RANGE IS .13834 + OR - .037596
THE NUMBER OF RECORDINGS TO ACHIEVE .035 PERCENT ACCURACY AT 3 SIGMA IS 875

TOTAL NUMBER OF OBSERVATIONS TO DATE ARE 759

Printout 7-2

OFFICE STUDY 4 CLERKS

WORK SAMPLING WORK SHEET   *Day 5*

DATE   01/01/81

```
         TYPE---PHONE---FILE---WRITE---AWAY---IDLE---
 8 : 1                                              ////
 8 : 20     /        /        /        /
 8 : 27     /                 /        /        /
 8 : 38     /        //                /        /
 8 : 52              /        //       /
 9 : 0      /                 /                 /        /
 9 : 20     //       //
 9 : 33     ///      /
 9 : 38     ιι                /                          /
 9 : 55     //       /                 /
10 : 2      /        /        /        /
10 : 11     //       /                 /
10 : 16     /        /                 //
10 : 24     /        //       /        /
10 : 31     /·       //       /
10 : 33     //                         /        /
10 : 45     //       /        /
10 : 55     /        //                /        /
11 : 4      /        //       /                          /
11 : 16     //       /                 /
11 : 19     /        //                /        /
11 : 37     ιι       /                                   /
11 : 55     /                                  //       /

 1 : 15                       /        /        /        //
 1 : 34     /        //                /        /        /
 1 : 39     //       /                                   /
 1 : 51     /        //       ι        /
 2 : 4      ι        /        ι        /
 2 : 15     /        ι        ι        /
 2 : 32     //                         /        /
 2 : 53     //                         /                 /
 3 : 8      ι        //       ι        /
 3 : 16     ι        ιι                         ι        ι
 3 : 20     ιι       ιι
 3 : 38     ι        /        /        /
 3 : 49     ι                 /        /        /
 4 : 1      //       /                          /        /
 4 : 21     ιι                         ι        /
 4 : 27     ιι       ι                 /        /
 4 : 38     /        ι        /        /        /
 4 : 49     /        ι                 /        /
 4 : 51     ι        //       /        /
 4 : 56              ι                 ι        /        ι
           ___      ___      ___      ___      ___      ___
TOTAL       56       45       20       23       19       17
```

OFFICE STUDY 4 CLERKS

SUMMARY

                                                    01/02/81

ITEM   TYPE
PERCENT FOR THIS ELEMENT IS .323749
ABSOLUTE ACCURACY NOW IS .0458086 OR THE RANGE IS .323749 + OR - .0458086
THE NUMBER OF RECORDINGS TO ACHIEVE .035 PERCENT ACCURACY AT 3 SIGMA IS 1608

Printout 7-2 continued

```
ITEM   PHONE
PERCENT FOR THIS ELEMENT IS .230032
ABSOLUTE ACCURACY NOW IS .0412021 OR THE RANGE IS .230032 + OR - .0412021
THE NUMBER OF RECORDINGS TO ACHIEVE  .035  PERCENT ACCURACY AT 3 SIGMA IS 1301

ITEM   FILE
PERCENT FOR THIS ELEMENT IS .127796
ABSOLUTE ACCURACY NOW IS .0326855 OR THE RANGE IS .127796 + OR - .0326855
THE NUMBER OF RECORDINGS TO ACHIEVE .035 PERCENT ACCURACY AT 3 SIGMA IS 818

ITEM   WRITE
PERCENT FOR THIS ELEMENT IS .109691
ABSOLUTE ACCURACY NOW IS .0305946 OR THE RANGE IS .109691 + OR - .0305946
THE NUMBER OF RECORDINGS TO ACHIEVE .035 PERCENT ACCURACY AT 3 SIGMA IS 717

ITEM   AWAY
PERCENT FOR THIS ELEMENT IS .0788073
ABSOLUTE ACCURACY NOW IS .0263783 OR THE RANGE IS .0788073 + OR - .0263783
THE NUMBER OF RECORDINGS TO ACHIEVE .035 PERCENT ACCURACY AT 3 SIGMA IS 533

ITEM   IDLE
PERCENT FOR THIS ELEMENT IS .129925
ABSOLUTE ACCURACY NOW IS .0329165 OR THE RANGE IS .129925 + OR - .0329165
THE NUMBER OF RECORDINGS TO ACHIEVE .035 PERCENT ACCURACY AT 3 SIGMA IS 830

TOTAL NUMBER OF OBSERVATIONS TO DATE ARE 939


1 REM PROGRAM NAME RATIO
2 REM WRITTEN BY J.E.NICKS
3 REM COMPUTER APPLICATIONS FOR THE MANUFACTURING ENGINEER
4 REM COPYRIGHT 1981 ALL RIGHTS RESERVED
10 CLS:CLEAR500
20 PRINT"THIS PROGRAM CALCULATES WORK SAMPLING RATIOS"
30 PRINT"THE PROGRAM IS DEVELOPED IN 3 PARTS"
40 PRINT"PART 1 GENERATES A WORK SHEET WITH RANDOM TIMES BETWEEN 8 & 5PM"
50 PRINT"THIS WORK SHEET CAN BE USED TO RECORD SAMPLINGS OF THE STUDY"
60 PRINT"PART 2 SETS UP THE STUDY HEADINGS IN THE FORM OF DATA STATEMENTS"
65 PRINT"IF THE WORK SHEET HAS NOT BEEN SET UP , USE PART 2"
70 PRINT"PART 3 PERMITS THE USER TO INPUT EACH DAYS RANDOM SAMPLES AND"
80 PRINT"CALCULATES THE TOTALS AND PERCENTAGES"
90 PRINT"TYPE IN THE MODULE YOU WISH TO WORK WITH"
100 INPUTX
110 ONXGOTO120,2000,500
120 RANDOM
130 DIMC(1200)
140 INPUT"TYPE IN THE NAME OF THE STUDY";X$
150 LPRINTCHR$(27);CHR$(14);X$
160 LPRINTCHR$(138)
170 READA
180 LPRINT"WORK SAMPLING WORK SHEET"
185 LPRINTCHR$(138)
190 INPUT"TYPE IN TODAYS DATE";A$
200 LPRINT"DATE   ";A$
210 FORI=1TOA
220 READB$
230 LPRINTTAB(10);B$;"---";
240 NEXTI
245 LPRINTCHR$(138)
250 FORI=800TO1200STEPB
260 A=RND(35)
270 C(I)=I+B
280 IFC(I)=800THEN330
290 IFC(I)>1200THEN346
300 X=INT(C(I)/100):Y=((C(I)/100)-X)*60:Z=INT(Y)
```

Printout 7-2 continued

187

```
310 IFX>12THEN346
320 LPRINTX;":";Z
330 B=B+A
340 NEXTI
346 DIMD(2000)
347 LPRINTCHR$(138)
350 FORI=100TO500STEPD
360 C=RND(35)
365 D(I)=D+I
370 IFD(I)=500THEN420
375 IFD(I)=100THEN400
380 X=INT(D(I)/100):Y=((D(I)/100)-X)*60:Z=INT(Y)
390 IFX=5THEN420
395 LPRINTX;":";Z
400 D=D+C
410 NEXTI
420 END
500 REM EACH DAYS ENTRY AND CALCULATION:CLS
501 CLS
510 PRINT"AFTER EACH DAYS RECORDINGS THE SUMMARY IS ENTERED AS DATA"
520 PRINT"TO ENTER DATA--BREAK--LIST--ENTER DATA--RE-RUN LINE 600"
530 PRINT"LINE 2070 SHOULD CONTAIN THE NUMBER OF DAYS DATA"
540 PRINT"LINE 2080 ETC SHOULD CONTAIN A SUMMARY OF RECORDINGS    FOR THAT DAY"
550 PRINT"RECORDINGS SHOULD BE ENTERED IN THE SAME ORDER AS HEADINGS"
560 PRINT"EXP: DATA LOAD,PROCESS,UNLOAD"
570 PRINT"ENF: DATA 15,23,10
580 STOP
600 READA
610 FORI=1TOA
620 READB$(I)
630 NEXTI
640 READN
650 FORI=1TON
660 FORJ=1TOA
670 READT(I,J)
680 NEXTJ
690 NEXTI
700 FORI=1TON
710 FORJ=1TOA
720 T1=T1+T(I,J)
730 IFJ=1THENT2=T2+T(I,J)
740 IFJ=2THENT3=T3+T(I,J)
750 IFJ=3THENT4=T4+T(I,J)
760 IFJ=4THENT5=T5+T(I,J)
770 IFJ=5THENT6=T6+T(I,J)
780 IFJ=6THENT7=T7+T(I,J)
790 IFJ=7THENT8=T8+T(I,J)
800 IFJ=8THENT9=T9+T(I,J)
810 NEXTJ
820 NEXTI
830 CLS
831 PRINT"CONFIDENCE LIMITS ARE EXPRESSED IN UNITS OF SIGMA"
832 PRINT"68 %CONFIDENCE =1------90 % CONDIDENCE =1.64"
833 PRINT"95 % CONFIDENCE =1.96-----95.45 % CONDIDENCE = 2"
834 PRINT"AND 99.73 % CONFIDENCE IS EQUAL TO 3 SIGMA"
840 INPUT"TYPE IN THE SIGMA EQUAL TO THE CONFIDENCE REQUIRED";G
850 PRINT"TYPE IN THE ABSOLUTE ACCURACY REQUIRED IN DECIMAL FORM"
860 INPUTK
861 INPUT"TYPE IN THE NAME OF THE STUDY";X$
862 LPRINTCHR$(27);CHR$(14);X$
863 LPRINTCHR$(138)
864 LPRINT"SUMMARY"
865 LPRINTCHR$(138)
866 INPUT"ENTER TODAYS DATE";A$
867 LPRINT,,,A$
```

Printout 7-2 continued

```
870 P2=T2/T1:Q2=G*(SQR((P2*(1-P2))/T1)):N2=((G[2)*(P2*(1-P2)))/(K[2)
880 LPRINT"ITEM   ";B$(1)
890 LPRINT"PERCENT FOR THIS ELEMENT IS";P2
900 LPRINT"ABSOLUTE ACCURACY NOW IS";Q2;"OR THE RANGE IS";P2;"+ OR -";Q2
910 LPRINT"THE NUMBER OF RECORDINGS TO ACHIEVE";K;"PERCENT ACCURACY AT";G;"SIGMA
 IS";INT(N2)
920 P3=T3/T1:Q3=G*(SQR((P3*(1-P3))/T1)):N3=((G[2)*(P3*(1-P3)))/(K[2)
930 LPRINTCHR$(138)
940 LPRINT"ITEM   ";B$(2)
950 LPRINT"PERCENT FOR THIS ELEMENT IS";P3
960 LPRINT"ABSOLUTE ACCURACY NOW IS";Q3;"OR THE RANGE IS";P3;"+ OR -";Q3
970 LPRINT"THE NUMBER OF RECORDINGS TO ACHIEVE ";K;" PERCENT ACCURACY AT";G;"SIG
MA IS";INT(N3)
980 IFT4=0THEN1400
990 P4=T4/T1:Q4=G*(SQR((P4*(1-P4))/T1)):N4=((G[2)*(P4*(1-P4)))/(K[2)
1000 LPRINTCHR$(138)
1010 LPRINT"ITEM   ";B$(3)
1020 LPRINT"PERCENT FOR THIS ELEMENT IS";P4
1030 LPRINT"ABSOLUTE ACCURACY NOW IS";Q4;"OR THE RANGE IS";P4;"+ OR -";Q4
1040 LPRINT"THE NUMBER OF RECORDINGS TO ACHIEVE";K;"PERCENT ACCURACY AT";G;"SIGM
A IS";INT(N4)
1050 IFT5=0THEN1400
1060 P5=T5/T1:Q5=G*(SQR((P5*(1-P5))/T1)):N5=((G[2)*(P5*(1-P5)))/(K[2)
1070 LPRINTCHR$(138)
1080 LPRINT"ITEM   ";B$(4)
1090 LPRINT"PERCENT FOR THIS ELEMENT IS";P5
1100 LPRINT"ABSOLUTE ACCURACY NOW IS";Q5;"OR THE RANGE IS";P5;"+ OR -";Q5
1110 LPRINT"THE NUMBER OF RECORDINGS TO ACHIEVE";K;"PERCENT ACCURACY AT";G;"SIGM
A IS";INT(N5)
1120 IFT6=0THEN1400
1130 P6=T6/T1:Q6=G*(SQR((P6*(1-P6))/T1)):N6=((G[2)*(P6*(1-P6)))/(K[2)
1140 LPRINTCHR$(138)
1150 LPRINT"ITEM   ";B$(5)
1160 LPRINT"PERCENT FOR THIS ELEMENT IS";P6
1170 LPRINT"ABSOLUTE ACCURACY NOW IS";Q6;"OR THE RANGE IS";P6;"+ OR -";Q6
1180 LPRINT"THE NUMBER OF RECORDINGS TO ACHIEVE";K;"PERCENT ACCURACY AT";G;"SIGM
A IS";INT(N6)
1190 IFT7=0THEN1400
1200 P7=T7/T1:Q7=G*(SQR((P7*(1-P7))/T1)):N7=((G[2)*(P7*(1-P7)))/(K[2)
1210 LPRINTCHR$(138)
1220 LPRINT"ITEM   ";B$(6)
1230 LPRINT"PERCENT FOR THIS ELEMENT IS";P7
1240 LPRINT"ABSOLUTE ACCURACY NOW IS";Q7;"OR THE RANGE IS";P7;"+ OR -";Q7
1250 LPRINT"THE NUMBER OF RECORDINGS TO ACHIEVE";K;"PERCENT ACCURACY AT";G;"SIGM
A IS";INT(N7)
1260 IFT8=0THEN1400
1270 P8=T8/T1:Q8=G*(SQR((P8*(1-P8))/T1)):N8=((G[2)*(P8*(1-P8)))/(K[2)
1280 LPRINTCHR$(138)
1290 LPRINT"ITEM   ";B$(7)
1300 LPRINT"PERCENT FOR THIS ELEMENT IS";P8
1310 LPRINT"ABSOLUTE ACCURACY NOW IS";Q8;"OR THE RANGE IS";P8;"+ OR -";Q8
1320 LPRINT"THE NUMBER OF RECORDINGS TO ACHIEVE";K;"PERCENT ACCURACY AT";G;"SIGM
A IS";INT(N8)
1330 IFT9=0THEN1400
1340 P9=T9/T1:Q9=G*(SQR((P9*(1-P9))/T1)):N9=((G[2)*(P9*(1-P9)))/(K[2)
1350 LPRINTCHR$(138)
1360 LPRINT"ITEM   ";B$(8)
1370 LPRINT"PERCENT FOR THIS ELEMENT IS";P9
1380 LPRINT"ABSOLUTE ACCURACY NOW IS";Q9;"OR THE RANGE IS";P9;"+ OR -";Q9
1390 LPRINT"THE NUMBER OF RECORDINGS TO ACHIEVE";K;"PERCENT ACCURACY AT";G;"SIGM
A IS";INT(N9)
1400 LPRINTCHR$(138)
1410 LPRINT"TOTAL NUMBER OF OBSERVATIONS TO DATE ARE";T1
1420 END
2000 CLS:PRINT"HEADINGS MUST BE ENTERED AS DATA STATEMENTS"
```

Printout 7-2 continued

```
2010 PRINT"START BY TYPING THE NUMBER OF HEADINGS AS DATA EXAMPLE"
2015 PRINT"LINE 2050 DATA 5"
2020 PRINT"THEN ENTER AND TYPE IN EACH HEADING NAME IN THE NEXT LINE"
2025 PRINT"EXAMPLE LINE 2060 DATA TYPE,FILE,"
2030 PRINT"WHEN COMPLETE RE-RUN THE PROGRAM"
2040 PRINT"SAVE THE PROGRAM WHEN COMPLETE"
2050 DATA6
2060 DATA"TYPE","PHONE","FILE","WRITE","AWAY","IDLE"
2070 DATA5
2080 DATA60,40,24,20,10,30
2090 DATA56,56,28,20,10,34
2100 DATA76,40,20,16,20,20
2110 DATA56,35,28,24,15,21
2120 DATA56,45,20,23,19,17
```

Printout 7-2 continued

Bibliography

Barnes, Ralph M. *Motion and Time Study*. 6th Ed., New York. John Wiley & Sons, 1968.

Konz, Stephan. *Work Design*. Columbus, OH. Grid Publishing Company, 1979.

Smith, George L. Jr. *Work Measurement, a System Approach*. Columbus, OH. Grid Publishing Company, 1978.

Optional Lab Assignments

Lab Assignment 7-1 (least difficult)
Write a computer program that evaluates storage requirements for a storeroom. The program should display several different sized standard containers for different sized parts. Limits could be written in the program for height of storage racks. The objective is to determine how much floor space is required including aisle space.

Lab Assignment 7-2 (moderate)
Using Queuing Theory, write a computer program that will evaluate the optimum location for the placement of a machine tool on the shop floor. This program would be of value for doing plant layout work. Any good statistics text will contain the formulas.

Lab Assignment 7-3 (difficult)
Write a computer program that calculates manning tables for indirect labor. The manning tables should reflect a step variable condition for indirect labor to direct labor. The objective of the program is to determine different manning levels for indirect labor service people as a production schedule varies.

CHAPTER 8

Analysis with Computer Graphics

One of the more glamorous yet tedious aspects of computer programming is computer graphics. Generally, there are three ways computer graphics can be used by the Manufacturing Engineer:

1. For illustration of an idea.
2. For analysis.
3. For charting.

Computer graphics used for illustration of an idea requires more than a modest amount of programming skill. There are five examples of this usage in Chapter Two. The fundamental intention is to convey an idea or message to the user which cannot be accomplished by description. A good example is the relationship of the mill cutter to the part being milled. There are no less than five different ways this relationship can be shown and each way requires a different formula for cutter approach. Without the aid of graphics, it would be difficult to illustrate these relationships.

Graphics used for analysis can best be described by reviewing the bar chart or histogram printout shown in Chapter Four. The data collected by the engineer is printed out in histogram form to permit the engineer to analyze whether the histogram looks normal. With the use of computer graphics, the engineer can tell if the histogram is bimodal, skewed, or peaked. This use of computer graphics is not difficult to program; in addition to its utility, it provides an expression of programming style.

Charting is the third way computer graphics can be used. Some examples of charting used by the Manufacturing Engineer are: "GANTT" charting, curve charting and "P.E.R.T." charting. Computer charting can be further subdivided into two classifications—scaled and nonscaled charting. Nonscaled charting means there is no scale across the top of the chart. This method of charting requires only one axis—the Y axis. Scaled charting, on the other hand, requires two axes—the X axis and the Y axis.

This chapter is devoted to the use of computer graphics and charting as might be used by the Manufacturing Engineer. Where necessary, a line-by-line description of each program presented in this chapter will be defined in detail. The following programs are included:

1. "BAR"—a program for charting a bar graph.
2. "MACH"—a scaled program for machine loads.
3. "GANTT"—a program for project control chart.
4. "MAN"—a program that calculates a one-man, two-machine relationship.

Program Name: "BAR"

The memory required is 659 bytes.

This program, even though simple, embraces all of the techniques used to produce nonscaled charts.

Line Explanation

Line 5 DIM B(13), D(13), S(13)

Line 5 is a dimension statement that sets aside 13 bytes of memory for each variable B, D and S. Without the "DIM" statement, the computer will default after 10 entries of any subscripted variable.

Line 10 INPUT "TYPE IN THE NUMBER OF BARS ON THE CHART";N
Line 20 FOR I=1 TO N

Line 10 permits the user to input the number of bars on the chart and Line 20 sets the start of the FOR-NEXT loop to that number, N.

Line 30 INPUT "TYPE IN THE FREQUENCY AND CELL SIZE, SEPARATE BY A COMMA";B(I),S(I)

Line 30 is a multiple input line. Notice that the subscripts match the I in the FOR-NEXT loop. Subscripting is necessary because these variables will be recalled from memory later in the program.

Line 40 D(I)=B(I)*S(I)

This line multiplies the frequency by the cell size for later calculations and stores this figure in memory as D(I).

Line 50 E=E+D(I)
Line 60 T=T+B(I)

These two lines are accumulators that sum E and T.

Line 70 NEXT I

Line 70 continues the loop until all entries have been made.

Line 100 LPRINT TAB (3);"FREQUENCY"; TAB (10);"CELL SIZE";
TAB(30); "BAR CHART"

This line sets up the heading. The TAB statements position the printer head before it prints. It is imperative that the punctuation be precise, otherwise, the computer will default.

Line 101 LPRINT

This statement prompts the computer to skip a line.

Line 102 FOR X=0TO60:LPRINT"=";:NEXT

Line 102 is a compressed line. The line number was placed in the program as an afterthought. Essentially, it is window dressing.

Line 110 FORI=1TON

This line starts the printout loop.

```
1 REM PROGRAM NAME BAR
2 REM WRITTEN BY J.E.NICKS
3 REM COMPUTER APPLICATIONS FOR THE MANUFACTURING ENGINEER
4 REM COPYRIGHT 1981 ALL RIGHTS RESERVED
5 DIMB(13),D(13),S(13)
6 CLS
7 PRINT"THIS PROGRAM PRINTS OUT A BAR CHART"
10 INPUT"TYPE IN THE NUMBER OF BARS ON THE CHART";N
20 FORI=1TON
30 INPUT"TYPE IN THE FREQ.&CELL SIZE,SEPARATE BY A COMMA";B(I),S(I)
40 D(I)=B(I)*S(I)
50 E=E+D(I)
60 T=T+B(I)
70 NEXTI
80 CLS
100 LPRINTTAB(3);"FREQ";TAB(10);"CELL SIZE";TAB(30);"BAR CHART"
101 LPRINT
102 FORX=0TO60:LPRINT"=";:NEXT
105 LPRINT
110 FORI=1TON
120 LPRINTTAB(3);B(I);TAB(10);"SIZE";S(I);
130 FORA=1TOB(I)
140 LPRINTTAB(25);"X";
150 NEXTA
160 LPRINT
170 NEXTI
175 LPRINT
180 LPRINT"THE AVERAGE IS";E/T
185 LPRINT"THE SUM OF ALL THE FREQUENCY IS",T
190 END
```

```
   FREQ    CELL SIZE           BAR CHART
============================================================
    4       SIZE .994          XXXX
    6       SIZE .995          XXXXXX
    9       SIZE .996          XXXXXXXXX
   11       SIZE .997          XXXXXXXXXXX
   15       SIZE .998          XXXXXXXXXXXXXXX
   19       SIZE .999          XXXXXXXXXXXXXXXXXXX
   27       SIZE 1             XXXXXXXXXXXXXXXXXXXXXXXXXXX
   23       SIZE 1.001         XXXXXXXXXXXXXXXXXXXXXXX
   20       SIZE 1.002         XXXXXXXXXXXXXXXXXXXX
   16       SIZE 1.003         XXXXXXXXXXXXXXXX
   12       SIZE 1.004         XXXXXXXXXXXX
    9       SIZE 1.005         XXXXXXXXX
THE AVERAGE IS 1.00019
THE SUM OF ALL THE FREQUENCY IS   171
```

Printout 8-1

Line 120 LPRINT TAB(3);B(I);TAB(10);"SIZE";S(1);

Note that the tab positions match the heading line. Also note B(I), or whatever was entered as the first B(I), will be recalled from memory and printed at location TAB(3). The trailing semicolon at the end of the line prevents the printer from terminating the print statement.

Line 130 FOR A=1TOB(I)

This line starts a nested FOR-NEXT loop, the length of which is B(I), or the frequency of the first input.

Line 140 LPRINT TAB (25);"X";

This line directs the printer to print as many X's as there are B(I)'s. Again, note the trailing semicolon; the printer does not shift yet.

Line 150 NEXT A

Line 150 finish line prints the X's in that row.

Line 160 LPRINT

Line 160 shifts the printer carriage.

Line 170 NEXT I

Line 170 asks the computer to go back and start at line 110 for the second row of data.

General Comments

This program is very simple and straightforward. Other features could be written into the program to test where the specification lines should be drawn, to expand print headings and to add other elements of window dressing.

Charting on a printer terminal, whether scaled or nonscaled, depends on the X axis for variability. Many bar charts use the Y axis, which permits the reader to see vertical lines or bars. Because the printer variability is only in the X axis, any charting program must be written so the chart is turned around.

While this program was written expressly for displaying a bell shaped curve, it also can be used to display other data.

Scaled Graphing on the Computer Terminal

The next two programs contain scaling features. Before these programs are reviewed, we should understand what scaling means and how it works.

Scaling produces a two-axes graph on the terminal screen or printer. The longitudinal axis (X axis) has 64 terminal spaces or 80 printer spaces. The vertical axis (Y axis) is limited to 16 rows on the terminal screen. For practical purposes, the printer is limited to 11 inches (the length of an 8-1/2 x 11-inch sheet).

Two-axes graphing on a terminal screen or printer is not complicated if you follow several easy to remember rules. For the first example, review the sine curve shown in *Figure 8-1*. Every engineer knows that a sine curve produces negative numbers as shown below.

The computer terminal operates much like a typewriter carriage with the exception that it cannot be backspaced. Therefore, the first rule for graphing on the computer terminal is to set all values equal to positive numbers. Where a sine curve equals +1 to -1, this value must be set to 0 to +2. If we wish that 0 to +2 be equal to 50 terminal spaces, then equate as shown in *Figure 8-2*.

The second rule for graphing is that variability for charting on the terminal screen or printer is available only in the X axis. In the sine curve example, this means the sine curve must be turned on its end to produce a curve on the CRT or printer.

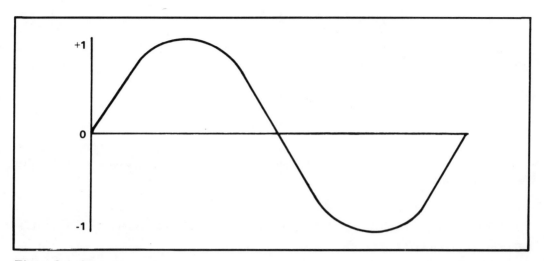

Figure 8-1. *Sine curve.*

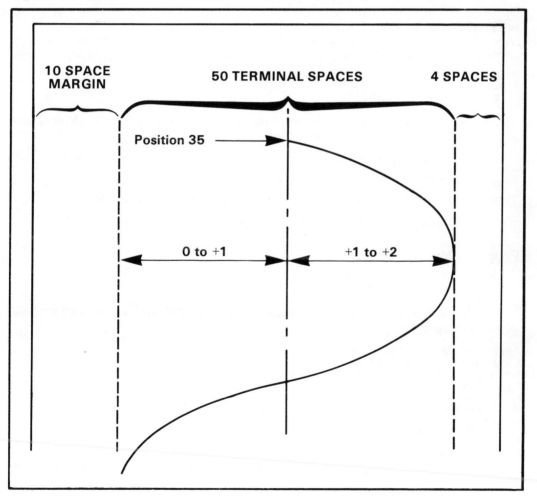

10 SPACE MARGIN   50 TERMINAL SPACES   4 SPACES

Position 35 →

0 to +1   +1 to +2

Figure 8-2. *Terminal screen.*

```
10 FOR I = 0 to 6.4 STEP .2
20 Y = SIN(I)*25
30 PRINT TAB (Y+35);"*"
40 NEXT I
```

This short program produces a sine curve on the terminal screen.

Line 10 FOR I=0 TO 6.4 STEP .2

This line equates the length of the curve to approximately $2 * \pi$. The STEP .2 part of the line increments the computer (6.4/.2=32) for 32 steps, 16 steps or points above the zero line, and 16 steps or points below the zero line.

Line 20 Y = SIN(I)*25

This line sets Y equal to the sine of .2*25 for the first print position. Or, expressed as a formula:

$$SIN(.2)*25=.08726$$

Line 30 PRINT TAB (Y+35);"*"

In *Figure 8-2*, the first asterisk is printed on the screen at position 35 + .08726. Position 35 is the center of the screen plus 10 terminal spaces for a margin. The sine curve is produced in a range of 50 terminal spaces by multiplying the +1 and the -1 by the 25 in line 20. Line 30 tells where to print it out. Next, add the following line.

Line 25 PRINT Y;

Rerunning the program will permit the user to see what the Y values are. Y can be changed into a whole number by adding and changing these lines:

Line 22 Y1 = INT(Y+35)
Line 25 PRINT Y1;

These two lines permit the user to see where the asterisk is printed on the CRT.

Finally, change the PRINT statements to LPRINT statements for hard copy.

Program Name: "MACH"

The memory required is 862 bytes.

The "MACH" program is a machine-load chart program, and represents the first example of scaled charting.

```
1 REM PROGRAM NAME MACH
2 REM WRITTEN BY J.E.NICKS
3 REM COPYRIGHT 1981 ALL RIGHTS RESERVED
4 REM COMPUTER APPLICATIONS FOR THE MANUFACTURING ENGINEER
10 A=20:B=60
15 LPRINTCHR$(27);CHR$(14);"MACHINE LOAD CHART"
20 LPRINT"MACHINE NAME-----GRINDER-----OCT-NOV 1980"
21 LPRINTCHR$(138)
30 LPRINT"HOURS LOAD PER WEEK"
31 LPRINTCHR$(138)
40 LPRINTTAB(5);"WEEK";TAB(15);"HOURS THIS WEEK";TAB(35);"OVER TIME";TAB(55);"DO
WN"
```

Printout 8-2

198

```
50 FORI=ATOBSTEP5
55 LPRINTTAB(I*.75);I;
60 NEXTI
65 LPRINTCHR$(138)
70 FORX=1TO10
75 READH,D
76 H1=H1+H:D1=D1+D
77 IFH>40THEN78ELSE80
78 O1=O1+(H-40)
80 LPRINTTAB(5);X;TAB(H*.75+3);"*";TAB(55);D;
85 LPRINTCHR$(13)
86 LPRINT"          --------------------------I---------------"
90 NEXTX
100 DATA30,3,35,6,38,6,40,0,42,5
110 DATA44,8,48,10,25,12,32,10,36,4
120 LPRINTCHR$(138)
130 LPRINTCHR$(27);CHR$(14);"ANALYSIS"
140 LPRINTCHR$(138)
150 LPRINT"AVERAGE HOURS OPERATED THIS PERIOD HAS BEEN";H1/10
160 LPRINT"TOTAL DOWN TIME HOURS HAS BEEN";D1
170 LPRINT"TOTAL OVERTIME HOURS HAS BEEN";O1
180 END
```

———————————————— **Printout 8-2 continued** ————————————————

MACHINE LOAD CHART
MACHINE NAME-----GRINDER-----OCT-NOV 1980

HOURS LOAD PER WEEK

WEEK	HOURS THIS WEEK				OVER TIME					DOWN
	20	25	30	35	40	45	50	55	60	
1			*							3
2				*						6
3				*						6
4					*					0
5					*					5
6						*				8
7							*			10
8	*									12
9			*							10
10				*						4

ANALYSIS

AVERAGE HOURS OPERATED THIS PERIOD HAS BEEN 37
TOTAL DOWN TIME HOURS HAS BEEN 64
TOTAL OVERTIME HOURS HAS BEEN 14

Printout 8-3

Line Explanation

Line 10 A=20: B=60.

Line 10 establishes the minimum and maximum hours per week that the machine will operate.

Line 50 FOR I=A TO B STEP 5

After the heading is tabbed in line 40, line 50 essentially states:

FOR I=20 TO 60 STEP 5

starting with 20, then 25, 30, etc. The STEP 5 is arbitrary. If 30 terminal or printer spaces are to be used, equate 30 terminal spaces to the X legend. X will equal 60 minus 20 or 40 so 40/30=.75. This method is used to establish the X scale.

Line 55 LPRINT TAB (I*.75);I;

The LPRINT line above condenses the 40 X spaces into 30 terminal spaces, incremented in steps of five. Pay special note to the trailing semicolon which prevents the printer from indexing until the entire line is printed.

Line 70 FOR X=1 TO 10

There are 10 weeks in this report, therefore, 10 sets of data to be read. This line also could be variable and could be:

Line 70 FOR X=S TO F

Where S equals "start" and F equals "finish":

Line 75 READ H,D

The hours worked (H) and downtime (D) are stored in the program as data statements, which simplifies the program. To update the program, two options are available.

First option. Delete the top line of DATA, or the first week, and add another last line of DATA. If this method is used, line 70 would change to read:

Line 70 FOR X = 2 TO 11

or

Line 70 FOR X = S TO F

If the latter is used, two more lines for inputting S and F are required.

Second option. The second option is to produce a longer report by adding the 11th week. To do this, change line 70 to read:

Line 70 FOR X = 1 TO 11

Line 76 H1 = H1 +H: D1= D1 +D

This line is an accumulator for the total hours worked (H1) and downtime (D1).

Line 77 IF H>40 THEN 78 ELSE 80
Line 78 01 = 01 + (H-40)

If there has been overtime in any week, line 77 tests for the condition and line 78 accumulates this figure. If there has been no overtime in this week, the computer is directed to line 80.

Line 80 LPRINT TAB (5);X;TAB(H*.75+3);"*";TAB(55);D;

With scaled graphing, it is necessary to line up the X axis data with the heading produced earlier. TAB(5);X; prints out the week. TAB(H*.75+3);"X"; multiplies the hours worked (h) by .75 (the column factor used earlier), then adds three to line up the one multiplication character (*). TAB(55);D; is the part of the line that prints out the downtime read earlier.

Line 86 LPRINT "---------I----"

This line positions an "I" under the 40 column to provide ease in reading the chart for hours in excess of 40 (overtime).

General Comments

This program was written to illustrate the ease in generating charts on the computer. If engineers in industry were asked to keep track of several machines in this manner, the program should be rewritten for purposes of convenience. For example, the DATA statements should be separate lines, and the FOR-NEXT loops should contain variables read from DATA statements. This idea permits the user to update the program with DATA statements only, without reprogramming any of the FOR-NEXT loops.

One last point should be stressed. This program also could be written using the filing system discussed in Chapter Nine. However, programming with DATA statements is much easier for this type of application.

Program Name: "GANTT"

The memory required for this program is 578 bytes.

Line Explanation

The use of project control charts, like the sample shown on the following page, are fundamental to Manufacturing Engineering. The "GANTT" program is a very simple program written much like the "MACH" program just reviewed. Therefore, the line explanation provided for this program will show only the scaling differences.

```
1 REM PROGRAM NEME GANTT
2 REM WRITTEN BY J.E.NICKS
3 REM COPYRIGHT 1981 ALL RIGHTS RESERVED
4 REM COMPUTER APPLICATIONS FOR THE MANUFACTURING ENGINEER
10 LPRINTCHR$(27);CHR$(14);"PROJECT CONTROL CHART FOR PROJECT 1"
20 LPRINTCHR$(138)
30 LPRINT"ITEM";TAB(30);"WEEKS";TAB(60);"TIME";TAB(66);"START";TAB(72);"FINISH"
40 LPRINTCHR$(138)
50 FORI=0TO52STEP4
60 LPRINTTAB(I*.4+7);I;
70 NEXTI
80 LPRINTCHR$(138)
90 FORX=1TO10
100 READA$,S,F
110 T=F-S
120 LPRINTA$;
130 FORY=STO(F-1)
140 LPRINTTAB(S+7);"I";
150 NEXTY
160 LPRINTTAB(60);T;TAB(66);S;TAB(72);F;
170 LPRINTCHR$(138)
```

Printout 8-4

```
180 LPRINTCHR$(138)
190 NEXTX
200 DATADES.A,1,10
210 DATABUILD,10,20
220 DATADES.B,4,8
230 DATABUILD,8,16
240 DATAASSY,20,30
250 DATATRY,31,35
260 DATADEBUG,35,40
270 DATAREWRK,40,42
280 DATASHIP,42,43
290 DATACOLLECT,44,45
300 END
```

PROJECT CONTROL CHART FOR PROJECT 1

ITEM	WEEKS														TIME	START	FINISH
	0	4	8	12	16	20	24	28	32	36	40	44	48	52			
DES.A	IIIIIIIII														9	1	10
BUILD				IIIIIIIIII											10	10	20
DES.B	IIII														4	4	8
BUILD		IIIIIIII													8	8	16
ASSY						IIIIIIIIII									10	20	30
TRY								IIII							4	31	35
DEBUG									IIIII						5	35	40
REWRK											II				2	40	42
SHIP											I				1	42	43
COLLECT												I			1	44	45

Printout 8-4 continued

First, 35 print spaces are equated to 52 weeks, stepped by four. There are 14 steps from 0 to 52, and we wish to use 35 print spaces for the data; therefore:

$$0 \text{ to } 52 = 14 \text{ STEPS}$$

$$14 \div 35 = .4$$

Line 60 LPRINT TAB (I *.4 + 7);I;

I is part of the FOR-NEXT loop in line 50, .4 is the factor and +7 is the margin.

Line 140 LPRINT TAB (S+7); "I";

S is equal to the start week and again +7 is the margin.

General Comments

Updating the "GANTT" program is accomplished the same way as the "MACH" program, by updating DATA statements.

The "GANTT" program could be rewritten to include programming logic to permit a new critical path to be calculated.

There are other project control devices that the Manufacturing Engineer uses such as "P.E.R.T." and "L.O.B." which also can be programmed.

"P.E.R.T." programs usually require more memory than a microcomputer has available, therefore, most existing programs for "P.E.R.T." are written for a mainframe computer. There are two major advantages in using this type of computer charting. First, when a revised data statement is entered as a single unit, the chart will show conflicts; that is, another unit might slide because the change or stack time produced might pull the program up. The second advantage is ease of testing for project changes. If the chart is a long one, i.e., 30 to 40 events, the lineup of the chart could be achieved with the use of spacing markers, such as "I", which will save time by eliminating the need to mark-up the chart by hand. This technique was used in the "MACH" program for marking overtime.

Program Name: "MAN"

The memory required for the "MAN" program is 2398 bytes.

The next problem to be discussed is man-machine charting. Man-machine charting was an Industrial Engineering tool that was borrowed by the Manufacturing Engineer to determine the relationship of man-time to machine-time where one man is asked to operate more than one piece of equipment. The technique is simple to determine answers to these questions:
1. What is the production rate for one man operating two machines?
2. What is the part cost for one man operating two machines?
3. What is the utilization for the man and the machine?

The engineer marks off the time scaled chart for load, process and unload for each of the machines until a repeating pattern develops. Once the pattern develops, the engineer can then determine the total cycle time for two parts, one piece from Machine One and one piece from Machine Two. Next, he continues to calculate the remaining data such as wait-time, utilization and total parts per hour. One rather interesting aside, the author has used man-machine charts for at least 25 years and also has seen them referenced in textbooks, yet not once has a math model been included to perform man-machine charting by calculation, only by charting. Also, it was not until the author considered doing this by computer that a math model was developed. Another interesting fact: the fundamental idea of charting this relationship at all is to develop time values per cycle. Once a math model is developed, the computer does not need the chart to evaluate data. This renders the chart useless. Therefore, this program is included in this chapter not because it produces a chart, but because it does not produce a chart. A line-by-line explanation of the program will not be provided for two reasons. First, it would take a chapter just to discuss the logic. Secondly, the math model does nothing more than add and subtract. What might be of interest to the reader, however, is the logic as to how the math model was developed. *Figure 8-5* is a decision tree that displays the rationale of man-machine charting.

ACTIVITY CHART

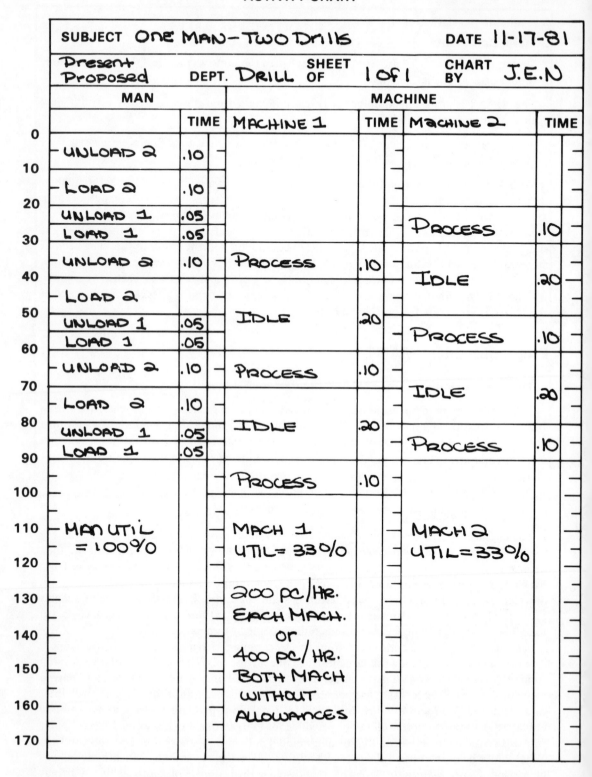

SUBJECT ONE MAN—TWO DRILLS			DATE 11-17-81			
Present Proposed		DEPT. DRILL SHEET OF 1 of 1	CHART BY J.E.N			
MAN		MACHINE				
	TIME	MACHINE 1	TIME	MACHINE 2	TIME	
UNLOAD 2	.10					
LOAD 2	.10					
UNLOAD 1	.05			PROCESS	.10	
LOAD 1	.05					
UNLOAD 2	.10	PROCESS	.10	IDLE	.20	
LOAD 2	.10					
UNLOAD 1	.05	IDLE	.20	PROCESS	.10	
LOAD 1	.05					
UNLOAD 2	.10	PROCESS	.10	IDLE	.20	
LOAD 2	.10					
UNLOAD 1	.05	IDLE	.20	PROCESS	.10	
LOAD 1	.05					
		PROCESS	.10			
MAN UTIL =100%		MACH 1 UTIL= 33%		MACH 2 UTIL=33%		
		200 PC/HR. EACH MACH. or 400 PC/HR. BOTH MACH WITHOUT ALLOWANCES				

(Time scale at left: 0, 10, 20, 30, 40, 50, 60, 70, 80, 90, 100, 110, 120, 130, 140, 150, 160, 170)

Figure 8-3. *This chart provides an example of an activity chart used in drilling.*

```
MAN-MACHINE CHARTING VARIABLES
         Machine One              Machine Two

    L1 = Load                 L2 = Load
    U1 = Unload               U2 = Unload
    P1 = Process              P2 = Process

    T1 = Total cycle          T2 = Total cycle
    T1 = L1 + U1 + P1         T2 = L2 + U2 + P2

    E1 = External time        E2 = External time
    E1 = L1 + U1              E2 = L2 + U2

                   MAN VARIABLE

                 M1 = Man waits

                 OTHER VARIABLES

    W1 = Machine One waits
    W2 = Machine Two waits
     C = Cycle time per piece
    M2 = Man utilization
    M3 = Machine One utilization
    M4 = Machine Two utilization
     D = Dollars per hour for the man
    D1 = Dollars per hour for Machine One
    D2 = Dollars per hour for Machine Two
    C1   = Cost per hour Machine One = D1 + (D/2)
    C2   = Cost per hour Machine Two = D2 + (D/2)
     P = Piece per hour
    R1 = Rate Machine One
    R2 = Rate Machine Two
```

Figure 8-4. Man-machine charting variables.

When the decision tree analysis started, there were 12 possible alternatives which finally reduced to three.

"MAN" Summary

After reviewing the two printouts for the "MAN" program, note the following: to conduct the same analysis by hand that was conducted by the computer would take an experienced engineer about one-and-a-half hours. The computer accomplished this analysis in three minutes, including input time.

Is there a computer program for one man—three machines or more? Several important problems arise when one person is asked to operate three or more machines. First, while there is a slight gain in production with the addition of the third machine, in most cases, there is usually an increase in cost per part when each machine has a separate cost element for it. Secondly, while the person's utilization improves, the machine's utilization drops. The best condition in actual practice is a balance of the best utilization of all factors possible. Thirdly, in most one man—three machine conditions where setup is a factor, actual downtime, due to setup or

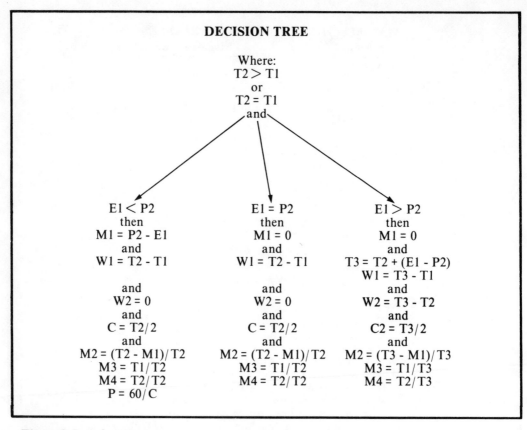

DECISION TREE

Where:
$T2 > T1$
or
$T2 = T1$
and

$E1 < P2$	$E1 = P2$	$E1 > P2$
then	then	then
$M1 = P2 - E1$	$M1 = 0$	$M1 = 0$
and	and	and
$W1 = T2 - T1$	$W1 = T2 - T1$	$T3 = T2 + (E1 - P2)$
		$W1 = T3 - T1$
and	and	and
$W2 = 0$	$W2 = 0$	$W2 = T3 - T2$
and	and	and
$C = T2/2$	$C = T2/2$	$C2 = T3/2$
and	and	and
$M2 = (T2 - M1)/T2$	$M2 = (T2 - M1)/T2$	$M2 = (T3 - M1)/T3$
$M3 = T1/T2$	$M3 = T1/T2$	$M3 = T1/T3$
$M4 = T2/T2$	$M4 = T2/T2$	$M4 = T2/T3$
$P = 60/C$		

Figure 8-5. *A decision tree.*

machine downtime, becomes more difficult to supervise than it is worth. Some readers may take exception to this logic. Perhaps those who do might wish to write a computer program to prove their point.

```
             MAN   —    MACHINE   ANALYSIS
    ITEM          MACHINE 1      MAN         MACHINE 2
    ----------------------------------------------------------------
    EXTERNAL       .1                          .3
    PROECSS        .35                         .2


    WAIT TIME      .05                         0
    CYCLE          .25                         .25
    MAN WAITS                     .1
    MAN UTIL %                    .8
    MACH UTIL %    .9                           100
    MAN COST                    $ 8.5
    MACH COST    $ 12.5                       $ 8.25
    TOT RATE     $ 16.75                      $ 12.5
    COST PER PC  $ .0697917                   $ .0520833
    PC PER HR                    240
    IF THE MAN OPERATES ONLY ONE MACHINE THE FOLLOWING DATA APPLIES

    PC PER HR      133.333                      120
    COST PER PC  $ .1575                      $ .139583
```

Printout 8-5

206

```
              MAN   —   MACHINE  ANALYSIS
     ITEM          MACHINE 1        MAN           MACHINE 2
    -----------------------------------------------------------------
     EXTERNAL        .3                            .25
     PROECSS         .15                           .25


     WAIT TIME       .1                            .05
     CYCLE           .275                          .275
     MAN WAITS                        0
     MAN UTIL %                       1
     MACH UTIL %     .818182                       .909091
     MAN COST                       $ 8.5
     MACH COST     $ 9.5                         $ 8.25
     TOT RATE      $ 13.75                       $ 12.5
     COST PER PC   $ .0630208                    $ .0572917
     PC PER HR                      218.182
     IF THE MAN OPERATES ONLY ONE MACHINE THE FOLLOWING DATA APPLIES

     PC PER HR      133.333                        120
     COST PER PC   $ .135                        $ .139583
```

```
1 REM PROGRAM NAME MAN
2 REM WRITTEN BY J.E.NICKS
3 REM COMPUTER APPLICATIONS FOR THE MANUFACTURING ENGINEER
4 REM COPYRIGHT 1981 ALL RIGHTS RESERVED
5 CLS
10 PRINT"THIS PROGRAM CALCULATES TIME AND PRODUCTION"
11 PRINT"RATES FOR 1 MAN OPERATING 2 MACHINES"
12 PRINT"IF YOU NEED INSTRUCTIONS TYPE 1 IF NOT TYPE 2"
20 INPUTZ
30 ONZGOTO40,140
40 PRINT"INSTRUCTIONS"
50 PRINT"THERE ARE A SERIES OF INPUTS NECESSARY FOR THIS PROGRAM."
60 PRINT"THIS PROGRAM ACCEPTS DATA FOR ONE MAN TWO MACHINES."
70 PRINT"IT IS NOT NECESSARY FOR THE TWO MACHINES TO HAVE THE"
80 PRINT"SAME CYCLE TIMES OR COSTS. IT IS NECESSARY HOWEVER TO INPUT"
90 PRINT"THE DATA IN THE SEQUENCE ASKED FOR"
100 PRINT"DATA FOR THE LONGEST CYCLE IS INPUTTED FIRST."
110 PRINT"ALL TIME VALUES ARE IN DECIMAL MIN."
120 PRINT"MACHINE AND MAN DOLLARS RATES ARE INPUTTED SEPARATLY"
140 PRINT"TYPE IN THE DATA FOR THE MACHINE THAT HAS THE LONGEST"
150 PRINT"TOTAL CYCLE FIRST"
160 INPUT"LOAD TIME , MACHINE 2";L2
170 INPUT"UNLOAD TIME , MACHINE 2";U2
180 INPUT"PROCESS TIME , MACHINE 2";P2
190 INPUT"COST PER HOUR FOR THE MAN";D
200 INPUT"COST PER HOUR FOR MACHINE 2";D2
210 INPUT"LOAD TIME , MACHINE 1";L1
220 INPUT"UNLOAD TIME , MACHINE 1";U1
230 INPUT"PROCESS TIME , MACHINE 1";P1
240 INPUT"COST PER HOUR FOR MACHINE 1";D1
241 REM T1,E1,T2,E2 = TOT TIME AND EXTERNAL TIME
242 REM M1,MAN WAIT,W1,W2 MACHINE WAIT
243 REM C,CYCLE,M2,M3,M4=UTIL FOR MAN,MACH1&2
244 REM P,PC PER HR,R1,R2=MACH RATE,C1,C2 COST PER HR
250 T1=L1+U1+P1:E1=L1+U1
260 T2=L2+U2+P2:E2=L2+U2
270 IFE1<P2THEN300ELSE280
280 IFE1=P2THEN340ELSE290
290 IFE1>P2THEN380
300 M1=P2-E1:W1=T2-T1:W2=0
310 C=T2/2:M2=(T2-M1)/T2
320 M3=T1/T2:M4=100
```

Printout 8-5 continued

```
330 GOTO420
340 M1=0:W1=T2:W2=0
350 C=T2/2:M2=(T2-M1)/T2
360 M3=T1/T2:M4=100
370 GOTO420
380 M1=0:T3=T2+(E1-P2)
390 W1=T3-T1:W2=T3-T2
400 C=T3/2:M2=(T3-M1)/T3
410 M3=T1/T3:M4=T2/T3
420 GOTO421
421 P=60/C:R1=(D/2)+D1:R2=(D/2)+D2
430 C1=R1/P:C2=R2/P
431 P3=60/T1:P4=60/T2:C3=(D+D1)/P3:C4=(D+D2)/P4
440 LPRINTCHR$(27);CHR$(14);TAB(8);"MAN -  MACHINE ANALYSIS"
450 LPRINT"ITEM","MACHINE 1","MAN","MACHINE 2"
460 FORX=0TO 64:LPRINT"-";:NEXT
465 LPRINT
470 LPRINT"EXTERNAL",E1,,E2
480 LPRINT"PROECSS",P1,,P2
490 LPRINT" "
491 LPRINT" "
500 LPRINT"WAIT TIME",W1,,W2
510 LPRINT"CYCLE",C,,C
520 LPRINT"MAN WAITS",,M1
530 LPRINT"MAN UTIL %",,M2
540 LPRINT"MACH UTIL %",M3,,M4
550 LPRINT"MAN COST",,"$";D
560 LPRINT"MACH COST","$";D1,,"$";D2
570 LPRINT"TOT RATE","$";R1,,"$";R2
580 LPRINT"COST PER PC","$";C1,,"$";C2
590 LPRINT"PC PER HR",,P
591 LPRINTCHR$(13)
592 LPRINT"IF THE MAN OPERATES ONLY ONE MACHINE THE FOLLOWING DATA APPLIES"
593 LPRINTCHR$(138)
594 LPRINT"PC PER HR",P3,,P4
595 LPRINT"COST PER PC","$";C3,,"$";C4
600 INPUT"TYPE 1 TO CONTINUE 2 TO EXIT";Y
610 ONYGOTO10,620
620 END
```

Printout 8-5 continued

Bibliography

Dwyer, Thomas A. and Margot Critchfield. *BASIC and the Personal Computer.* Philippines: Addison-Wesley Publishing Company, Inc., 1978.

Inman, Don. *Introduction to TRS-80 Graphics.* Portland, Oregon: Dilithium Press, 1979.

Optional Lab Assignments

Lab Assignment 8-1 (least difficult)

Write a computer program for a typical Manufacturing Engineer Department that displays the cost reduction efforts of those in the department by project. A departmental goal line can be established for time and dollars saved. Design the program for easy updating.

Lab Assignment 8-2 (moderate)

Design and write a computer program using the "GANTT" charting idea presented in this chapter. The program should include a feature to permit slack time to be calculated. Once new data is entered, a new project time is calculated. This exercise will sharpen the programmer's abilities in computer logic usage.

Lab Assignment 8-3 (difficult)

Write a computer program which can handle a "P.E.R.T." network. The program should also calculate the network based on the following input:

1. Least time.
2. Expected time.
3. Most time.

CHAPTER 9

Computer Filing

The TRS-80[1] microcomputer permits a system for random filing and a system for sequential filing. Random filing is, as the name implies, locating a file on disk at random. Sequential filing for the TRS-80 microcomputer is reading a file from disk in sequential order, or the order in which the file was placed on disk.

As a language, BASIC has often been referred to as a high-level language, or scientific language. The term scientific, loosely defined, means that BASIC has the ability to perform higher level math problems with ease. BASIC was not originally developed as a business language, but as a math problem-solving language. Other languages like COBOL of RPG are specifically designed to perform typical business operations, such as filing and word processing, but are not the best number processing languages available.

BASIC And Filing

Almost 20% of the statements and commands used in TRS-80 BASIC are used exclusively for filing. Many useful computer programs may be written without learning the filing part of the language, (or what might be referred to as the extension of BASIC that permits filing).

There are, however, many examples of filing that can and should be used in an engineering department. Several examples are:
1. Capital equipment budgeting.
2. Tooling cross references.
3. Usage values for bills of material.
4. Processing status for new projects.
5. Quality control records.
6. Maintenance records and inventory.
7. Preventative maintenace records.
8. Address mailing files.

The list, of course, is almost endless. There are advantages and disadvantages to small stand-alone computer filing systems. Any department or function that must maintain some quantity of records, where the records are generated and used internally to that department or function, is a candidate for a stand-alone filing system. Put another way, some data processing can best be accomplished by a mainframe computer, and some data processing can best be

---

[1]TRS-80 is a trademark of the Radio Shack Division of Tandy Corporation.

accomplished by a stand-alone computer.

The following example will illustrate the point. Suppose a medium-sized plant needs to update its record-keeping in the maintenance department. The objective is threefold:

1. Provide a preventative maintenance and oiling schedule each day.
2. Record maintenance labor and downtime for each piece of equipment.
3. Maintain a running inventory of spare and/or replacement parts for each machine.

If programs are written for the company's mainframe computer, someone from the data processing department must do the programming. Based on the author's experience, after many months of trying to communicate one's needs, one begins to wonder if the objective is worthwhile. On the other hand, if a company employed a Manufacturing Engineer who understood computer programming and the maintenance department's problems, the objective could be achieved much more easily.

Nevertheless, the major test is not the question of who can write computer programs. The major test is who else in the organization must use the programs. For example, if the maintenance programs are to be a sub-system of a much larger set of programs used by other elements of the organization, then data processing personnel must write and maintain the programs. If, however, the maintenance programs are to be used only by the maintenace function, anyone could write and maintain the programs. Another factor should be considered from the engineer's point of view. Some companies have moved in the direction of providing "on-line" service to various departments via the telephone lines connected to a keyboard and a CRT. If such were the case for the maintenance example, this could provide both advantages and disadvantages. "On-line" processing is not without its problems. Often there are time delays when the mainframe is busy. As more departments go "on-line", this problem is frequently solved with a larger mainframe. Reprogramming is usually required, with more costs and delays. Another problem is language compatibility. Without trying to sound too critical, most professional programmers tend to "over-program", or provide more than what is necessary, to have a good working system.

Microcomputers

Microcomputers, on the other hand, can perform these types of tasks "on-line" in the department without much of the inconvenience of mainframes. What size system is necessary? Can a 32K or 48K micro really take care of your needs? Data storage should not be a problem. In the last two years, disk drive manufacturers have made major advances in storage capacity. Most disk drive advertisements in computer magazines show, "1.5 MEGA BYTE STORAGE FOR THE TRS-80". One-and-a-half million characters of storage on disk are equivalent to many large mainframe systems nearly five years ago.

This chapter discusses how to write filing type programs in some degree of detail. The format for this chapter is somewhat different than other chapters of this book. Each of the sample programs will be explained line-by-line. New programming words that are used will be explained in detail. More attention to detail is provided for the random filing methods than the sequential filing methods because the random filing system is much more useful and powerful.

Program Name: "RFILE"

The memory required for this program is 2514 bytes.

"RFILE" is a random filing program that is inventory oriented. This program is developed in three modules. The first module permits the user to place part number information in a file. The second module permits the user to read a specific file or bring it to the CRT for viewing. The third module permits the user to print out the file and calculate the usage value (usage times cost) of each part number and the entire inventory. The part number series begins with 81200. When BASIC is booted from DOS, the computer asks "HOW MANY FILES?" If the user presses ENTER, the computer sets aside buffer storage for three files by default. If the user

```
1 REM PROGRAM NAME RFILE
2 REM BASIC AND THE MANUFACTURING ENGINEER
3 REM WRITTEN BY J.E.NICKS
4 REM COPYRIGHT 1981
10 CLEAR500:CLS
20 OPEN"R",1,"PART"
30 FIELD1, 10 AS A$(1),10 AS B$(1),10 AS C$(1),8 AS D$(1),2 AS E$(1)
40 FIELD1, 63 AS DU$,10 AS A$(2),10 AS B$(2),10 AS C$(2),8 AS D$(2),2 AS E$(2)
50 FIELD1,126 AS DU$,10 AS A$(3),10 AS B$(3),10 AS C$(3),8 AS D$(3),2 AS E$(3)
60 FIELD1,189 AS DU$,10 AS A$(4),10 AS B$(4),10 AS C$(4),8 AS D$(4),2 AS E$(4)
70 REM OPTIONS
80 PRINT"USER OPTIONS ARE"
90 PRINT"TYPE 1 TO WRITE TO THE FILE"
100 PRINT"TYPE 2 TO READ FROM THE FILE"
110 PRINT"TYPE 3 TO PRINT OUT THE FILE"
120 PRINT"TYPE 4 TO EXIT"
125 INPUT"WHICH ONE DO YOU WISH";X
130 ONXGOTO140,260,370,999
140 INPUT"ENTER THE PART NUMBER";A1
141 PRINT"LENGTH OF FILE";LOF(1)
145 A2=A1-82100
150 R=1+INT((A2-1)/4):P=A2-4*INT((A2-1)/4)
151 PRINT"RECORD NO";R;"POSITION";P
160 GET1,R
170 INPUT"ENTER THE PART NAME";B$
180 INPUT"ENTER THE ANNUAL USAGE";C
190 INPUT"ENTER THE PART COST";D
200 INPUT"ENTER THE CLASS OF PART I.E. A , B , C , X";E$
210 LSETB$(P)=B$:LSETC$(P)=MKI$(C):LSETD$(P)=MKS$(D)
220 LSETE$(P)=E$
230 PUT1,R
240 INPUT"FOR ANOTHER RECORD TYPE 1 OR 2 TO EXIT";X
250 ONXGOTO140,255
255 CLOSE:END
260 REM READ FROM THE FILE
265 PRINT"LENGTH OF FILE";LOF(1)
270 INPUT"TYPE IN THE PART NUMBER";A1
280 A2=A1-82100
290 R=1+INT((A2-1)/4):P=A2-4*INT((A2-1)/4)
295 PRINT"RECORD NUMBER";R;"POSITION";P
300 GET1,R
310 PRINT"PART NUMBER";A1
320 PRINT"PART NAME","USAGE","COST","CLASS"
325 PRINT
330 PRINTB$(P),CVI(C$(P)),CVS(D$(P)),E$(P)
340 PRINT"FOR ANOTHER ENTRY TYPE 1 OR 2 TO EXIT"
350 INPUTX
360 ONXGOTO260,999
370 LPRINT"PART NUMBER RECORD FILE"
380 LPRINTCHR$(138)
390 LPRINT"PART NO.","NAME","USAGE","COST","CLASS"
400 LPRINTCHR$(138)
410 A1=82100
420 REM PRINT OUT THE FILE
430 FORR=1TOLOF(1)
440 FORP=1TO4
```

Printout 9-1

```
445 A1=A1+1
455 PRINTR,P
460 GET1,R
470 LPRINTA1,B$(P),CVI(C$(P)),CVS(D$(P)),E$(P)
475 B=CVI(C$(P))*CVS(D$(P))
476 LPRINT"TOTAL USAGE VALUE FOR THIS PART IS $";B
477 C=C+B
478 LPRINTCHR$(138)
480 NEXTP
490 NEXTR
500 LPRINTCHR$(138)
510 LPRINT"TOTAL INVENTORY VALUE IS $";C
999 CLOSE
1000 END
```

PART NUMBER RECORD FILE

PART NO.	NAME	USAGE	COST	CLASS
82101	CASTING	1000	10.3	A

TOTAL USAGE VALUE FOR THIS PART IS $ 10300

PART NO.	NAME	USAGE	COST	CLASS
82102	MACH CAST	1000	12.23	A

TOTAL USAGE VALUE FOR THIS PART IS $ 12230

82103	GEAR	250	5.87	B

TOTAL USAGE VALUE FOR THIS PART IS $ 1467.5

82104	SHAFT	100	1.12	C

TOTAL USAGE VALUE FOR THIS PART IS $ 112

82105	SHAFT2	700	3.12	B

TOTAL USAGE VALUE FOR THIS PART IS $ 2184

82106	HOUSING	1000	5.67	B

TOTAL USAGE VALUE FOR THIS PART IS $ 5670

82107		0	0	

TOTAL USAGE VALUE FOR THIS PART IS $ 0

82108	NOSE	1000	1.26	B

TOTAL USAGE VALUE FOR THIS PART IS $ 1260

82109		0	0	

TOTAL USAGE VALUE FOR THIS PART IS $ 0

82110	PIN	1000	.12	X

TOTAL USAGE VALUE FOR THIS PART IS $ 120

82111		0	0	

TOTAL USAGE VALUE FOR THIS PART IS $ 0

82112		0	0	

TOTAL USAGE VALUE FOR THIS PART IS $ 0

TOTAL INVENTORY VALUE IS $ 33343.5

Note: Space has been reserved for Part No. 82107. Data for this part no. has not been entered yet.

Printout 9-1 continued

wishes to work with more than three files, the user must answer with a number, such as 5 or 6. The maximum number of buffers or open files the user can assign is 15. A buffer is a holding area for the data of a file. The buffer is assigned to hold a file length of information until it is told to do something with the information. Therefore, the buffer acts as a temporary storage area. Buffers are used for both sequential and random filing. *Figure 9-1* will help you understand how the buffer works.

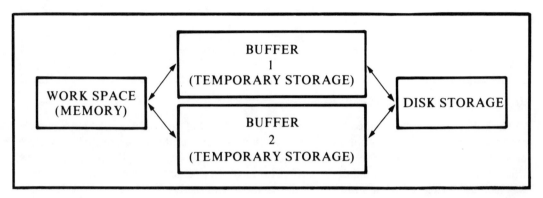

Figure 9-1. *This figure illustrates the relationship of the buffer to the computer and disk storage. The arrows indicate that data can travel in both directions.*

Line 20   OPEN "R",1,"PART"

Line 20 opens the file for random "R" input or output and keeps buffer number 1 clear for the contents of the file. The file name is "PART" and the program name is "RFILE."

Line 30   FIELD 1, 10 AS A$(1), 10 AS B$(1), 10 AS C$(1), 8 AS D$(1), 2 AS E$(1)

Each buffer length is 256 bytes. Fielding the buffer can be accomplished any number of ways. In this program, the data to be stored on disk file looks like this:

PART NUMER = 82100 = 8 BYTES = A$ = 10 BYTES FIELDED
PART NAME = CASTING = 7 BYTES = B$ = 10 BYTES FIELDED
ANNUAL USAGE = 100000 = 6 BYTES = C$ = 10 BYTES FIELDED
PART COST = 23.50 = 5 BYTES = D$ = 8 BYTES FIELDED
CLASS = A = 1 BYTE = E$ = 2 BYTES FIELDED

Only 40 bytes are used in this example out of the possible 256 available in buffer 1. Therefore more than one part number file can reside in the buffer. In this case, four blocks of part number data can easily reside in the buffer, as shown in *Figure 9-2*.

DATA FOR 81201	DATA FOR 81202	DATA FOR 81203	DATA FOR 81204
256 BYTES			

Figure 9-2. *This illustration shows that at least four sets of part number data can reside in the buffer if fielded properly.*

Some type of code is necessary to find the area of the buffer that holds specific part number information. This will be explained later. The reader should note that more information can be stored in the file in the unused section of the buffer, if desired. This is shown in *Figure 9-3*.

Buffer = 256/4. Part number = 64.

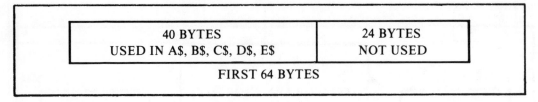

Figure 9-3. *The first one-fourth of the buffer.*

The buffer could be "re-fielded" later to use the unused part of the buffer, i.e., 24 bytes, which might be called F$. The subscript, B$(1), denotes that the part number data is stored in the first of four parts of the buffer. For example, in lines 40, 50 and 60, B$(2), B$(3), and B$(4) define where the next B$ data is stored in the buffer. Lines 40, 50 and 60 field the buffer in the same way as line 30, except for the subscript as noted above and the DU$. The DU$, or DUMMY STRING (which is not printed out), is used to direct the computer over the first block of data stored in the first one-fourth of the buffer to the second one-fourth of the buffer. This is illustrated in *Figure 9-4*.

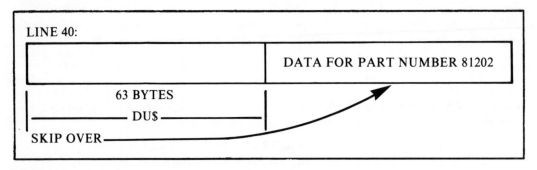

Figure 9-4. *The dummy string is used to direct the computer to skip over blocks of data.*

If the buffer contains six blocks of data, six fielding statements would be necessary. If the buffer contains a single block of data, the fielding would be: FIELD 1, 256 OR A$. Subscripting is necessary only if the buffer is divided into sections or blocks. Further, it should be noted that buffer 2 or 3 can also be fielded to hold the same data.

Line 141   PRINT "LENGTH OF FILE"; LOF(1)

This line permits the user to see how many files have been created. For example, if the computer prints out FOUR, this means there are four buffer lengths of files and each file contains four part number data sets, or in this case, 16 sets of data. The 5¼" floppy diskette is formatted into 35 tracks. Each track has 10 sectors and each sector contains 256 bytes of storage. Storage available for the user on a TRSDOS diskette is 58,880 bytes, or 23 of the 35 tracks. The other 12 tracks on a TRSDOS diskette contain utility programs and BASIC.

In the "RFILE" program example, if each buffer contains four sets of data per each 256 byte sector, and if there are 10 sectors per track (40 part numbers per track), and if there are 23 tracks that can be used (40 x 23 = 920), a total of 920 different sets of part number data can be stored on one 5¼″ diskette.

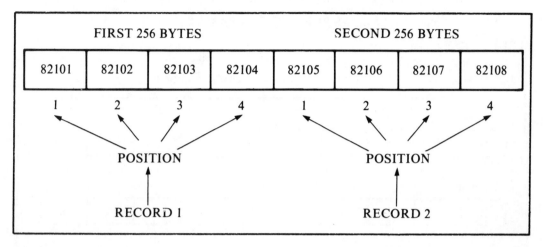

Figure 9-5. This figure shows how the data on file must be accessed by record number then by position number.

The term, "random filing", is somewhat misleading unless you understand exactly what it means. Data is not stored on disk by part numbers, such as 82101 or 82110 randomly. Data is stored on disk in blocks of 256 bytes and must be accessed by record number and position number in the buffer. This means that some code must be devised to convert the part number into information that the computer can understand. *Figure 9-5* will help you understand this point.

Data is stored on diskette in sequential form but can be accessed randomly. When the user types in PART NUMBER 82107, the computer must convert the number to record 2, position 3. The coding system that performs this conversion is:

        Line 145   A2 = A1 - 82100
        Line 150   R=1+INT ((A2-1)/4):P=A2-4*INT ((A2-1)/4)

Where:
        R = Record Number
        P = Position

If the user entered 82107 in answer to the computer's question in line 140, then:

        Line 140   INPUT "ENTER THE PART NUMBER";A1=82107 ENTER
        Line 145   A2 = 82107 - 82100 = 7
        Line 150   R = 1 + INT ((7-1)/4) = 2
        Line 151   P = 7 - 4 * INT ((7-1)/4) = 3

The data for part number 82107 resides in record number 2 at position 3. Line 151 prints this out for the user to see.

        Line 160   GET 1, R

The computer "gets" record number 2 and "brings" it into buffer number 1. All four sets of data in record number 2 are retrieved, i.e., 82105 through 82108. Now that the buffer is available for record number 2, lines 170 to 200, the data to be placed in the file is inputted. Note that STRINGS are used for alpha data and regular variables are used for numeric data.

Line 210   LSET B$(P)=B$:LSET C$(P)=MKI$(C):LSETD$(P)=MKS$(D)

LSET or RSET places data into the buffer and sets it (L = left justification or R = right justification). For example, earlier we "fielded" B$ = 10. If B$ is the part name, GEAR, in the buffer, LSET and RSET would be positioned as shown in *Figure 9-6*.

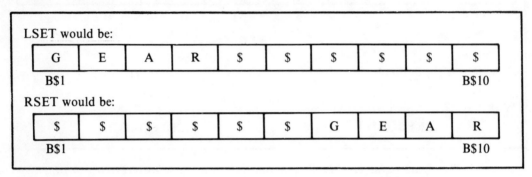

Figure 9-6. *This figure shows left and right justification. The S is a blank space.*

B$(P) places B$ (GEAR) into the third position of records 2, i.e., part number 82107. Space in the file was reserved for A$, the part number A1, and is not used. This means the first 10 spaces of each record are unused but nonetheless available, as shown in *Figure 9-7*.

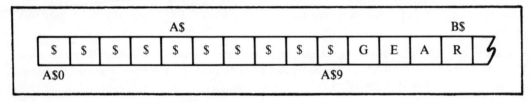

Figure 9-7. *The part number is not part of the file however this space could be used later as shown in this figure.*

All data in a file must be stored as STRINGS. The three functions available for the conversion from numeric data to STRING data are:

MKD$ = returns an eight-byte STRING.
MKI$ = returns a two-byte STRING.
MKS$ = returns a four-byte STRING.

Data that is already STRING data does not need to be converted.

Line 230   PUT 1,R

This line places the data in the buffer on disk file.

Line 255   CLOSE: END

It is very important to "close" the file before exiting the program. If this is not accomplished, file data could be lost. Lines 260 through 350 comprise the section of the program where the user "gets" data from the file. The same routine is used to convert the part number to record and position numbers.

Line 300   GET 1,R

This line of program "gets" the record.

Line 330   PRINT B$(P), CVI(C$(P)), CVS(D$(P)), E$(P)

This line converts the stored STRING data back to numeric data. The CVI and CVS functions are the inverse of MKI and MKS functions. *Table 9-1* illustrates this point.

Table 9-1
Relationship of CVI and CVS to MKI and MKS

Convert to STRING	Convert back to numbers
MKD$ = eight bytes	= CVD
MKI$ = two bytes	= CVI
MKI$ = four bytes	= CVS

The last section of the program is used to print out the entire file and calculate the usage value. This can be done in a nested FOR-NEXT loop using R for record and P for position.

Line 430   FOR R = 1 TO LOF(1)
Line 440   FOR P = 1 TO 4

The user may not know how many records there are, therefore, the LOF(1), LENGTH OF FILE (1), is a number the computer understands and is used in the FOR-NEXT loop. Because we have used four sub-records or positions in the FIELD statements, the P loop is 1 to 4.

Note that in Line 475 we can perform math functions while the data is stored in memory and before the computer starts its second round through the loop. B in line 475 is usage value.

Line 475   B = CVI(C$(P))*CVS(D$(P))

Summary

For those who are accustomed to writing programs that perform number crunching, the filing routines may seem awkward at first. But the engineer who has some experience in BASIC programming should be encouraged to try several filing routines. As stated earlier in this chapter, over 900 sets of part number data can be stored in files on a single disk. This represents a valuable tool that has numerous applications. The program is not that long, just different. A sample printout is shown as Printout 9-2.

Program Name: "SFILE"

The memory required for "SFILE" is 3303 bytes.

"SFILE" is a sequential filing mailing address program that requires 3303 bytes of computer memory. This program is actually three programs in one. The three programs, or files, each do something different and when combined into one program provide an easy way for the user to accomplish the following:

1. Create a file.
2. Update that file.
3. Merge these files into a third file in alphabetical order.

The utility of this program is readily apparent. As stated before, the filing methods used by most microcomputers are awkward to work with until you have had some programming experience. For that reason, a detailed description of the program itself is necessary. First, stated in more detail, the general idea of the program is shown below in steps.

1. The original mailing list in alphabetical order is typed in and stored on disk as File 1.
2. An update to the mailing list is typed in alphabetically and stored on disk as File 2.
3. A sorting routine is provided where the first record of each file is loaded and tested by the lowest order of the alphabet and placed on disk under File 3.
4. This process continues until both files are merged.
5. Files 1 and 2 are killed, or erased from disk.
6. File 3 is renamed File 1.
7. The process can then start over again.

The general idea of sequential filing is to place data on disk file in sequential order and then read the data from disk in the order in which it was placed on disk. Sequential filing and random filing differ in that a record number and position number of the invidual record is not necessary because data is read to or from disk in sequential order. Also, the mode "O" for output to disk or "I" input from disk must be declared as part of a program line. The reason for this is that the computer's data buss is a bi-directional data buss and the computer must be told which direction data is moving—in or out.

```
1 REM PROGRAM NAME SFILE
2 REM WRITTEN BY J.E.NICKS
3 REM BASIC FOR THE MANUFACTURING ENGINEER
4 REM COPY RIGHT 1981
5 Z$=CHR$(13):CLS
10 PRINT"THIS PROGRAM IS A MAILING LIST PROGRAM"
20 PRINT"MADE UP OF 3 SECTIONS. SECTION 1 CREATES THE ORIGINAL FILE"
30 PRINT"SECTION 2 UP DATES THE FILE AND SECTION 3 MERGES FILES"
40 PRINT"1 AND 2 INTO A NEW FILE , CALLED FILE 3."
50 PRINT"AFTER THE FILE HAS BEEN UP DATED AND MERGED INTO FILE 3"
60 PRINT"FILES 1 AND 2 ARE KILLED. AFTER THIS IS DONE ENTER DOS AND"
70 PRINT"RENAME FILE 3 TO FILE 1"
90 CLEAR1000
100 INPUT"PRESS ENTER TO CONTINUE";X:ONXGOTO110
110 CLS:PRINT"OPTIONS"
120 PRINT"TYPE 1 TO CREATE THE FILE"
130 PRINT"TYPE 2 TO UP DATE THE FILE"
140 PRINT"TYPE 3 TO MERGE FILES 1 AND 2"
150 PRINT"TYPE 4 TO PRINT OUT FILE 1 ON THE CRT"
160 PRINT"TYPE 5 TO PRINT OUT FILE 2 ON THE CRT"
170 PRINT"TYPE 6 TO PRINT OUT FILE 3 , HARD COPY"
180 PRINT"TYPE 7 TO KILL FILES 1 AND 2"
190 PRINT"TYPE 8 TO EXIT"
195 PRINT"TYPE 9 TO KILL FILE 3"
200 INPUTX
210 ONXGOTO220,400,600,1050,1130,1270,1400,1410,1420
220 OPEN"O",1,"FILE1":CLS
230 PRINT"SECTION 1 CREATE A MAILING LIST FILE"
240 PRINT"DATA MUST NOT HAVE ANY COMMAS"
250 PRINT"ENTERIES MUST BE IN ALPHABETICAL ORDER"
260 PRINT"ENTER LAST NAME FIRST"
270 PRINT"TO TERMINATE ENTERIES TYPE &"
280 INPUT"TYPE IN FULL NAME , LAST NAME FIRST";A$
290 IFA$="&"THEN350
300 INPUT"TYPE IN THE ADDRESS";A1$
310 INPUT"TYPE IN THE CITY , STATE , AND ZIP CODE";A2$
320 INPUT"TYPE IN THE PHONE NUMBER";A3$
325 Z$=CHR$(13)
330 PRINT#1,A$;Z$;A1$;Z$;A2$;Z$;A3$
335 PRINT
340 GOTO270
350 CLOSE1
360 GOTO110
```

Printout 9-2

```
400 OPEN"O",2,"FILE2":CLS
410 PRINT"SECTION 2 , UP DATING THE FILE"
420 PRINT"DATA MUST NOT HAVE ANY COMMAS"
430 PRINT"ENTERIES MUST BE IN ALPHABETICAL ORDER"
440 PRINT"LAST NAME FIRST"
450 PRINT"TO TERMINATE ENTERIES TYPE &"
460 INPUT"TYPE IN THE FULL NAME";B$
470 IFB$="&"THEN530
480 INPUT"TYPE IN THE ADDRESS";B1$
490 INPUT"TYPE IN THE CITY , STATE , AND ZIP CODE";B2$
500 INPUT"TYPE IN THE PHONE NUMBER";B3$
505 Z$=CHR$(13)
510 PRINT#2,B$;Z$;B1$;Z$;B2$;Z$;B3$
515 PRINT
520 GOTO450
530 CLOSE2
540 GOTO110
600 CLS:OPEN"I",1,"FILE1"
610 OPEN"I",2,"FILE2"
620 OPEN"O",3,"FILE3"
630 INPUT#1,A$,A1$,A2$,A3$:INPUT#2,B$,B1$,B2$,B3$:GOTO660
640 INPUT#1,A$,A1$,A2$,A3$:GOTO660
650 INPUT#2,B$,B1$,B2$,B3$
660 IFEOF(1)ANDEOF(2)THEN710
670 IFEOF(1)THEN800
680 IFEOF(2)THEN900
690 GOTO1000
700 Z$=CHR$(13)
710 IFA$>B$THEN730ELSEPRINT#3,A$;Z$;A1$;Z$;A2$;Z$;A3$:PRINT
720 PRINT#3,B$;Z$;B1$;Z$;B2$;Z$;B3$:PRINT:CLOSE:GOTO110
730 PRINT#3,B$;Z$;B1$;Z$;B2$;Z$;B3$:PRINT
740 PRINT#3,A$;Z$;A1$;Z$;A2$;Z$;A3$:PRINT:CLOSE:GOTO110
800 IFA$>B$THEN820ELSEPRINT#3,A$;Z$;A1$;Z$;A2$;Z$;A2$:PRINT
810 PRINT#3,B$;Z$;B1$;Z$;B2$;Z$;B3$:PRINT:GOTO840
820 PRINT#3,B$;Z$;B1$;Z$;B2$;Z$;B3$:PRINT
830 GOTO650
840 INPUT#2,B$,B1$,B2$,B3$
850 PRINT#3,B$;Z$;B1$;Z$;B2$;Z$;B3$:PRINT
860 IFEOF(2)THEN870ELSE840
870 CLOSE
880 GOTO110
900 IFA$>B$THEN920ELSEPRINT#3,A$;Z$;A1$;Z$;A2$;Z$;A3$:PRINT
910 GOTO640
920 PRINT#3,B$;Z$;B1$;Z$;B2$;Z$;B3$:PRINT
930 PRINT#3,A$;Z$;A1$;Z$;A2$;Z$;A3$:PRINT
940 INPUT#1,A$,A1$,A2$,A3$
950 PRINT#3,A$;Z$;A1$;Z$;A2$;Z$;A3$:PRINT
960 IFEOF(1)THEN970ELSE940
970 CLOSE
980 GOTO110
1000 Z$=CHR$(13):IFA$>B$THEN1010ELSEPRINT#3,A$;Z$;A1$;Z$;A2$;Z$;A3$:PRINT:GOTO64
0
1010 PRINT#3,B$;Z$;B1$;Z$;B2$;Z$;B3$:PRINT:GOTO650
1050 OPEN"I",1,"FILE1":CLS
1060 INPUT#1,A$,A1$,A2$,A3$
1070 PRINTA$:PRINTA1$:PRINTA2$:PRINTA3$
1080 INPUT"PRESS ENTER TO CONTINUE";X
1090 ONXGOTO1100
1100 IFEOF(1)THEN1110ELSE1060
1110 PRINT:PRINT:PRINT"END OF FILE"
1120 CLOSE1:END
1130 OPEN"I",2,"FILE2":CLS
1140 INPUT#2,B$,B1$,B2$,B3$
1150 PRINTB$:PRINTB1$:PRINTB2$:PRINTB3$
1160 INPUT"PRESS ENTER TO CONTINUE";X
1170 ONXGOTO1180
```

Printout 9-2 continued

```
1180  IFEOF(2)THEN1190ELSE1140
1190  PRINT:PRINT:PRINT"END OF FILE"
1200  CLOSE2:END
1270  OPEN"I",3,"FILE3":CLS
1280  INPUT#3,A$,A1$,A2$,A3$
1290  PRINTA$,A1$,A2$,A3$
1330  IFEOF(3)THEN1340ELSE1280
1340  PRINT"END OF FILE"
1350  CLOSE3:END
1400  KILL"FILE1":KILL"FILE2":END
1410  CLOSE1:CLOSE2:CLOSE3:END
1420  KILL"FILE3":END
```

Printout 9-2 continued

Lines 10 to 100 provide the user with instructions on using the program. Lines 100 to 195 provide the nine different options in using the program. Lines 200 to 210 are the ON. . .GO statements of unconditional branching that direct the computer to each of the nine options stated above.

Line 220   OPEN "O",1, "FILE 1":CLS

FILE 1 is opened for "O", output to disk, and its contents are temporarily stored on buffer 1. The comments about the use of buffers that were made earlier in this chapter apply.

Line 240   "DATE MUST NOT HAVE ANY COMMAS."

The comma acts as a terminator for data placed on file.

Line 290   IF A$ = "&" THEN 350

This line of program provides a way for the user to terminate entries by typing in lower-case key 6 or &. This section also could be written using a FOR-NEXT loop.

Line 325   Z$ = CHR$(13)

CHR$(13) is ASCII code for carriage return, and Z$ is set equal to CHR$(13) to avoid typing in CHR$(13) which would separate data variables. Other terminators could also be used.

Line 330   PRINT #1, A$;Z$;A1$;Z$;A2$;Z$;A3$

Line 330 takes the data just inputted into computer memory and places it on buffer 1 for later transfer to disk. The Z$ acts as a terminator to keep the data separated.

Line 335   PRINT

This line is required to index the carriage again before starting the next round of inputs.

Line 350   CLOSE 1

This closes buffer 1. Care must be taken to close files before proceeding because data can be lost if a file "drawer" is not closed.

In Lines 400 to 530, the logic and programming is the same as for those just reviewed, except that variable names have been changed from A$ to B$.

Line 600   CLS: OPEN "I",1,"FILE 1"

This opens file 1 for "I", inputs and assigns its contents to buffer 1.

Line 610   OPEN "I",2,"FILE 2"

This completes the same operation for file 2.

Line 620   OPEN "0",3; "FILE 3"

This opens file 3 for output "O" and assigns its contents to buffer 3.

General Comments

Lines 630 to 1010 provide a sorting routine that tests the input from file 1 and file 2 by name (A\$ versus B\$) and then places the contents on file 3 in alphabetical order. Data is stored on disk in ASCII form and STRINGS can be sorted by using math operators.
Example:

A\$ = AAAB and B\$= AAAA

Using the logic, if A\$ is greater than B\$, then do something, else do something else. A\$ and B\$ can be sorted into the proper alphabetical order, i.e., B\$ first, then A\$ next. The programming logic also must include a test check if the end of file (EOF) has been read. If the computer is directed to read past the end of a file where there is no data, an error message will be displayed on the CRT such as "PAST END OF FILE IN LINE NUMBER". The computer then shows "READY" or it has booted itself out of the program where it incurred the error. For these reasons, two sets of logic must be written into the program: the first set to test if A\$ is greater than B\$, and the second set to test the end of file. This sorting problem has many facets. There are six sets of logic steps or tests that must be written into the program. These logic tests are shown in *Figure 9-8*. A study of the logic steps will provide a better understanding of what the computer is doing in this section of the program rather than trying to provide the line-by-line logic.

Lines 1050 to 1120. After File 1 has been established, the user may wish to review what is on the file. This section of the program performs this review. It has five steps.
1. The file is opened for input.
2. A\$, A1\$, A2\$ and A3\$ are inputted and printed on the screen.
3. To prevent the screen from scrolling, the user looks at each entry of the file and then presses ENTER when he wishes to see the next entry.
4. An end of file test is provided.
5. After all data has been viewed, the file is closed and the program ends.

Lines 1130 to 1200. These lines provide the same features for File 2 as shown for File 1.

Lines 1270 to 1350. In their present form, these lines perform the same operations as the sections reviewed earlier. At this point, we should discuss how the address mailing program can be used. By changing several lines in this section, we could print out a hard copy of the mailing list. Another alternative would be to replace the printer paper with mailing labels and print out a sticker-type mailing list. Other possibilities also arise. The mailing list could be sorted into one of seven sub-lists. For example, the mailing list could be sorted using A2\$, which is the city, state and zip code. The zip code could be separated from the STRING by using LEFT\$ (A2\$,5), then tested to provide a zip code sort. Another possibility is to sort by state using the same logic. Still other possibilities are available. A sort could be made for all of the people on the mailing list with a last name that starts with, for example, the letter J.

Line 1400 KILL "FILE1":KILL "FILE 2":END

After the merge of files 1 and 2 into file 3 has been completed, files 1 and 2 are killed. After this has been accomplished, the user should then ENTER DOS and rename file 3 as file 1, which permits the cycle to start over again.

```
                        FILE 1              FILE 2
                        INPUT A$            INPUT B$
                              First logic test
```

If EOF 1 and EOF 2, then test A$ is greater than B$ and print in proper order of File 3 and close File 3. If not, then:

Second logic test

If EOF 1 and not EOF 2, then test A$ is greater than B$ and print in proper order on File 3 and go back to File 2, input the remaining B$'s and print on File 3, then close files.

Third logic test

If EOF 2 and not EOF 1, then test A$ is greater than B$, print in proper order on File 3, go back to File 1 and input the remaining A$'s and print on File 3, then close files.

Fourth logic test

If not EOF 1 or EOF 2, then:

Fifth logic test

If A$ is greater than B$, then print B$ on File 3 and go back to the start and get another B$.

or:

Sixth logic test

If B$ is greater than A$, then print A$ on File 3 and go back to the start and get another A$.

Figure 9-8. *Sorting logic.*

General Comments on Sequential Filing

Writing computer programs using sequential filing is easier than writing programs using random filing techniques. There are several cautions that should be understood. First, the way data is stored on disk must be understood before data can be retrieved and used. Secondly, there are several ASCII codes that can be used for data separation on disk. These codes should be experimented with and understood before any serious programming effort is undertaken.

The filing systems can be used to store large quantities of data. The main advantage of filing systems is the ability to store vast quanitities of information far beyond the computer's memory capacity.

No sample printout is provided for this program because the reader reviewing this chapter would find little value in looking at names, addresses and telephone numbers, unless they happen to be those of Hollywood stars.

Bibliography

Radio Shack Disk Operating System, Disk Basic, TRSDOS & DISK BASIC Reference Manual, Ft. Worth, TX: Radio Shack, A Division of Tandy Corp., 1979.

Optional Lab Assignments

Lab Assignment 9-1R (least difficult)
Write a computer program for a capital equipment budget using the random filing mode that stores data. The file should contain the following:
1. Line item number.
2. Equipment description.
3. Budgeted amount.
4. Status.
   a. Vendor.
   b. Date order was placed.
   c. Expected delivery date.
   d. Comments.
5. Name of engineer in charge.

The program should be able to retrieve any line item number and/or print out the entire budget status.

Lab Assignment 9-2R (moderate)
Write a project control type program for a new product that stores all the bill of materials status on file. The printout should be in "GANTT" chart form. (See Chapter Eight on "GANTT" charting.)

Lab Assignment 9-1S (least difficult)
Write a sequential filing program that stores an equipment inventory on disk. The program should include updating abilities. Typical items included in the inventory should be:
1. Brass tag number.
2. Serial number.
3. Equipment description.
4. Data acquired.
5. Cost.

Lab Assignment 9-2S (moderate)
Using a sequential filing mode, write a computer program for preventative maintenance. The program should include:
1. Brass tag number.
2. Equipment description.
3. Service to be provided.
4. Weekday or day number service is to be completed.

The program should include a sorting feature by day or day number, which, when printed out, is today's work schedule.

CHAPTER 10

Microcomputer Assisted Process Planning

Process planning is one of the most important aspects of the Manufacturing Engineer's duties in industry. Process planning can be accomplished on several different levels. At the lowest level, a process plan is little more than an operation lineup where the process plan results in a shop floor routing displaying the sequence of operations a part must be processed through before its completion. At the other end of the spectrum, a process plan can be very detailed and encompass all the details necessary to set up the machines on which the part is being manufactured. The latter plan is a more complete engineering effort. The very act of process planning is a blend of technical knowledge, skill and engineering imagination and if completed properly, it is a very time-consuming task. The general steps in the development of a process plan that a Manufacturing Engineer must complete are:

1. Study of all blueprint specifications.
2. Establishment of a sequence of operations.
3. Refinement of the general sequence by mentally reviewing the equipment available.
4. Further refinement of the sequence by selecting the machines for each operation.
5. Development of shop floor picture sheets which include the following:
    a. Speeds and feeds and setup information required.
    b. A sequence of events on the machine.
    c. Tooling layouts as required.
    d. Inspection and gaging considerations.
    e. Development of time values.
    f. A pictorial sketch of the cuts required.
6. Development of process dimensions and tolerances for each operation using tolerance charting, if required.
7. Design of the jigs, fixtures, tools, cutting tools and gages necessary.

The approach to process planning is a very logical but nonetheless lengthy process. Throughout this book the following idea has been presented: The engineer should do what he does best and the computer should do what it does best. This chapter will explore how a microcomputer can be used to assist the engineer's effort in the process planning routine.

Before we begin, a general review of the subject of computer assisted process planning is necessary.

Computer Assisted Process Planning

This complex subject can be examined by looking at the two very different directions of computer usage as the technology is now developing. The first is called Group Technology and

227

the second is what the author will call Microcomputer Assisted Process Planning, or MiCAPP.

Group Technology

Group Technology can be defined as an attempt to convert small lot production technology into mass production technology. If this can be achieved, the benefits can be substantial. The general ideas of Group Technology are to classify parts or groupings of machines into logical processes or manufacturing cells for the purposes of:

1. Reduction of setup times.
2. Reduction of inventory.
3. Reduction of queueing.
4. Achievement of automated process planning.
5. Reduction of costs.
6. Reduction of material handling costs.

The activity starts with the classification of piece parts into logical groupings by process, geometry, function and manufacturing characteristics or materials. This classification system concludes with the development of a numbering system which is then computerized. A re-examination of the numbering system results in the establishment of family processing and finally the physical placement of machines into logical manufacturing cells. The manufacturing cells can best be defined as job shop production lines. These production lines are physical in the sense that they depart from the traditional job shop plant layout where all like machines are in one department. The biggest advantage to this type system is that most of the process planning is contained in the number codes which simplifies production flow over groups of machines. Management's dedication to achieving these goals is vast to say the least. There is hardly an element of the organization which is untouched from a standpoint of redoing or reorganizing their efforts. The Manufacturing Engineering effort to achieve these ends is at the center of the activity. Generally, more computer capacity is required.

Automated process planning comes about as a natural extension of the Group Technology effort. As parts are classified by size, shape, etc., the processes required to manufacture these parts also are computerized. If a new part is to be processed, it must follow some sequence of manufacturing that fits into the existing structure of the manufacturing cell. There are both advantages and disadvantages to this idea. First, the time necessary for the computer to recognize what the process should be and to fit the part into an existing manufacturing cell is short. While the computer is making these decisions, it also can check scheduling requirements for that specific cell and determine if the new part fits the existing cell's capacity. To achieve this goal, the engineer's interaction with the computer is modest.

There, is however, one major disadvantage to this idea. The design of the Group Technology system is rigid by necessity. Rigid in the sense that parts processed are made somewhat to conform to a general processing plan to fit the system. This, of course, can be both good and bad. Improvement comes about with change. If change is difficult to achieve, we might well be doing tomorrow what we did yesterday.

Author Viewpoint. The author has had two different experiences in industry using the Group Technology ideas and principles. Without going into a detailed explanation of each of these events, neither of these two experiments concluded with earth-shattering results. As in many activities, the actual practice seldom yields what the theory predicted.

At this point, the reader may observe that the author's view of this endeavor is negative.

Understanding the day-to-day activities necessary to manage a job shop operation, the author observes that while the realization of these goals is worthy, the work necessary to achieve them in a job shop atmosphere is monumental. Yet another aspect of the problem is the never ending change of a job shop manufacturing facility—change in parts being produced, change in more modern equipment, and most importantly of all, change in process development to produce more product in less time. While the theory of Group Technology is difficult to refute without sounding like a reactionary, for most companies the 21st century has not yet arrived. Perhaps some interim steps are required to bridge the gap of "future shock".

Microcomputer Assisted Process Planning

MiCAPP in itself is a definition and provides another direction in the evolution of the totally automated factory. Before we can define in more detail how the microcomputer can be used by the Manufacturing Engineer in the process planning effort, it is necessary to take another look at the process planning effort. Referring to steps three and four stated earlier in the chapter, most of the engineer's time spent in process planning is devoted to creating the detail for each machine operation. An overview of what the engineer does to accomplish this task could be stated as:
1. Thinking
2. Calculating
3. Writing or printing instructions.

These factors also represent the three major elements of process planning on a computer:
1. Thinking—the engineer's job.
2. Calculating—the computer's job.
3. Printing instructions—the printer's job.

Hence, MiCAPP could be redefined as a step toward the automation of the Manufacturing Engineer's effort in process planning without the use of Group Technology. There are advantages and disadvantages to this concept. Among the major advantages: MiCAPP can be accomplished in the Manufacturing Engineering Department without interruption of another department's activity.

In Chapter Two, we posed a question concerning the detail of cost estimating versus the use of this paperwork by the Manufacturing Engineer once an order is received. This question can now be answered. Perhaps we can improve our cost estimating skills by improving the level of detail, if the time required to estimate the cost of a part versus the time to process the part is the same. The overall improvement of accuracy by the elimination of using shortcuts in estimating also should be apparent. Without trying to oversell the concept, we should conclude by saying that the major advantage of MiCAPP is speed. With the use of MiCAPP, the typical process planning effort is reduced by 75%.

To help balance the scale, the disadvantages will be reviewed next. The major disadvantage of MiCAPP is the programming effort required. The Manufacturing Engineer is the only person in industry qualified to write computer programs to assist in the process planning effort. A generous amount of programming skill is usually required; in addition, an intimate knowledge of the specific machine tool is mandatory. Another disadvantage is that this field is still very new and most companies involved in some effort to use the microcomputer are not very anxious to share their experience with the public. Most, if not all, of the work done in this new field could be classified as proprietary effort.

Computer Program for Process Planning

This chapter presents one computer program for process planning on the Warner & Swasey 2 AC Chucker. The Warner & Swasey AC and AB single spindle chucking and bar machines are very popular job shop machines used in industry. Most Manufacturing Engineers, at one time or another, have processed parts on these machines. For this reason, the Warner & Swasey machine was selected as an example for MiCAPP. For those readers who may not be familiar with this machine and its operation, a brief review of its capabilities is in order.

The Automatic Chucker (AC) is a single spindle chucking machine with an end working pentagon, or end slide, which has five tooling faces. The machine also has a front and rear tool slide. The rear tool slide can be used in conjunction with the main pentagon slide to perform recessing, grooving and backfacing operations. The machine has two sets of speeds, each having a high-low range and 36 feeds available, six of which can be used in one setup.

Another reason this machine was selected for a demonstration program is that writing a module which calculates machine speeds and feeds must be reconciled to what is available in the machine itself. This provides the reader with an example of how computer programming can be accomplished to satisfy physical machine constraints. Another programming challenge was the almost endless number of combinations of operations this machine can perform.
The machine is designed to perform drilling, reaming, turning, boring, grooving, facing and forming operations will all three slides simultaneously in motion, each using more than one tool. The machine also is designed to provide other standard features by setting limit switches. For example, at the end of a cut from the pentagon, three options are available:
1. Stop spindle and rapid off.
2. Rapid off while the spindle is in motion.
3. Turn or bore, reverse feed off.
Similar options are provided for the cross slide:
1. Standard cross slide.
2. Late cross slide.
3. Late cross slide—second feed.

From this general description of the AC, it should be obvious that although the machine is a standard machine, it can be tooled in a variety of ways. This machine is typical of many found in industry, and from a programming standpoint, it embraces most of the problems associated with programming.

Steps in Working With the AC Program

Before examining a sample printout from the AC program, here is a review of how the engineer, with the assistance of a microcomputer, performs the process planning task.

The Engineer

Briefly stated, here are the tasks performed by the engineer.
1. Review blueprints and specifications.
2. Use the AC worksheet (see *Figure 10-1*) to accomplish the following:
   a. Record the cuts to be made.
   b. Establish the machining sequence.

WARNER & SWASEY 2AC WORKSHEET

Part Name: Sleeve Oper. 10 1st Chucking
Part No.: 12345
Date: 1-1-81
Material: Mall

DESCRIPTION	DIA. & TOL.	LENGTH & TOL.	1. HSS	2. Carbide	3. Rough	4. Finish	5. Rapid Off	6. Stop Spin.	7. Rev. Feed	8. Std. C.S.	9. Late C.S.	10. Late C.S. 2d FD.	11. Cored Hole	12. Drilled Hole	13. RH THD	14. LH THD
Pentagon Face 1																
Tool 1 Turn A	9.27 ± .005	1.5 ± .005		✓	✓		✓									
2 Face 1	9.27 ± .005	1.44 ± .005		✓												
3																
4																
Pentagon Face 2																
Tool 1 Bore D	7.84 ± .005	1.49 ± .005		✓	✓			✓								
2 Bore H	5.36 ± .005	1.49 ± .005		✓												
3																
4																
Pentagon Face 3																
Tool 1 Slab E	7.5 ± .010	.060 ± .005		✓		✓	✓			✓						
2																
3																
4																
Pentagon Face 4																
Tool 1 Turn B	9 ± .010	.75 ± .010		✓		✓		✓								
2 Cham D	7.84 ± .005	.06 ± .005		✓												
3																
4																
Pentagon Face 5																
Tool 1 Bore D	7.86 ± .002	1.5 ± .005		✓		✓			✓							
2 Form C	8.738 ± .002	.266 ± .002		✓						✓						
3																
4																

OPTIONS

Figure 10-1. This worksheet records an engineer's idea of how the part should be produced in operation 10.

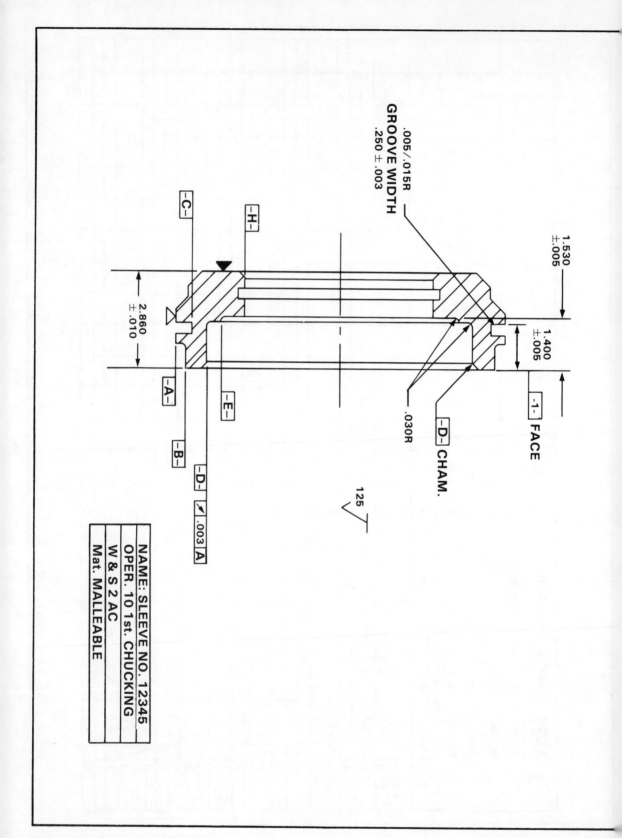

Figure 10-2. *This figure is a 2 A C worksheet for Operation 10. It shows the options selected and the recording of the cuts to be completed.*

232

```
2 A/C PROCESS PLANNING SUMMARY

PART NAME SLEEVE          PART NUMBER  12345          DATE 01/01/81

FIRST CHUCKING  O.D. CHUCK     ENGINEER NICKS

MATERIAL GROUP C

SPEEDS SELECTED
  22   37   44   62   72   104   121   170   203   290   334   568

FEEDS SELECTED
                 FEED          GEAR          FEED          GEAR
FEEDS 1 & 4      2.8E-03        22           .011           38
FEEDS 2 & 5      6E-03          27           .025           33
FEEDS 3 & 6      .015           33           .06            27

OPERATION DESCRIPTION
OPER          DIAMETER              LENGTH              FEED      RPM

TURN & FACE FRT SLIDE, ROUGH CUT, STOP SPINDLE RAPID OFF, ,

 1   1   TURN A    9.27 +- 5E-03        1.5 +- 5E-03        .025      121
 1   2   FACE 1    9.27 +- 5E-03        1.44 +- 5E-03       .025      121
TIME FOR THIS OPERATION IS .502479  +  .11 INDEX

BORING MULTIPLE TOOLS, ROUGH CUT, STOP SPINDLE RAPID OFF, ,

 2   1   BORE D    7.84 +- 5E-03        1.49 +- 5E-03       .025      170
 2   2   BORE H    5.36 +- 5E-03        1.49 +- 5E-03       .025      170
TIME FOR THIS OPERATION IS .355294  +  .11 INDEX

TURN AND SLAB CUT, FINISH CUT, RAPID TURRET FACE OFF, ,

 3   1   SLAB E    7.5 +- .01           .06 +- 5E-03        6E-03     203
TIME FOR THIS OPERATION IS .0656815  +  .11 INDEX

TURNING MULTIPLE TOOLS, FINISH CUT, STOP SPINDLE RAPID OFF, ,

 4   1   TURN B    9 +- .01             .75 +- .01          .015      170
 4   2   CHAM D    7.84 +- 5E-03        .06 +- 5E-03        .015      170
TIME FOR THIS OPERATION IS .301961  +  .11 INDEX

BORE & FACE REAR SLIDE, FINISH CUT, REVERSE FEED OFF, ,

 5   1   BORE D    7.86 +- 2E-03        1.4 +- 5E-03        6E-03     203
 5   2   FORM C    8.738 +- 2E-03       .266 +- 2E-03       6E-03     203
TIME FOR THIS OPERATION IS 2.33169  +  .11 INDEX

TOTAL OPERATION IS 4.10711 PLUS LOAD & UNLOAD EQUALS 4.45711
TOTAL PARTS PER HOUR ARE 13.4616
SET UP ALLOWANCE IS 2.49333 HOURS
```

Printout 10-1

    c. Record diameters and tolerances to be cut.

    d. Record lengths of cut and tolerances.

    e. Determine the options for each cut.

  3. Enter this data into the computer via the keyboard.

The Microcomputer

Briefly stated, these are the tasks performed by the microcomputer.

1. Select surface feet per minute (SFPM), depending on the type cut and material being processed.

2. Calculate the RPM required.
3. Reconcile the RPM calculated to what is available in the machine.
4. Calculate the revolutions required.
5. Calculate cutting times.
6. Calculate total time and production rate.

The Printer

The printer provides hard copy printout suitable for shop floor use which includes:
1. The sequence of events for each pentagon face and cross slide.
2. Records of the operation being performed, diameter and tolerance, length and tolerance.
3. Most of the setup data required for:
    a. Speeds and feeds.
    b. Other setup data described befre, such as, late cross slide, rapid off, or reverse feed, etc.
    c. Change gears for feed and threading.

Items b and c above are information required by the setup man to establish the machine's sequence of operation. This is accomplished by setting a bank of switches for each turret face and setting trip dogs on the machine's rear drum.

Sample Printout for Part No. 12345, Part Name: Sleeve

The blueprint for the sample part, sleeve, was studied to determine the best machining sequence, just as in conventional processing. Once the engineeer formulated his ideas on how the part should be produced, this was recorded on the AC worksheet. (See *Figure 10-1* for operation 10 and *Figure 10-2* for operation 20.) The purpose of the worksheet is to prevent the engineer from overlooking something once interacting with the computer. This entire process took about an hour. The operation 10 printout provides the shop floor with a hard copy of the tooling sequence and cuts to be made for each tool slide used. The reader should note that the AC program records lengths of cuts which are the basis for calculating time values. There will be more about this later.

Figure 10-3 is a picture sheet that would accompany the printout to the shop floor. This picture sheet is unlike a typical picture sheet in that it does not record diameters, lengths and tolerances. This picture sheet references only the surfaces being machined; i.e., turn A, bore B, etc. These liberties with the picture sheet have been taken to further shorten the engineer's time on the drawing board. The reader should also notice that several dimensions appear on the picture sheets. For example, on *Figure 10-3* there is a length dimension of 1400 ±.005 from face 1. To understand this length dimension, refer to pentagon face 5.2 Form C on the planning summary sheet. Note that the diameter for the formed groove is 8.738 ±.002 and the length of the cut is .266 ±.002. When working with the end slide, the length of cut also shows the position of that cut from a locating surface, but working from the front or rear cross slide, some additional reference is necessary. The program provides for a diameter and length of cut for calculation purposes, but in this example a third dimension is required, namely a locating point. The picture sheet contains the least amount of information required to produce the part. With the exception of the gaging requirements, the combination of the computer printout and the picture sheet is all that is necessary. Gaging requirements could be programmed. However, this might best be handled with the picture sheet.

To recap, the engineer spent one hour planning the process, the computer and engineer required 15 minutes to input the requirements and print out the plannings summaries for both

WARNER & SWASEY 2AC WORKSHEET

Part Name: Sleeve Oper.20 2d Chucking
Part No. 12345
Date: 1-1-81
Material: Mall

OPTIONS

DESCRIPTION	DIA. & TOL.	LENGTH & TOL.	1. HSS	2. Carbide	3. Rough	4. Finish	5. Rapid Off	6. Stop Spin.	7. Rev. Feed	8. Std. C.S.	9. Late C.S.	10. Late C.S. 2d FD.	11. Cored Hole	12. Drilled Hole	13. RH THD	14. LH THD
Pentagon Face 1																
Tool 1 Turn A	9.249 ±.002	2.34 ±.010		✓		✓			✓							
2 Turn F	8.75 ±.010	.49 ±.010		✓												
3																
4																
Pentagon Face 2																
Tool 1 Skip																
2																
3																
4																
Pentagon Face 3																
Tool 1 Face 2	8.75 ±.010	1.64 ±.010		✓		✓	✓			✓						
2 Cham H	5.38 ±.005	.060 ±.005		✓												
3																
4																
Pentagon Face 4																
Tool 1 GRV G	5.75 ±.002	8.5 ±.002		✓		✓	✓				✓					
2																
3																
4																
Pentagon Face 5																
Tool 1 Bore H	5.38 ±.002	1.43 ±.005		✓		✓			✓							
2																
3																
4																

Figure 10-3. This figure illustrates a floor picture sheet for Operation 20.

235

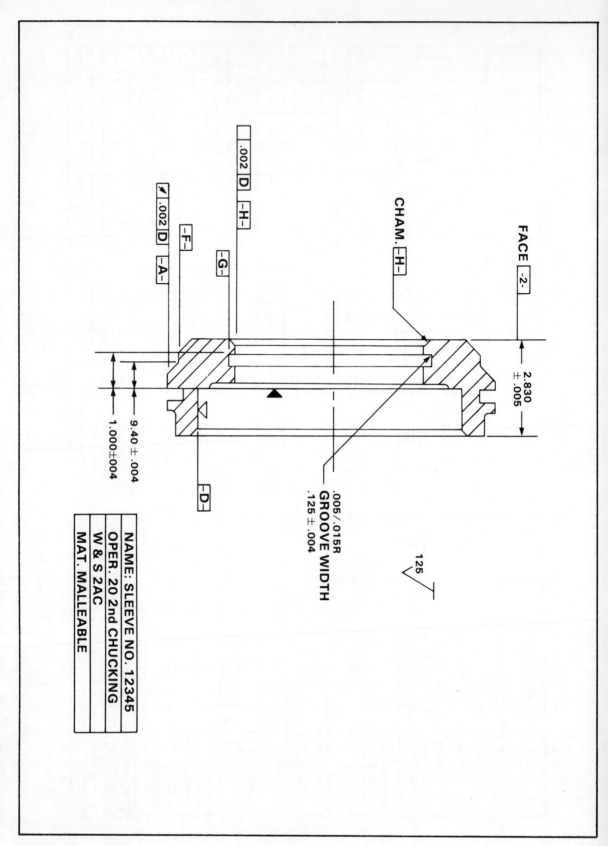

Figure 10-4. *This figure illustrates floor picture sheet for Operation 20.*

236

```
2  A/C  PROCESS  PLANNING  SUMMARY

PART NAME SLEEVE              PART NUMBER  12345          DATE 01/01/81

SECOND CHUCKING I.D. CHUCK    ENGINEER NICKS

MATERIAL GROUP C

SPEEDS SELECTED
 22  37  44  62  72  104  121  170  203  290  334  568

FEEDS SELECTED
                 FEED         GEAR          FEED          GEAR
FEEDS 1 & 4     2.8E-03        22           .011           38
FEEDS 2 & 5     4.4E-03        22           .017           38
FEEDS 3 & 6     .015           33           .06            27

OPERATION DESCRIPTION
OPER            DIAMETER            LENGTH            FEED       RPM

TURNING MULTIPLE TOOLS, FINISH CUT, REVERSE FEED OFF, ,

 1   1   TURN A   9.249 +- 2E-03        2.34 +- .01       .011       170
 1   2   TURN F   8.75 +- .01            .49 +- .01       .011       170
TIME FOR THIS OPERATION IS 2.52406  +  .11 INDEX


SKIP INDEX TIME =.02

TURN & FACE FRT SLIDE, FINISH CUT, STOP SPINDLE RAPID OFF, ,

 3   1   FACE 2   8.75 +- .01           1.64 +- .01       .015       170
 3   2   CHAM H   5.38 +- 5E-03          .06 +- 5E-03     .015       170
TIME FOR THIS OPERATION IS .65098  +  .11 INDEX

RAPID ADVANCE - GROOVE, FINISH CUT, RAPID OFF, CARBIDE, LATE CROSS SLIDE

 4   1   GRV G    5.75 +- 2E-03          .185 +- 2E-03    2.8E-03    170
TIME FOR THIS OPERATION IS .451681  +  .15 INDEX

BORING SINGLE TOOL, FINISH CUT, REVERSE FEED OFF, ,

 5   1   BORE     5.38 +- 2E-03         1.43 +- 5E-03     .011       290
TIME FOR THIS OPERATION IS .909091  +  .11 INDEX

TOTAL OPERATION IS 5.03582 PLUS LOAD & UNLOAD EQUALS 5.38582
TOTAL PARTS PER HOUR ARE 11.1404
SET UP ALLOWANCE IS 2.17667 HOURS
```

Printout 10-2

operations 10 and 20. The engineer then spent another hour drawing the picture sheets. All total, the job is floor ready in two hours and 15 minutes.

Program Name: "AC"

The memory required for "AC" is 18,441 bytes. This is the longest computer program included in this book. Therefore, no effort will be made to provide a line-by-line review. The nature of our review will be to examine the 11 different elements of this program and point out, when necessary for the reader's understanding, how specific things are accomplished in the program. The 11 elements to be reviewed are:

1. Material Selection
2. Select Feeds

3. Select Speeds
4. Inputting General Data
5. First Printout
6. Tooling Each Pentagon Face
7. Cut Selection
8. Universal PRINT Statements
9. Threading
10. Load and Unload Time
11. Setup Time

Material Selection

Warner & Swasey groups 34 different types of materials into six major classifications—Class A through E. The "AC" program accomplishes this also.

> Line 200 INPUT "PRESS ENTER TO SEE THE MATERIAL";X
> Line 210 ONX GOSUB 20000

Viewing the GOSUB routine, the reader will see a similar listing for materials and the user is directed by the computer to type in the number next to the material to be worked with. Notice also that the GOSUB includes all of Warner & Swasey's recommended SFPM for each material selected. There are constants in line 20210 for Group C material, TR=320, TF=420, etc. TR is the variable SFPM for turning rough and TF is the variable SFPM for turning finish. Also note the REM line, 20320, which defines the variable names for turning, boring, drilling, etc.

As pointed out in Chapter Two, selection or calculation of SFPM is a necessary first step in any machining program. When writing a machining program, selection versus calculation depends on what the program is to do and the variability of the machine tool.

Select Feeds

As stated earlier, the AC has 36 feeds, six of which can be used in one setup. The computer begins this selection process in line 220.

> Line 220 INPUT "PRESS ENTER TO SELECT FEEDS";X
> Line 230 GOSUB 10000

In this GOSUB, the CRT screen is cleared and the first set of feeds available is shown. The user is then asked to type in the number next to the feeds selected.

Feeds in the AC are selected by the use of change gears. Refer to either of the Process Planning Summaries to review a typical printout. The printout shows trip dog numbers for feed selection, gears required and the feed itself.

This selection process continues until the engineer has selected all six feeds he wishes to use.

Select Speeds

> Line 240 INPUT "PRESS ENTER TO SELECT MACHINE SPEEDS";X
> Line 250 ONX GOSUB 15000

In this GOSUB, all speeds available in the machine are shown on the CRT screen. The user is asked to select group 1 or group 2 speeds. Once the selection is made, the specific speeds are in the computer's memory for later use.

Inputting General Data

In line 260 through 290, the engineer is coached to input the part number, name, data and so on.

One interesting programming technique used throughout this program to save memory is defined below. The same string variables are used again and again to conserve memory and shorten the printing routines. For example:

> Line 277 INPUT "ENTER 1 FOR OD CHUCK OR 2 FOR ID CHUCK";M1
> Line 278 IF M1=1 THEN B6$="O.D.CHUCK"ELSE B6$+"I.D.CHUCK"

A second example: P$ is used no less than 48 times in this program.

First Printout

At this point, all the data selected or inputted thus far is printed out.

Tooling Each Pentagon Face

> Line 490 FOR Z=1 TO 5

Line 490 starts a FOR-NEXT loop. The 5, of course, is for the five pentagon faces. The loop continues until it reaches line 8530.

The screen scrolls clear and the user sees instructions on how the machine is tooled and then selects the type of cut he wishes to make, as shown below.

> 1. - - - - - TURNING.
> 2. - - - - - BORING.
> 3. - - - - - DRILLING
> 4. - - - - - REAMING.
> 5. - - - - - THREADING.
> 6. - - - - - TREPANNING.
> 7. - - - - - SKIP INDEX.

Cut Selection

If, for example, the user selects TURNING, the computer boots to line 610 where a user further selects which type of turning operation he wishes to use.

> 1. - - - - - TURNING SINGLE TOOL.
> 2. - - - - - TURNING MULTIPLE TOOLS.
> 3. - - - - - TURNING & DRILLING.
> 4. - - - - - TURNING & CORE DRILLING.
> 5. - - - - - TURNING & REAMING.
> 6. - - - - - TURN & BORE.
> 7. - - - - - TURN & SLAB CUT.
> 8. - - - - - TURN & FACE FROM THE CROSS SLIDE.
> 9. - - - - - TURN & FORM FROM THE CROSS SLIDE.
> 9. - - - - - TURN - FACE AND FORM.
> 9. - - - - - TURN - BORE - FACE & FORM.

This program permits 48 different types of standard operations to be used. Each operation, except for single tool operations, uses another FOR-NEXT loop to input the number of tools for that station. The number of combinations of cuts this program will accept is endless. Incidentally, in an effort to determine the exact number of combinations, the author wrote a computer program. But alas, the computer defaulted at 33 factorial—far short of the mark. Thirty-three factorial has 39 zeros in the answer. Everything has its limits!

After selecting multiple tool turning, the computer is directed to line 920. Every effort has been made in writing this program to have the user do as little typing as possible. Most engineers are proficient on a calculator keypad, but not a typewriter or keyboard.

Other selections such as "stop spindle", "reverse feed", or "rapid off" are made by pressing one numbered key. Once all diameters and cut lengths are inputted, the computer calculates the RPM necessary for the operation. After this has been accomplished, the computer is directed to line 9000 which is also a GOSUB routine. Lines 9000 through 9120 comprise a sorting subroutine that takes the calculated RPM and finds the nearest RPM that the user has selected and uses the closest RPM for calculations. Once the station is tooled, the computer boots to line 8500.

Universal PRINT Statements

Lines 8500 to 8525 should be studied very carefully because they are LPRINT lines for the entire program. As mentioned earlier, the same use of strings permits this. P$ (P STRING), whether "turning" or "reaming" is P$. Also not that line 8525 sets the string back to μ again before encountering line 8530, NEXT Z.

Threading

Although threading was not used in the sample printout, the program does accept the following:
1. Threading - solid tap.
2. Threading - internal, collapsible
3. Threading - external, die head.
Threading is accomplished in lines 4500 through 4970. Threading change gears is also part of the computer's memory and therefore it is printed out when threading is selected.

Load and Unload Time

Once the part has been tooled, the user selects load and unload time by estimating the part weight.

The last step in the process is a review, on the screen, of typical types of setup conditions, where the user enters the number of times used or zero if not used. See lines 8720 through 8900.

General Comments

The "AC" program is an important programming example from several viewpoints. First of all, as stated earlier, this program was written for a Warner & Swasey 2 AC. There are other AC's and AB's in the Warner & Swasey family. For example, there is an 0 AC, 1 AC, 3 AC and 4 AC, and a like number of AB machines. Changing only the speeds and feeds data, this program is valid for any of the AC machines. The same idea is true for the AB machines, however, several other changes must be made because these machines are bar machines.

This observation leads us to the next point. Even though this is a long program, it is typical of what one would expect to find in industry. Families of machines can be umbrellaed under one program. Most of the work involved in writing this type of program is in understanding the peculiarities of a specific machine tool and trying to find a universal approach to programming so that the programming effort can be utilized for other machine tools in or out of the family.

These are important statements and should be considered before launching off in a direction that must be reversed later.

For those who are wondering how long it took to write this program, the answer is 44 man-hours. This may seem like a long time for the resulting effort but this program, if written in industry, would pay for itself after the first 25 to 30 jobs processed using the program. The engineer's time- savings, on the average, is about one-and-one quarter hours per job.

In addition, for an engineer to write such a program he must be intimately familiar with the machine he is working with. Many times in industry, this is not the case. To gain the familiarity necessary is a definite plus to the organization.

```
1 REM PROGRAM NAME A/C
2 REM WRITTEN BY J.E.NICKS
3 REM COMPUTER APPLICATIONS FOR THE MANUFACTURING ENGINEER
4 REM COPYRIGHT 1981 ALL RIGHTS RESERVED
10 DIMG(12),F(12),R(12),S(12),S1(12)
20 CLS:PRINT"THIS PROGRAM IS DESIGNED TO ASSIST THE ENG. IN PROCESS PLANNING"
30 PRINT"ON THE WARNER & SWASEY 2 A/C CHUCKER"
40 PRINT"THE PROGRAM WILL COACH THE ENGINEER THROUGH EACH STEP."
50 PRINT"FIRST, MATERIAL IS SELECTED FROM THE MATERIAL LIST."
60 PRINT"NEXT, SPEEDS AND FEEDS ARE SELECTED."
70 PRINT"THEN THE ENGINEER STARTS THE PROCESS PLANNING ROUTINE."
80 PRINT"THIS PROGRAM USES THE APPROACH OF THE A/C BEING TOOLED AS SHOWN BELOW:"
:PRINT
90 PRINT"PENTAGON FACES 1 , 2 & 3 ARE TOOLED FOR:"
100 PRINT"TURNING , BORING , DRILLING , REAMING AND THREADING"
110 PRINT"PENTAGON FACE 4 IS TOOLED FOR LATE CROSS SLIDE OPERATIONS."
120 PRINT"PENTAGON FACE 5 IS TOOLED WITH AN ADJUSTABLE BORING HEAD"
130 PRINT:PRINT
200 INPUT"PRESS ENTER TO SEE THE MATERIAL LIST";X
210 GOSUB20000
220 CLS:INPUT"PRESS ENTER TO SELECT FEEDS";X
230 GOSUB10000
240 CLS:INPUT"PRESS ENTER TO SELECT MACHINE SPEEDS";X
250 GOSUB15000
260 CLS:INPUT"ENTER THE DATE I.E. 01/01/81";B$
270 INPUT"ENTER THE PART NAME";B1$
275 INPUT"ENTER 1 FOR 1ST CHUCKING OR 2 FOR 2ND CHUCKING";M
276 IFM=1THENB5$="FIRST CHUCKING"ELSEB5$="SECOND CHUCKING"
277 INPUT"ENTER 1 FOR OD CHUCK OR 2 FOR ID CHUCK";M1
278 IFM1=1THENB6$="O.D. CHUCK"ELSEB6$="I.D. CHUCK"
280 INPUT"ENTER THE PART NUMBER";B1
290 INPUT"ENTER THE ENGINEER'S NAME";B2$
300 LPRINTCHR$(27);CHR$(14);"2 A/C PROCESS PLANNING SUMMARY"
310 LPRINTCHR$(138):LPRINT"PART NAME ";B1$,,"PART NUMBER ";B1,"DATE ";B$
320 LPRINTCHR$(138):LPRINTB5$,B6$,"ENGINEER ";B2$
330 LPRINTCHR$(138):LPRINT"MATERIAL ";A$
340 LPRINTCHR$(138):LPRINT"SPEEDS SELECTED"
350 FORI=1TO12:LPRINTS(I);:NEXTI
360 LPRINTCHR$(138):LPRINT"FEEDS SELECTED"
370 LPRINT,"FEED","GEAR","FEED","GEAR"
380 LPRINT"FEEDS 1 & 4",F1,G1,F4,G4
390 LPRINT"FEEDS 2 & 5",F2,G2,F5,G5
400 LPRINT"FEEDS 3 & 6",F3,G3,F6,G6
410 LPRINTCHR$(138):LPRINT"OPERATION DESCRIPTION"
420 LPRINT"OPER","DIAMETER";TAB(40);"LENGTH";TAB(60);"FEED";TAB(70);"RPM":LPRINT
CHR$(138)
490 FORZ=1TO5
500 CLS:PRINT"PENTAGON FACES 1, 2 & 3 , MULTIPLE TURNING HEAD"
501 PRINT"PENTAGON FACE 4 LATE CROSS SLIDE OPERATIONS"
502 PRINT"PENTAGON FACE 5 ADJUSTABLE BORING HEAD"
503 PRINT"YOU ARE NOW TOOLING PENTAGON FACE ";Z
```

Printout 10-3

```
510 PRINT"ENTER THE TYPE OPERATION YOU WISH TO WORK WITH"
520 PRINT"1-----TURNING"
530 PRINT"2-----BORING"
540 PRINT"3-----DRILLING"
550 PRINT"4-----REAMING"
560 PRINT"5-----THREADING"
570 PRINT"6-----TREPANNING"
580 PRINT"7-----SKIP INDEX"
590 INPUTX
600 ONXGOTO610,2000,3000,4000,4500,5000,5010
610 CLS:PRINT"TURNING OPERATIONS"
620 PRINT"ENTER THE TYPE TURNING OPERATION"
630 PRINT"1-----TURNING SINGLE TOOL"
640 PRINT"2-----TURNING MULTIPLE TOOLS"
650 PRINT"3-----TURNING AND DRILLING"
670 PRINT"4-----TURNING AND CORE DRILLING"
680 PRINT"5-----TURN AND REAM"
690 PRINT"6-----TURN AND BORE"
700 PRINT"7-----TURN AND SLAB CUT"
710 PRINT"8-----TURN AND FACE FROM THE CROSS SLIDE"
720 PRINT"9----TURN AND FORM FROM THE CROSS SLIDE"
740 PRINT"9----TURN , FACE AND FORM"
750 INPUT"9----TURN , BORE , FACE AND FORM FROM THE CROSS SLIDE";X:CLS
760 ONXGOTO800,920,1080,1110,1140,1150,1160,1170,1280
800 CLS:P$="TURNING SINGLE TOOL":P3$="TURN"
810 INPUT"ENTER THE DIA. & TOLERANCE,SEPARATE BY A COMMA";D,D1
820 INPUT"ENTER THE LENGTH & TOLERANCE,SEPARATE BY A COMMA";L,L1
830 INPUT"ENTER 1 FOR ROUGH CUT OR 2 FOR FINISH CUT";N
840 IFN=1THENR=(TR*12)/(D*3.1416)ELSER=(TF*12)/(D*3.1416)
845 IFN=1THENP2$="ROUGH CUT"ELSEP2$="FINISH CUT"
850 GOSUB9000:GOSUB9200
860 T=((L+.02)/F)/R:T1=.11:T2=T+T1
865 TR=TA:TF=TB
870 INPUT"ENTER 1 FOR STOP SPIN., 2 FOR REV. FEED, 3 FOR RAPID OFF";N1
880 ONN1GOTO890,900,910
890 P1$="STOP SPINDLE RAPID OFF":GOTO8500
900 P1$="REVERSE FEED OFF":T=T*2:T2=T+T1:GOTO8500
910 P1$="RAPID TURRET FACE OFF":GOTO8500
920 CLS:P$="TURNING MULTIPLE TOOLS":P3$="TURN"
930 INPUT"ENTER THE NUMBER OF TOOLS";J
935 PRINT"ENTER THE LONGEST CUT FIRST"
936 PRINT"CUT NAMES SHOULD BE SHORT I.E. FACE A ,FORM B "
940 PRINT"ENTER THE LARGEST DIA. & LONGEST LENGTH FIRST"
945 FORI=1TOJ
946 INPUT"TYPE IN THE OPER. NAME I.E. BORE,DRILL,TURN ETC.";P3$(I)
950 INPUT"ENTER THE DIA. & TOLERANCE , SEPARATE BY A COMMA";D(I),D1(I)
960 INPUT"ENTER THE LENGTH & TOLERANCE , SEPARATE BY A COMMA";L(I),L1(I)
970 NEXTI
980 INPUT"ENTER 1 FOR ROUGH CUT OR 2 FOR FINISH CUT";N
990 IFN=1THENR=(TR*12)/(D(1)*3.1416)ELSER=(TF*12)/(D(1)*3.1416)
1000 IFN=1THENP2$="ROUGH CUT"ELSEP2$="FINISH CUT"
1010 GOSUB9000:GOSUB9200
1020 T=((L(1)+.02)/F)/R:T1=.11:T2=T+T1
1025 TR=TA:TF=TB
1030 INPUT"ENTER 1 FOR STOP SPIN.,2FOR REV. FEED,3 FOR RAPID OFF";N1
1040 ONN1GOTO1050,1060,1070
1050 P1$="STOP SPINDLE RAPID OFF":GOTO8500
1060 P1$="REVERSE FEED OFF":T=T*2:T2=T+T1:GOTO8500
1070 P1$="RAPID TURRET FACE OFF":GOTO8500
1080 P$="TURNING AND DRILLING":GOTO930
1110 P$="TURNING AND CORE DRILLING":GOTO930
1140 P$="TURNING AND REAMING":GOTO930
1150 P$="TURNING AND BORING":GOTO930
1160 P$="TURN AND SLAB CUT":GOTO930
1170 CLS:PRINT"TURNING & FACING"
```

Printout 10-3 continued

```
1180 PRINT"ENTER WHICH OPTION YOU WISH"
1190 PRINT"1----TURN & FACE FRONT SLIDE"
1200 PRINT"2----TURN & FACE REAR SLIDE"
1210 PRINT"3----TURN & FACE BOTH SLIDES"
1220 INPUT"4----TURN , BORE & FACE";X
1230 ONXGOTO1240,1250,1260,1270
1240 P$="TURN & FACE FRT SLIDE":GOTO930
1250 P$="TURN & FACE REAR SLIDE":GOTO930
1260 P$="TURN & FACE BOTH SLIDES":GOTO930
1270 P$="TURN,BORE & FACE":GOTO930
1280 CLS:PRINT"TURNING - BORING & FORMING"
1290 PRINT"NOTE ALL FORMING OPERATIONS ARE COMPLETED WITH FORMING SPEEDS"
1300 PRINT"ENTER THE OPTION YOU WISH TO USE"
1310 PRINT"1----TURN & FORM FRONT SLIDE"
1320 PRINT"2----TURN & FORM REAR SLIDE"
1330 PRINT"3----BORE & FORM FRONT SLIDE"
1340 PRINT"4----BORE & FORM REAR SLIDE"
1341 PRINT"5----TURN - BORE & FORM"
1342 PRINT"6----TURN - BORE - FACE & FORM"
1350 INPUTX
1360 ONXGOTO1370,1380,1390,1400,1401,1402
1370 P$="TURN & FORM FRT SLIDE":GOTO1410
1380 P$="TURN & FORM REAR SLIDE":GOTO1410
1390 P$="BORE & FORM FRT SLIDE":GOTO1410
1400 P$="BORE & FORM REAR SLIDE":GOTO1410
1401 P$="TURN - BORE - FORM R.S.":GOTO1410
1402 P$="TURN-BORE-FACE-FORM R.S.":GOTO1410
1410 CLS:INPUT"ENTER THE NUMBER OF TOOLS";J
1420 PRINT"ENTER THE LONGEST CUT FIRST----TIME IS CALCULATED ON THIS"
1430 FORI=1TOJ
1440 INPUT"TYPE IN THE OPER. NAME I.E. TURN A, FORM B, FORM C";P3$(I)
1450 INPUT"ENTER THE DIA. & TOLERANCE , SEPARATE BY A COMMA";D(I),D1(I)
1460 INPUT"ENTER LENGTH OF CUT & TOL., SEPARATE BY A COMMA";L(I),L1(I)
1470 NEXTI
1480 INPUT"TYPE 1 FOR HSS FORM TOOL OR 2 FOR CARBIDE";N
1490 IFN=1THENR=(FS*12)/(D(1)*3.1416)ELSER=(FC*12)/(D(1)*3.1416)
1500 IFN=1THENP4$="HIGH SS"ELSEP4$="CARBIDE"
1510 GOSUB9000:GOSUB9200
1520 T=((L(1)+.03)/F)/R:T1=.11:T2=T+T1
1530 PRINT"ENTER 1 FOR STANDARD CROSS SLIDE"
1540 PRINT"ENTER 2 FOR LATE CROSS SLIDE"
1550 INPUT"ENTER 3 FOR LATE CROSS SLIDE 2 ND FEED";N1
1560 ONN1GOTO1570,1580,1590
1570 P5$="STD CROSS SLIDE":GOTO1630
1580 P5$="LATE CROSS SLIDE":T1=.15:T2=T+T1:GOTO1630
1590 P5$="LATE C.S. 2ND FEED":T1=.15:T2=T+T1
1600 LPRINTCHR$(138):LPRINT"FIRST FEED FOR THIS OPERATION IS";F;"SECOND FEED IS
SHOWN IN THE FEED COL."
1610 INPUT"TYPE 1 TO SELECT THE SECOND FEED";U
1620 IFU=1THENGOSUB9200
1630 INPUT"ENTER 1 FOR ROUGH CUT OR 2 FOR FINISH CUT";V
1640 IFV=1THENP2$="ROUGH CUT"ELSEP2$="FINISH CUT"
1650 INPUT"ENTER 1 FOR STOP SPIN, 2 FOR REV FEED,3 FOR RAPID OFF";N1
1660 ONN1GOTO1670,1680,1690
1670 P1$="STOP SPINDLE":GOTO8500
1680 P1$="REVERSE FEED":T=T*2:T2=T+T1:GOTO8500
1690 P1$="RAPID OFF":GOTO8500
2000 CLS:PRINT"BORING OPERATIONS"
2010 PRINT"ENTER THE TYPE BORING OPERATION YOU WISH"
2020 PRINT"1----BORING SINGLE TOOL"
2030 PRINT"2----BORING MULTIPLE TOOLS"
2040 PRINT"3----BORING & FACING CROSS SLIDE"
2050 PRINT"3----BORING & FORMING CROSS SLIDE"
2060 PRINT"3----BORING , FORMING & FACING CROSS SLIDE"
2070 INPUT"4----BORING & GROOVING";X
```

Printout 10-3 continued

```
2100  ONXGOTO2110,2120,2130,2240
2110  P$="BORING SINGLE TOOL":P3$="BORE":TR=BR:TF=BF:GOTO810
2120  P$="BORING MULTIPLE TOOLS":P3$="BORE":TR=BR:TF=BF:GOTO930
2130  CLS:PRINT"BORING & FACING"
2140  PRINT"ENTER THE OPTION YOU WISH TO USE"
2150  PRINT"1----BORING & FACING FRONT SLIDE"
2160  PRINT"2----BORING & FACING REAR SLIDE"
2170  PRINT"3----BORING & FACING BOTH SLIDES"
2180  INPUT"4----BORING & FORMING";X
2190  ONXGOTO2200,2210,2220,2230
2200  P$="BORE & FACE FRT SLIDE":GOTO930
2210  P$="BORE & FACE REAR SLIDE":GOTO930
2220  P$="BORE & FACE BOTH SLIDES":GOTO930
2230  GOTO1280
2240  CLS:PRINT"ENTER THE OPTION YOU WISH"
2250  PRINT"1-----BORE THEN GROOVE"
2260  PRINT"2-----RAPID ADVANCE THEN GROOVE OR BACK FACE"
2265  PRINT"NOTE THE LENGTH OF CUT IS THE DEPTH OF GROOVE"
2270  INPUTX1
2280  ONX1GOTO2290,2300
2290  P$="BORE THEN GROOVE":GOTO1410
2300  P$="RAPID ADVANCE - GROOVE":GOTO1410
3000  CLS:PRINT"DRILLING MODULE"
3010  PRINT"ENTER THE NUMBER YOU WISH TO WORK WITH"
3020  PRINT"1-----DRILL HIGH SPEED STEEL"
3030  PRINT"2-----CORE DRILL - CORED HOLE"
3040  PRINT"3-----CORD DRILL - DRILLED HOLE"
3041  PRINT"4----DRILL & FACE"
3050  INPUTX
3060  ONXGOTO3070,3170,3270,3310
3070  CLS:P$="DRILL - HSS":P3$="DRILL"
3080  INPUT"ENTER THE DIA. & TOLERANCE SEPARATED BY A COMMA";D,D1
3090  INPUT"ENTER THE LENGTH & TOLERANCE SEPARATED BY A COMMA";L,L1
3100  R=(SD*12)/(D*3.1416)
3110  GOSUB9000:GOSUB9200
3120  T=((L+(D*.3))/F)/R:T1=.11:T2=T+T1
3130  INPUT"ENTER 1 FOR STOP SPINDLE OR 2 FOR RAPID OFF";N1
3140  ONN1GOTO3150,3160
3150  P1$="STOP SPINDLE RAPID OFF":GOTO8500
3160  P1$="RAPID TURRET FACE OFF":GOTO8500
3170  CLS:P$="CORE DRILL - CORED HOLE":P3$="CORE"
3180  INPUT"ENTER THE DIA. & TOLERANCE SEPARATED BY A COMMA";D,D1
3190  INPUT"ENTER THE LENGTH & TOLERANCE SEPARATED BY A COMMA";L,L1
3200  R=(CC*12)/(D*3.1416)
3210  GOSUB9000:GOSUB9200
3220  T=((L+.02)/F)/R:T1=.11:T2=T+T1
3230  INPUT"ENTER 1 FOR STOP SPINDLE OR 2 FOR RAPID OFF";N1
3240  ONN1GOTO3250,3260
3250  P1$="STOP SPINDLE RAPID OFF":GOTO8500
3260  P1$="RAPID TURRET FACE OFF":GOTO8500
3270  CLS:P$="CORE DRILL - DRILLED HOLE":P3$="CORE"
3280  INPUT"ENTER THE DIA. & TOLERANCE SEPARATED BY A COMMA";D,D1
3290  INPUT"ENTER THE LENGTH & TOLERANCE SEPARATED BY A COMMA";L,L1
3300  R=(CD*12)/(D*3.1416):GOTO3210
3310  CLS:PRINT"DRILL & FACE"
3320  PRINT"ENTER THE OPTION YOU WISH"
3330  PRINT"1----DRILL & FACE FRONT SLIDE"
3340  PRINT"2----DRILL & FACE REAR SLIDE"
3350  PRINT"3----DRILL & FACE BOTH SLIDES"
3360  INPUTX
3370  ONXGOTO3380,3390,3400
3380  P$="DRILL & FACE FRT SLIDE":GOTO930
3390  P$="DRILL & FACE REAR SLIDE":GOTO930
3400  P$="DRILL & FACE BOTH SLIDES":GOTO930
4000  CLS:PRINT"REAMING MODULE"
```

Printout 10-3 continued

```
4005 PRINT"NOTE OPTIONS 1 & 2 USE REAMING SPEEDS"
4010 PRINT"ENTER THE NUMBER YOU WISH TO WORK WITH"
4020 PRINT"1-----REAM HIGH SPEED REAMER"
4030 PRINT"2-----REAM CARBIDE REAMER"
4031 PRINT"3-----REAM & FACE USING FACING SFPM"
4040 INPUTX
4050 ONXGOTO4060,4150,4190
4060 CLS:P$="REAM - HSS REAMER":P3$="REAM"
4070 INPUT"ENTER THE DIA. & TOLERANCE SEPARATED BY A COMMA";D,D1
4080 INPUT"ENTER THE LENGTH & TOLERANCE SEPARATED BY A COMMA";L,L1
4090 R=(RS*12)/(D*3.1416)
4100 GOSUB9000:GOSUB9200
4110 INPUT"ENTER 1 FOR STOP SPINDLE OR 2 FOR RAPID OFF";N1
4120 ONN1GOTO4130,4140
4130 P1$="STOP SPINDLE RAPID OFF":GOTO8500
4140 P1$="RAPID TURRET FACE OFF":GOTO8500
4150 CLS:P$="REAM - CARBIDE REAMER":P3$="REAM"
4160 INPUT"ENTER THE DIA. & TOLERANCE SEPARATED BY A COMMA";D,D1
4170 INPUT"ENTER THE LENGTH & TOLERANCE SEPARATED BY A COMMA";L,L1
4180 R=(RC*12)/(D*3.1416):GOTO4100
4190 CLS:PRINT"REAMING & FACING"
4200 PRINT"ENTER THE OPTION YOU WISH TO USE"
4210 PRINT"1----REAM & FACE FRONT SLIDE"
4220 PRINT"2----REAM & FACE REAR SLIDE"
4230 PRINT"3----REAM & FACE BOTH SLIDES"
4240 INPUTX
4250 ONXGOTO4260,4270,4280
4260 P$="REAM & FACE FRT SLIDE":GOTO930
4270 P$="REAM & FACE REAR SLIDE":GOTO930
4280 P$="REAM & FACE BOTH SLIDES":GOTO930
4500 CLS:P$="THREADING"
4510 PRINT"ENTER THE NUMBER NEXT TO THE THREADS PER INCH AND"
4515 PRINT"R.H. FOR RIGHT HAND OR L.H. FOR LEFT HAND, SEPARATE BY COMMA"
4520 PRINT"1---7 TPI        9---14 TPI"
4530 PRINT"2---8           10---16"
4540 PRINT"3---9           11---18"
4550 PRINT"4---10          12---20"
4560 PRINT"5---11          13---24"
4570 PRINT"6---11.5        14---27"
4580 PRINT"7---12          15---28"
4590 PRINT"8---13          16---32"
4600 INPUTX1,P3$
4610 ONX1GOTO4620,4630,3640,4650,4660,4670,4680,4690,4700,4710,4720,4730,4740,47
50,4760,4770
4620 S=TW:Q=7:P6$="7 TPI":P4$="64-UU-14":GOTO4780
4630 S=TX:Q=8:P6$="8 TPI":P4$="51   -   12":GOTO4780
4640 S=TX:Q=9:P6$="9 TPI":P4$="50   -   12":GOTO4780
4650 S=TX:Q=10:P6$="10TPI":P4$="49-U-12":GOTO4780
4660 S=TX:Q=11:P6$="11 TPI":P4$="39   -   10":GOTO4780
4670 S=TX:Q=11.5:P6$="11.5 TPI":P4$="39-U-10":GOTO4780
4680 S=TX:Q=12:P6$="12 TPI":P4$="46-U-12":GOTO4780
4690 S=TX:Q=13:P6$="13 TPI":P4$="44   -   12":GOTO4780
4700 S=TX:Q=14:P6$="14 TPI":P4$="35   -   10":GOTO4780
4710 S=TY:Q=16:P6$="16 TPI":P4$="46-0-14":GOTO4780
4720 S=TY:Q=18:P6$="18 TPI":P4$="25   -   8":GOTO4780
4730 S=TY:Q=20:P6$="20 TPI":P4$="48   -   16":GOTO4780
4740 S=TY:Q=24:P6$="24 TPI":P4$="34-U-12":GOTO4780
4750 S=TZ:Q=27:P6$="27 TPI":P4$="31   -   12":GOTO4780
4760 S=TZ:Q=28:P6$="28 TPI":P4$="35   -   14":GOTO4780
4770 S=TZ:Q=32:P6$="32 TPI":P4$="28   -   12":GOTO4780
4780 CLS:PRINT"ENTER THE NUMBER YOU WISH TO WORK WITH"
4790 PRINT"1-----THREAD SOLID TAP"
4800 PRINT"2-----THREAD INTERNAL COLLAPSIBLE"
4810 PRINT"3-----THREAD ENTERNAL DIE HEAD"
4820 INPUTX2
```

Printout 10-3 continued

```
4830 ONX2GOTO4840,4850,4860
4840 P5$="THREAD - SOLID TAP":GOTO4870
4850 P5$="THREAD - INTERNAL COLLAPSIBLE":GOTO4870
4860 P5$="THREAD - ENTERNAL DIE HEAD":GOTO4870
4870 INPUT"ENTER THE DIA. & TOLERANCE , SEPARATE BY A COMMA";D,D1
4880 INPUT"ENTER THE LENGTH & TOLERANCE, SEPARATE BY A COMMA";L,L1
4890 R=(S*12)/(D*3.1416):GOSUB9000
4900 F=1/Q:T=((L+.125)/F)/R:T1=.11:T2=T+T1
4910 IFX2=1THENT=T*2:T2=T+T1ELSE4920
4920 LPRINTCHR$(138)
4930 LPRINTP$;"   ";P6$;"                      GEARS"
4940 LPRINTCHR$(138)
4950 IFX2=1THEN4960ELSE4970
4960 P1$="REVERSE FEED OFF      ":GOTO8500
4970 P1$="RAPID TURRET FACE OFF":GOTO8500
5000 P$="TREPANNING":GOTO930
5010 LPRINTCHR$(138):LPRINT"SKIP INDEX TIME =.02"
5020 T2=.02:GOTO8520
8500 LPRINTP$;", ";P2$;", ";P1$;", ";P4$;", ";P5$:LPRINTCHR$(138):IFJ>0THEN8501E
LSE8510
8501 FORI=1TOJ
8502 LPRINTZ;I;"  ";P3$(I),D(I);"+-";D1(I);TAB(40);L(I);"+-";L1(I);TAB(60);F;TAB(
70);R
8503 NEXTI
8504 GOTO8515
8510 LPRINTZ;1;"  ";P3$,D;"+-";D1;TAB(40);L;"+-";L1;TAB(60);F;TAB(70);R
8515 LPRINT"TIME FOR THIS OPERATION IS";T; " + " ;T1;"INDEX"
8520 LPRINTCHR$(138):T3=T3+T2
8525 J=0:P4$="":P5$="":P2$="":P1$="":P3$=""
8530 NEXTZ
8540 CLS:PRINT"THE NEXT SECTION OF THE PROGRAM ADDS LOAD & UNLOAD TIMES"
8550 PRINT"TYPE IN THE NUMBER NEXT TO THE PART WEIGHT"
8560 PRINT"1-----UNDER 5 LBS."
8570 PRINT"2-----UNDER 10 LBS."
8580 PRINT"3-----UNDER 15 LBS."
8590 PRINT"4-----UNDER 20 LBS."
8600 PRINT"5-----OVER 20 LBS."
8610 INPUTH
8620 ONHGOTO8630,8640,8650,8660,8670
8630 H=.25:GOTO8680
8640 H=.35:GOTO8680
8650 H=.45:GOTO8680
8660 H=.55:GOTO8680
8670 H=.75:GOTO8680
8680 T4=T3+H:T5=60/T4
8690 LPRINT"TOTAL OPERATION IS";T3;"PLUS LOAD & UNLOAD EQUALS";T4
8700 LPRINT"TOTAL PARTS PER HOUR ARE";T5
8710 CLS:PRINT"THE LAST PART OF THE PROGRAM IS ADDING UP THE SET UP TIME"
8720 PRINT"AS THE SET UP DESCRIPTION APPEARS ON THE SCREEN,"
8730 PRINT"TYPE IN THE NUMBER OF TIMES IT IS USED OF 0 IF NOT USED."
8740 PRINT"NOTE-TO SHORTEN THE PROCESS SOME CONSTANTS ARE ADDED IN"
8750 PRINT:INPUT"INSTALL  TURRET SLIDE HEAD - FACING OR RECESSING CUT";MA
8760 MB=MA*16.5
8770 INPUT"OVER HEAD TURNING - CUTTER & HOLDER";MC
8780 MB=MB+(MC*10)
8790 INPUT"INSTALL BORING BAR & CUTTER";MD
8800 MB=MB+(MD*9.5)
8810 INPUT"INSTALL OVERHEAD CHAMFER CUTTER & HOLDER";ME
8820 MB=MB+(ME*6)
8830 INPUT"INSTALL BORING BAR CUTTER HEAD & CUTTER";MF
8840 MB=MB+(MF*5)
8850 INPUT"INSTALL DRILL , CORE DRILL , REAMER  OR TAP";MG
8860 MB=MB+(MG*5)
8870 INPUT"INSTALL FRONT OR REAR CROSS SLIDE CUTTER BLOCK & CUTTER";MH
8880 MB=MB+(MH*7)+64.6:MJ=MB/60
```

Printout 10-3 continued

```
8890 LPRINT"SET UP ALLOWANCE IS";MJ;"HOURS"
8900 END

9000 FORI=1TO12
9010 IFI=12ANDR>S(I)THEN9020ELSE9030
9020 S1=S(I):GOTO9110
9030 IFS(I)<RTHEN9100
9040 IFS(I)>RTHEN9050
9050 S1=(S(I)+S(I-1))/2
9060 IFS1<=RTHENS1=S(I)ELSE9080
9070 GOTO9110
9080 IFS1>RTHENS1=S(I-1)
9090 GOTO9110
9100 NEXTI
9110 R=S1
9120 RETURN
9200 CLS:PRINT@768,"FEED SELECTION"
9210 PRINT@832,F1;F2;F3;F4;F5;F6
9220 PRINT@896,"ENTER THE FEED NUMBER YOU WISH TO USE":INPUTX
9230 ONXGOTO9240,9250,9260,9270,9280,9290
9240 F=F1:RETURN
9250 F=F2:RETURN
9260 F=F3:RETURN
9270 F=F4:RETURN
9280 F=F5:RETURN
9290 F=F6:RETURN
10000 CLS:FORI=1TO12:READR(I):NEXTI
10010 DATA1,1,3,3,5,5,7,7,9,9,11,11
10020 FORI=1TO12:READG(I):NEXTI
10030 DATA17,43,22,38,27,33,33,27,38,22,43,17
10040 PRINT"ROW","FEED","ROW","FEED"
10050 FORI=1TO12:READF(I):PRINTR(I),F(I);,:NEXTI
10060 DATA.0019,.0077,.0028,.011,.004,.016,.006,.024,.008,.034,.012,.05
10070 INPUT"ENTER THE ROW NUMBER YOU WISH TO USE";I
10080 F1=F(I):F4=F(I+1):G1=G(I):G4=G(I+1)
10090 CLS:PRINT"ROW","FEED","ROW","FEED"
10100 FORI=1TO12:READF(I):PRINTR(I),F(I);,:NEXTI
10110 DATA.003,.012,.0044,.017,.006,.025,.009,.037,.013,.052,.019,.076
10120 INPUT"ENTER THE ROW NUMBER YOU WISH TO USE";I
10130 F2=F(I):F5=F(I+1):G2=G(I):G5=G(I+1)
10140 CLS:PRINT"ROW","FEED","ROW","FEED"
10150 FORI=1TO12:READF(I):PRINTR(I),F(I);,:NEXTI
10160 DATA.005,.019,.007,.028,.01,.04,.015,.06,.021,.084,.031,.124
10170 INPUT"ENTER THE ROW NUMBER YOU WISH TO USE";I
10180 F3=F(I):F6=F(I+1):G3=G(I):G6=G(I+1)
10190 RETURN
15000 CLS:PRINT"THE 2 A/C CHUCKER HAS 2 SETS OF RPM'S."
15010 PRINT"EACH SET HAS A HIGH AND A LOW SPEED RANGE"
15020 PRINT"              875 RPM MOTOR SPEED"
15030 FORI=1TO12:READS(I):PRINTS(I),;:NEXTI
15040 DATA22,37,44,62,72,104,121,170,203,290,334,568
15050 PRINT:PRINT:PRINT"              1750 RPM MOTOR SPEED"
15060 FORI=1TO12:READS1(I):PRINTS1(I),;:NEXTI
15065 DATA44,74,88,124,144,208,242,340,406,580,668,1136
15070 INPUT"ENTER 1 TO USE THE 875 SET OR 2 TO USE THE 1750 SET";X
15080 IFX=2THEN15090ELSE15100
15090 FORI=1TO12:S(I)=S1(I):NEXTI
15100 RETURN
20000 CLS:PRINT"MATERIAL LIST"
20010 PRINT"1--GROUP A"
20020 PRINT"B-1112,C-1118,BRONZE (P-64)"
20030 PRINT:PRINT"2--GROUP B"
20040 PRINT"416 S.S.,C-1010-1015 TUBING,C-1019,C-1037,C-1041"
20050 PRINT"NAVAL BRONZE 73, BRONZE (TOBIN), CAST IRON (SOFT)"
20060 PRINT:PRINT"3--GROUP C"
```

Printout 10-3 continued

```
20070 PRINT"C-1040-45-50,A-4140-50,A-4340,A-4615,302,304 STAINLESS STEEL"
20080 PRINT"BRONZE (ALUM), CAST IRON (HARD), MALLEABLE IRON"
20090 PRINT"4--GROUP D,-----E-3310, E-4160, CAST STEEL"
20100 PRINT"5--GROUP E,------C-1070, C-1090, MONEL"
20110 PRINT"6--GROUP F,-----ALUM, BRASS (FREE MACHINING)"
20120 PRINT:INPUT"ENTER THE NUMBER FROM 1 TO 6 THAT CORRESPONDS TO THE LETTER";N
20130 ONNGOTO20140,20170,20200,20230,20260,20290
20140 A$="GROUP A"
20150 TR=490:TF=560:TA=TR:TB=TF:BR=TR:BF=TF:SD=120:CD=150:CC=120:RS=60:RC=90:FS=
150:FC=320:TW=10:TX=20:TY=30:TZ=40
20160 RETURN
20170 A$="GROUP B"
20180 TR=420:TF=490:TA=TR:TB=TF:BR=TR:BF=TF:SD=80:CD=120:CC=100:RS=50:RC=75:FS=1
20:FC=320:TW=15:TX=25:TY=40:TZ=45
20190 RETURN
20200 A$="GROUP C"
20210 TR=320:TF=420:TA=TR:TB=TF:BR=350:BF=420:SD=60:CD=90:CC=80:RS=40:RC=60:FS=9
0:FC=245:TW=4:TX=8:TY=10:TZ=15
20220 RETURN
20230 A$="GROUP D"
20240 TR=245:TF=320:TA=TR:TB=TF:BR=260:BF=320:SD=50:CD=70:CC=60:RS=30:RC=45:FS=7
0:FC=220:TW=4:TX=8:TY=10:TZ=15
20250 RETURN
20260 A$="GROUP E"
20270 TR=220:TF=230:TA=TR:TB=TF:BR=175:BF=230:SD=50:CD=50:CC=50:RS=25:RC=35:FS=5
0:FC=200:TW=4:TX=5:TY=10:TZ=12
20280 RETURN
20290 A$="GROUP E"
20300 TR=1000:TF=TR:TA=TR:TB=TF:BR=TR:BF=TR:SD=200:CD=250:CC=200:RS=120:RC=180:F
S=250:FC=1000:TW=20:TX=50:TY=100:TZ=150
20310 RETURN
20320 REM VARIABLE NAMES TR=R TURN, TF=F TURN, FACE SAME AS TURNBR=R BORE, BF=F
BORE, SD=DRILL HSS, CD=CORE DRILLED,CC=CORED HOLE, RS=REAM HSS,RC=REAM CARBIDE,F
S=FORM HSS,FC=FORM CARBIDE, T=THD,TW=<7.5,TX=8-15,TY=16-24,TZ=>25
```

Printout 10-3 continued

Bibliography

Operating Instructions for the 2 AC (Ms920) Single Spindle Chucking Automatic. Cleveland: Warner & Swasey, 1973.

Wilson, R.C. and Henry, Robert A. *Introduction to Group Technology in Manufacturing and Engineering.* Ann Arbor, MI: Industrial Development Division, Institute of Science and Technology, University of Michigan, 1977.

Optional Lab Assignments

Lab Assignment 10-1 (least difficult)
Select a horizontal milling machine which has specific speeds and feeds and write a computer program similar to the "AC" program. This is considered least difficult because the number of different types of operations that a horizontal milling machine can perform is limited.

Lab Assignment 10-2 (moderate)
Select a twin spindle, vertical chucker and write a program similar to the "AC" program. The tooling variety is greater than the milling machine, however, less than the AC.

Lab Assignment 10-3 (difficult)
Select a six or eight spindle automatic screw machine and write a computer program similar to the "AC" program. The nature of the program will be somewhat different in respect to selection of speeds. Speeds can be reconciled in a subroutine that favors different types of cuts.

CHAPTER 11

Tolerance
Control

The establishment of manufacturing process dimensions and tolerances are fundamental to an engineer's effort in developing a new manufacturing process. As defined earlier, a process dimension is a dimension developed by the engineer to accommodate the manufacturing process, and is different than a final blueprint dimension. Examples of process dimensions are:
1. Dimensions required for rough cuts where finished cuts produce print dimensions.
2. Dimensions established for castings or forgings which are the rough sizes with which the engineer processing the part starts.
3. A dimension established for processing convenience where no print dimension exists.

Process tolerances are tolerances associated with process dimensions, and established by the Manufacturing Engineer. They are different than finished print tolerances.

The objectives of this chapter are three-fold.
1. To present an overview of tolerance control.
2. To review tolerance charting.
3. To present a computerized tolerance charting program.

Tolerance Control over Manufactured Parts

The idea of tolerance control is not new; it dates back to the days of Eli Whitney. Whitney's early efforts devoted to musket manufacturing gave birth to the American idea of interchangeable parts. The concept of interchangeable parts and the development of machines to produce them founded the American industrial revolution. It could be said that Whitney was, in fact, the first Manufacturing Engineer. However, the evolution from interchangeable parts to the present day concept of tolerance control over manufactured parts was many years in coming.

The practice of tolerance charting to control manufacturing tolerances is probably the least used and most misunderstood element of Manufacturing Engineering today.

Over the years, magazine articles have appeared on the subject, and occasionally one can find a chapter in an engineering text devoted to tolerance charting. To the author's knowledge, however, only one book has been written about the subject (see Bibliography). Due to the early pioneering efforts of Oliver R. Wade, who gathered all of the known information at that time and added many of his own thoughts, tolerance control today is more of a science than an art.

In many respects, computerized tolerance charting is a blessing. The many long hours an engineer now spends working up a tolerance chart by hand are significantly reduced. The problem arises because the skill is not well-understood. One rule always should be followed when working with computers: First, understand how the task is accomplished by hand, then computerize it. Unless one understands how something should be accomplished, how does one know if a computer printout is correct?

Review of Tolerance Charting

Tolerance charting is a method of establishing length dimensions and tolerances where process dimensions and tolerances are required to manufacture a part or assembly.

The tolerance chart itself has remained fairly standard for the last 30 years.

A brief review of the charting symbols is shown on *Figure 11-1*.

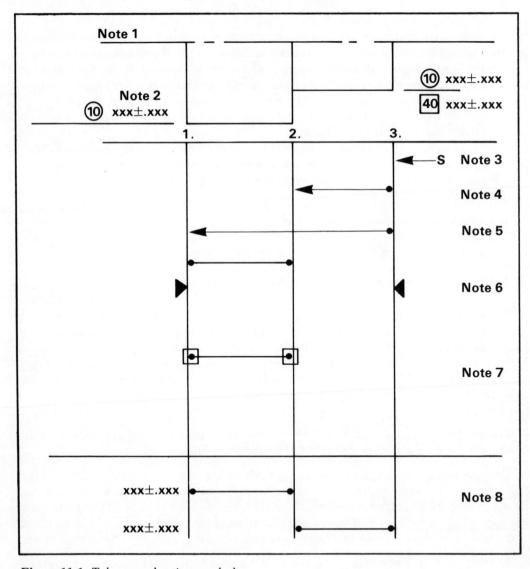

Figure 11-1. *Tolerance charting symbols.*

252

Notes for Figure 11-1

1. The piece part is shown in a manner that vertical lines can be extended from the part, creating planes. Each plane then represents a length dimension on the part. All lengths should be charted.

2. This portion of the chart records diametrical features and tolerances showing which operations created each feature. The 10 shown with a circle around it defines that the diameter was created by a direct machining cut. The 40 shown with a box around it defines that the diameter has been altered or redefined by an indirect operation. Typical indirect operations could be plating or painting.

3. The arrow shown with an "S" behind it defines that this end of the part is to be faced from bar stock or produced from the solid.

4. The dot and arrow line defines a machining cut. The dot indicates the locating point or where the dimension is measured from. The arrow indicates the length surface being machined. All direct machining cuts are shown in this manner.

5. The two dots joined by a line are called a balance dimension. There are two types of balance dimensions:
   a. A balance dimension can be created by adding or subtracting one machined cut from another machined cut or balance dimension to represent a length.
   b. A balance dimension can be created to define stock removal for a surface that previously existed.
   Both of these cases for balance dimensions are developed and illustrated in *Figure 11-3*.

6. The triangles represent locating points, and in this illustration they could be defined as locating the part between centers.

7. This type of balance dimension is created by an indirect processing operation. Indirect operations are heat-treat, plating, and so on. In the heat-treating example, this balance dimension would be a declaration of a dimension. For example, the part increased in length after the heat-treating operation.

8. Blueprint dimensions are shown as regular balance dimensions.

Also study *Figures 11-2, 11-3* and *11-4*, which show examples of balance dimensions being created by machined cuts and a balance dimension created for stock removed.

In *Figure 11-2,* what are the tolerances for Lines 1 and 2? The tolerances are additive. If Line 3 is given the full blueprint tolerance of ± .005 and if tolerances are additive, then Lines 1 and 2 must share this tolerance.

$$Line \ 1 = 1.000 \pm .002$$
$$Line \ 2 = 2.000 \pm .003$$

The proof being:

$$Line \ 2 - Line \ 1 = Line \ 3$$

or (if Line 2 is low and Line 1 is high):

$$1.997 - 1.002 = .995$$

If Line 2 is high and Line 1 is low:

$$2.003 - .998 = 1.005$$

Now add the low and high tolerances for Line 3.

$$.995 + 1.005 = \frac{2.000}{2} = 1.000 \pm .005$$

If Lines 1 or 2 are given full blueprint tolerance, Line 3 is over the print limit.

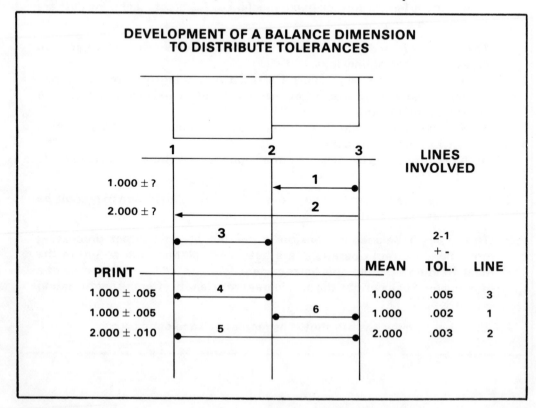

Figure 11-2. Development of a balance dimension to distribute tolerances.

Turn attention now to *Figure 11-3*. From this figure, you will notice:

Line 2 - Line 1 = Line 4
Line 3 - Line 1 = Line 5
Line 6 - Line 5 = Line 7

If the machined dimension of Line 1 is $1.000 \pm .005$; Line 2 is $2.000 \pm .005$, Line 6 is $2.980 \pm .005$, Line 3 is $3.000 \pm .005$, then the following holds true:

Line 2	$2.000 \pm .005$
-Line 1	$1.000 \pm .005$
Line 4	$1.000 \pm .010$

and:

Line 3	$3.000 \pm .005$
-Line 1	$1.000 \pm .005$
Line 5	$2.000 \pm .010$

and:

Line 6	$2.980 \pm .005$
-Line 5	$2.000 \pm .010$
Line 7	$.980 \pm .015$

Note that the balance dimension 7 represents the new length between planes 3 and 4 because the cut produced by Line 6, has altered that length. The proof being:

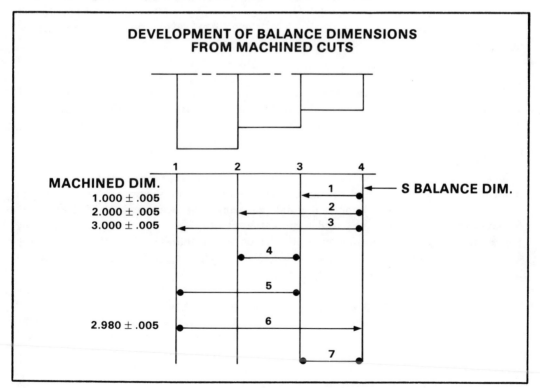

Figure 11-3. *Development of balance dimensions from machined cuts.*

Line 3 - Line 6 = Stock Removal

and then

Line 1 - Stock Removal = Line 7

If Line 3 is low and Line 6 is high:

$$2.995 - 2.985 = .010$$

The minimum Stock Removal is .010. If Line 3 is high and Line 6 is low:

$$3.005 - 2.975 = .030$$

The maximum Stock Removal is .030. To prove the length of Line 7 (Line 1 is high; Stock Removal is low):

$$1.005 - .010 = .995$$

or if Line 1 is low and the Stock Removal is high:

$$.995 - .030 = .965$$

Now add the low and high tolerances for Line 7.

$$.995 + .965 = \frac{1.960}{2} = .980 \pm .015$$

Finally, turn attention to *Figure 11-4*.

What is the length of Line 1? Line 1 is not involved in the tolerance stack. So, assume it has a tolerance of $\pm$ .005. Line 6 has a Stock Removal tolerance of $\pm$ .015 (Lines 1, 4 and 5). To this add + .005 for clean up, to equal + .020. Line 1 is 1.000 - .020 = .980 $\pm$ .005. Note that Line 1 is shorter not longer.

What is the length of Line 2?

Because Line 2 and 4 are the same length, add the Line 2 tolerance (.005) and the Line 4 tolerance (.005) which is $\pm$ .010. Next add + .005 for clean up, bringing the total to + .015. Line 2 is .015 longer than Line 4, 2.015 $\pm$ .005.

Locating Points

The choice of locating points by the engineer who is creating the process can have a dramatic influence on the distribution of tolerances and whether the full blueprint tolerances can be used. This is an extremely important point that cannot be over-emphasized. Use of the tolerance chart is a reliable way to determine the relationships that exist between locating points, machining cuts and print dimensions. All too often in industry, the engineer processing a part fails to see these relationships because tolerance charting is not practiced. There are many complicated aerospace parts that cannot be manufactured properly unless process dimensions and tolerances are established by charting methods. Many times, engineers processing simpler commercial or non-aerospace parts try to take shortcuts in establishing process dimensions and tolerances. This practice usually results in one of two conditions. In the first condition, defective parts are produced by the shop unknowingly, because the process is defective and the shop is following the process. The second condition results in the shop being given process tolerances to machines that do not reflect the best distribution of tolerances. To understand how the latter can happen, review *Figures 11-5, 11-6,* and *11-7* on the following pages. These figures are completed tolerance charts of a very simple non-aerospace part that

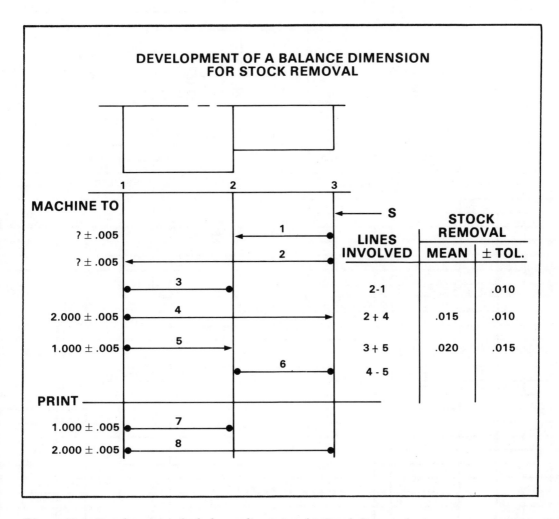

Figure 11-4. Development of a balance dimension for Stock Removal.

have been processed three different ways. In all, there are seven manufacturing cuts taken to manufacture each part, and the locating points of only the last two cuts change. The objective of this exercise is to answer the question: Will process tolerances change if locating points change? After a thorough review of the three machining examples is conducted, review *Table 11-1*. This shows a summary of the process tolerances associated with each manufacturing cut. Observe that process tolerances are different in each example because the locating point for cuts six and seven have changed.

Other tolerance dispersements could be made in these examples. Nevertheless, the point being made is a valid one. The way in which an engineer chooses to process a part will have an influence on the establishment of process tolerances. This relationship can be seen clearly through the use of tolerance charting.

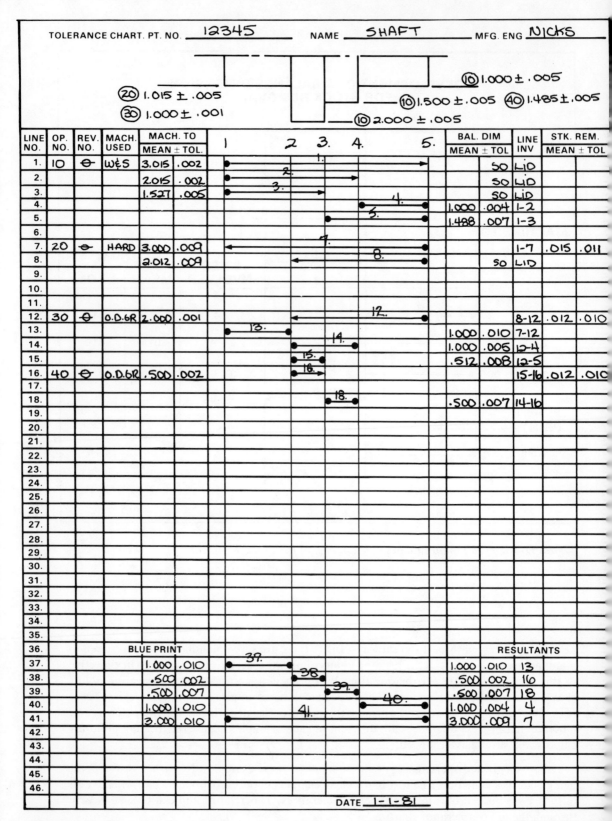

Figure 11-5. *This tolerance chart for a part machined in seven manufacturing cuts, establishes tolerance*
for cuts 7 and 12.

258

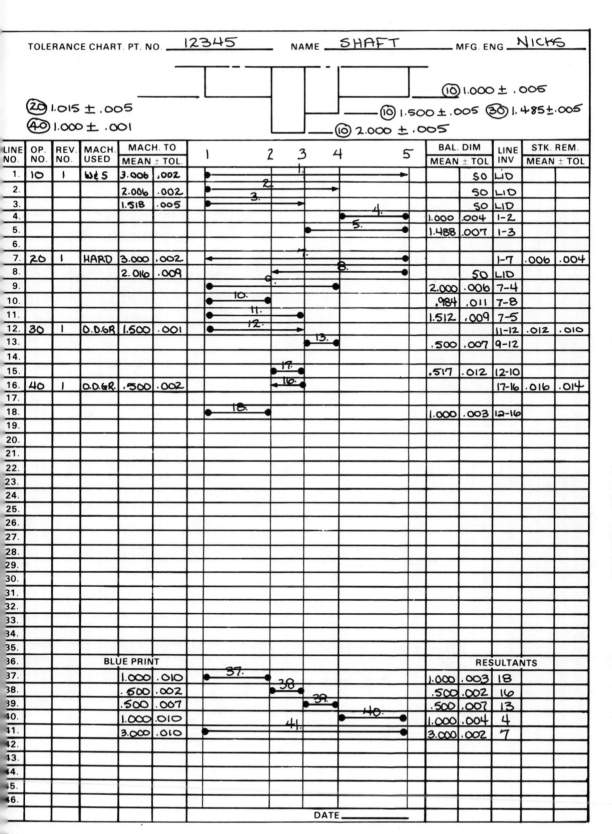

Figure 11-6. This figure represents the same part as shown in the previous figure. The located points for the first two cuts have changed, however. Note the tolerances established for cuts 7 and 12, then compare these to the next chart.

259

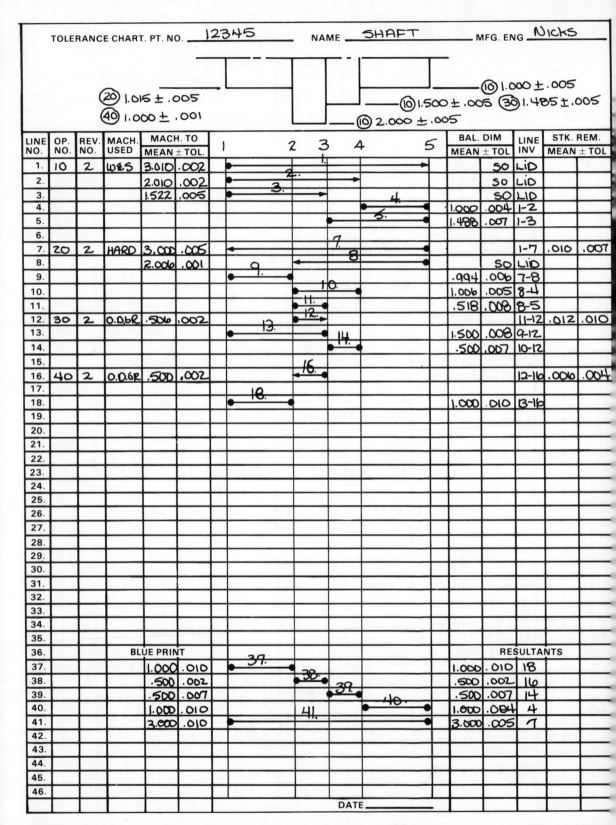

LINE NO.	OP. NO.	REV. NO.	MACH. USED	MACH. TO		1	2	3	4	5	BAL. DIM		LINE INV	STK. REM.	
				MEAN	± TOL.						MEAN	± TOL		MEAN	± TOL
1.	10	2	W&S	3.010	.002								SO	LID	
2.				2.010	.002								SO	LID	
3.				1.522	.005								SO	LID	
4.											1.000	.004	1-2		
5.											1.488	.007	1-3		
6.															
7.	20	2	HARD	3.000	.005								1-7	.010	.007
8.				2.006	.001								SO	LID	
9.											.994	.006	7-8		
10.											1.006	.005	8-4		
11.											.518	.008	8-5		
12.	30	2	O.D.GR	.506	.002								11-12	.012	.010
13.											1.500	.008	9-12		
14.											.500	.007	10-12		
15.															
16.	40	2	O.D.GR	.500	.002								12-16	.006	.004
17.															
18.											1.000	.010	13-16		
19.															
20.															
21.															
22.															
23.															
24.															
25.															
26.															
27.															
28.															
29.															
30.															
31.															
32.															
33.															
34.															
35.															
36.				BLUE PRINT								RESULTANTS			
37.				1.000	.010						1.000	.010	18		
38.				.500	.002						.500	.002	16		
39.				.500	.007						.500	.007	14		
40.				1.000	.010						1.000	.004	4		
41.				3.000	.010						3.000	.005	7		
42.															
43.															
44.															
45.															
46.															

TOLERANCE CHART. PT. NO. 12345   NAME SHAFT   MFG. ENG Nicks

20 1.015 ± .005
40 1.000 ± .001
10 1.000 ± .005
10 1.500 ± .005   30 1.485 ± .005
10 2.000 ± .005

DATE

Figure 11-7. This represents a third way a part can be machined. Note the tolerances established for cuts 7, 8 and 12.

Table 11-1

Table 11-1
Process Tolerances

Line Number		Revision Number		
		0	1	2
1	±	.002	.002	.002
2	±	.002	.002	.002
3	±	.005	.005	.005
7	±	.009	.002	.005
8	±	.009	.009	.001
12	±	.001	.001	.002
16	±	.002	.002	.002

Angle and Radius Control

Piece parts which have angle and/or radius features, and which are subject to second or finish cuts, present special problems. In such cases, special formulas for angle relationships and radius breakout must be developed. The scope of these are beyond the tolerance charting review in this chapter. The interested reader is directed to Mr. Wade's book metioned earlier in the chapter and listed in the Bibliography.

Tolerance Charting by Computer

Tolerance charting by computer is not new. General Motors developed a computer program that performs this task. However, this program is available only for General Motors divisions.

Mark Alder and Mike LaPierre, two Manufacturing Engineering students attending Ferris State College in Michigan, also wrote a computer program to perform tolerance charting. This program and a sample printout are included in this chapter. Before we review the program and sample printout, several comments should be made about the programming efforts of Alder and LaPierre.

Alder and LaPierre each spent several hundred man-hours working out the logic of tolerance charting. This effort concluded in producing a most complicated microcomputer program. It is, in fact, a study in logic.

Program Names: "T CHART 1" and "T CHART 2"

The memory required for "T CHART 1" is 11,157 bytes and the memory required for "T CHART 2" is 11,336 bytes. This computer program is written in two parts because of the computer memory required.

A 32K microcomputer has approximately 21,910 bytes of memory available to the user. The "T CHART" programs exceed this, and Alder and LaPierre developed an ingenious way around this problem. After the program computes all required balance dimensions, a sequential file on disk is established to hold all the variables. Once the variables are placed on file, "T CHART 1" is dumped from the computer's memory and "T CHART 2" is loaded into memory automatically. After "T CHART 2" is loaded, the sequential file is activated and the variables are returned to start the second round of calculations. Shown here is the sequence of inputs required by the user to execute those programs. In reviewing these steps, we also will review a typical printout produced by the program. The part selected for the printout is the same part used in *Figure 11-5*. Machining cuts 6 and 7 are again changed to represent a fourth way of machining the part.

Program Steps

1. The computer asks the user if instructions are required by the user. If answered yes, the computer then lists a series of instructions that include:
    a. How the program works.
    b. A definition of balance dimensions.
    c. A description of the final printout symbols.
    d. A definition of how planes on the part are labeled.
    e. A description of how planes on the part are labeled.
2. The user inputs the number of machining cuts and number of blueprint dimensions.
3. The computer then asks the user to input working tolerances for typical machining cuts. These tolerances will be used in the program as base tolerances unless a specific cut tolerance requires changing because it may be in the tolerance stack. Working tolerances are recorded on the first printout for user reference.
4. The number of planes of the part are inputted, which is then displayed on the CRT in chart form.
5. The computer asks the user to input each machining cut by identifying the planes. For example, the first cut is from plane one to plane five. After the input for each cut is entered, the CRT shows each cut in chart form with a dot at the locating end and an arrow at the cut end. This process continues until all cuts are entered. If a surface is not cut, the computer coaches the user to redo the input and provide this lacking information.
6. The user inputs print dimensions and tolerances by plane numbers. These data also are shown on the CRT in chart form.
7. Once the data is inputted, the screen scrolls clear and a message is printed out saying:
    a. THE COMPUTER IS CALCULATING BALANCE DIMENSIONS.
    b. THE COMPUTER IS ASSIGNING TOLERANCES.
8. The next step is to store all variables on disk file and load "T CHART 2".
9. After "T CHART 2" is loaded, and the variables are retrieved from disk file, the user is asked if he wishes a printout of instructions necessary to complete the tolerance chart. (Note: See sample printout entitled Work Sheet Instructions.)
10. Next the work sheet for tolerance distribution is printed out. (See printout example.)
    a. Note that the computer has made a preliminary tolerance assignment to all the cuts involved in the tolerance build-up or stack; i.e., cuts 1,2,4,6 and 7. Cuts 3 and 5 have no tolerance assignment because they are not involved in the tolerance build-up.
    b. The user can adjust any tolerances he wishes.
        1) Cuts 6 and 7 are given + .0002 to increase their tolerance from .0003 to .0005.
        2) Once this is accomplished, cut 4 must be adjusted because cuts 4,6 and 7 create the print dimension of .5 ± .002.
        3) Because cut 6 was adjusted by giving it more tolerance, either cut 1 or 2 must also be adjusted because cuts 1,2 and 6 form print dimension .5 ± .007.

Therefore, cut 1 is reduced by .0003.

    4)   Lastly, tolerances are assigned to cuts 3 and 5.

   c.   Once the engineer has completed the tolerance adjusting process, these new figures are entered into the computer.

11. A new work sheet is printed out that reflects the new tolerance assignments and the engineer is asked if any additional changes are to be made. If the engineer has inadvertently made any errors by exceeding the print tolerance in conducting the tolerance review, the computer coaches him about the nature of the error and how to correct it. If no such violations have been made, and if the engineer is satisfied with the tolerance assignment, the next step begins.

12. In this step, the computer asks the engineer to further define planes on the part. The computer asks if each plane is facing right or left. This information is necessary so the computer can determine if Stock Removal is to be added to or substracted from a surface.

13. Next the CRT displays each cut that has a Stock Removal and what the Minimum Stock Removal (MSR) is for that surface. The engineer than inputs a Stock Removal figure that exceeds the MSR, which the computer adds to or subtracts from the affected cut lines.

14. Next, the engineer is asked to input base dimensions for each cut.

15. The last step is a final printout of the tolerance chart.

The steps have taken much longer to explain than to perform.

WORKSHEET INSTRUCTIONS

INTRODUCTION :

    THE CHART ON THE WORKSHEET SHOWS THE BLUEPRINT DIMENSION AND TOLERANCE AS ORIGINALLY INPUTED, ALONG WITH THE NEW TOLERANCE THAT YOU MAY EXPECT AS A RESULT OF THE 'MACHINE CUT' TOLERANCES THAT ARE LISTED BELOW THE CHART.

    THE 'MACHINE CUT' TOLERANCES WERE DERIVED PROPORTIONALLY, USING (1) THE ORIGINAL BLUEPRINT TOLERANCE, (2) THE MACHINE CUTS INVOLVED IN CREATING THIS DIMENSION, AND (3) THE TYPE OF MACHINING TAKING PLACE AT EACH CUT.

    AN 'x' HAS BEEN PLACED UNDER EACH MACHINE CUT THAT THE COMPUTER HAS DETERMINED IS INVOLVED IN CREATING THIS DIMENSION.

    AT THIS POINT, THE COMPUTER HAS DONE AS MUCH AS POSSIBLE, AS FAR AS DISTRIBUTING TOLERANCES MATHEMATICALLY. IT IS UP TO YOU TO MAKE ANY NECESSARY CHANGES.

INSTRUCTIONS :

LET US SAY, FOR EXAMPLE, THAT WE HAVE A BLUEPRINT TOLERANCE OF .005 AND A NEW TOLERANCE OF .004. WE WISH TO MAKE A CHANGE TO INCREASE THE NEW TOLERANCE TO USE THE FULL .005.

(1) LOOK AT ALL THE MACHINE CUTS INVOLVED WITH THIS DIMENSION (AS MARKED 'x') AND DETERMINE WHICH OF THESE CUT TOLERANCES YOU WISH TO INCREASE BY .001. NOTE: THE .001 MAY BE DISTRIBUTED OVER MORE THAN ONE MACHINE CUT IF YOU SO DESIRE.

(2) NEXT TO THE 'x', FOR THE MACHINE CUT THAT YOU HAVE CHOSEN, WRITE IN '+.001'.

(3) NOW FOLLOW THIS MACHINE CUT COLUMN UP AND DOWN, PUTTING A '+.001' WHEREVER THERE IS A 'x' IN THAT COLUMN.

Printout 11-1

(4) TAKE NOTE THAT WHEREVER YOU HAVE ENTERED A '+.001', THE TOLERANCE OF THAT BLUEPRINT DIMENSION IS ALSO INCREASED BY .001.

(5) ADD THE .001 TO THAT MACHINE CUT IN THE BOTTOM TABLE.

(6) CONTINUE ON WITH ANY OTHER NEW TOLERANCES THAT YU WISH TO INCREASE OR DE-CREASE.

(7) ADD OR SUBTRACT ANY CHANGES IN THE BOTTOM CHART TO GET THE NEW TOLERANCE FOR EACH MACHINE CUT.

(8) ASSIGN WHATEVER TOLERANCE YOU DESIRE FOR MACHINE TOLERANCES MARKED 'NONE', AS THESE CUTS ARE NOT DIRECTLY INVOLVED IN BLUEPRINT TOLERANCES.
    NOTE: KEEP IN MIND-(A) THE HIGHER THE TOLERANCE, THE HIGHER THE STOCK REMOVAL, AND (B) THE MINIMUM TOLERANCE OF THIS OPERATION SHOULD BE OBEYED.

(9) INPUT THE NEW TOLERANCES TO RECEIVE AND UPDATED CHART INCORPORATING THE CHANGE. (YOU WILL BE ABLE TO MAKE FURTHER CHANGES IF NECESSARY.)

OPERATION TYPES

TYPE	NAME	MIN. TOL.	
1)	ROUGH CUTS	.0100	
2)	SEMI FINSH CUTS	.0050	
3)	FINISH CUTS	.0030	← —— *Working tolerances*
4)	ROUGH GRINDS	.0020	
5)	FINISH GRINDS	.0010	

REFER TO THIS TABLE WHEN ASKED FOR THE TYPE OF CUT.

WORKSHEET FOR TOLERANCE DISTRIBUTION

BLUEPRINT   MACHINE CUTS
DIMEN.+/-TOLER.

```
                    1  2  3  4  5  6  7
 1 +/-.0100        | |  |  |  |  |  |*|
(NEW) +/-.0003     | |  |  |  |  |  | |
-------------------------------------------
 .5 +/-.0020       | |  |  |*|  |*|*|
(NEW) +/-.0020     | |  |  | |  | | |
-------------------------------------------
 .5 +/-.0070       |*| *|  |  |  |*|  |
(NEW) +/-.0070     | |  |  |  |  | |  |
-------------------------------------------
 1 +/-.0100        |*| *|  |  |  |  |  |
(NEW) +/-.0067     | |  |  |  |  |  |  |
-------------------------------------------
 3 +/-.0100        | |  |  |*|  |  |  |
(NEW) +/-.0014     | |  |  | |  |  |  |
-------------------------------------------
```

MACHINE CUT	+/- TOLERANCE	CHANGES	= NEW TOLERANCE
1	.0034	– .0003	.0031
2	.0034		

Printout 11-2

264

3	NONE	+.005	.005
4	.0014	−.0004	.001
5	NONE	+.005	.005
6	.0003	+.0002	.0005
7	.0003	+.0002	.0005

WORKSHEET FOR TOLERANCE DISTRIBUTION

```
BLUEPRINT                     MACHINE CUTS
DIMEN.+/-TOLER.

                        1   2   3   4   5   6   7
 1 +/-.0100          |  |  |  |  |  |  |  |  |  |*|
(NEW) +/-.0005       |  |  |  |  |  |  |  |  |  |  |
------------------------------------------------------------
 .5 +/-.0020         |  |  |  |  |  |*|  |*|  |*|
(NEW) +/-.0020       |  |  |  |  |  |  |  |  |  |  |
------------------------------------------------------------
 .5 +/-.0070         |*|  |*|  |  |  |  |  |*|  |  |
(NEW) +/-.0070       |  |  |  |  |  |  |  |  |  |  |
------------------------------------------------------------
 1 +/-.0100          |*|  |*|  |  |  |  |  |  |  |
(NEW) +/-.0065       |  |  |  |  |  |  |  |  |  |  |
------------------------------------------------------------
 3 +/-.0100          |  |  |  |  |*|  |  |  |  |
(NEW) +/-.0010       |  |  |  |  |  |  |  |  |  |
```

MACHINE CUT	+/- TOLERANCE	CHANGES	= NEW TOLERANCE
1	.0031		
2	.0034		
3	.0050		
4	.0010		
5	.0050		
6	.0005		
7	.0005		

Final tolerance assignment

Printout 11-3

```
================================================================================
MACHINE CUTS & BALANCE DIMENSIONS

LINE
 NO.

        1           2           3           4           5        +/-    LINE
        |           |           |           |           |        TOL    INV.
  1     |*----------+-----------+-----------+----------->|        .0031  SOLID
  2     |*----------+-----------+---------->|            |        .0034  SOLID
 15     |           |           |           o-----------o        .0065  1-2
  3     |*----------+---------->|            |           |        .0050  SOLID
 18     |           |           o-----------+-----------o        .0081  1-3
  4     |<----------+-----------+-----------+-----------*        .0010  1
  5     |           |<----------+-----------+-----------*        .0050  SOLID
 17     o-----------o           |           |           |        .0060  4-5
  6     |           |           |<----------+-----------*        .0005  18
 13     o-----------+-----------o           |           |        .0015  4-6
 16     |           |           o-----------o           |        .0070  6-15
  7     |*-------->|            |           |           |        .0005  17
 14     |           o-----------o           |           |        .0020  13-7
        |           |           |           |           |
================================================================================
BLUEPRINT DIMENSIONS
                                                          LINE.INV.
        1           2           3           4           5
        |           |           |           |           |
  8     *-----------*           |           |           |        7
  9     |           *-----------*           |           |        14
 10     |           |           *-----------*           |        16
 11     |           |           |           *-----------*        15
 12     *-----------+-----------+-----------+-----------*        4
        |           |           |           |           |
================================================================================
PROCESS DIMENSIONS AND TOLERANCES

CUT
NUMBER          DIMENSION +/- TOLERANCE
  1               3.0080 +/-  .0031
  2               2.0080 +/-  .0034
  3               1.5160 +/-  .0050
  4               3.0000 +/-  .0010
  5               2.0080 +/-  .0050
  6               1.5000 +/-  .0005
  7               1.0000 +/-  .0005
```

This final printout is in standard tolerance chart form

Printout 11-4

```
5  '
10 '        TCHART      PART # 1
11 '
15 '            WRITTEN BY
16 '
17 '        MARK E. ALDER
18 '             &
19 '        MIKE A. LA PIERRE
20 REM COMPUTER APPLICATIONS FOR THE MANUFACTURING ENGINEER
21 CLS:FOR I=1 TO 6:PRINT:NEXT:PRINTCHR$(23)TAB(5)"TOLERANCE CHART":PRINTTAB(5)"
=============="
22 PRINT:PRINTTAB(8)"WRITTEN BY":PRINTTAB(6)"MARK E. ALDER":PRINT TAB(3)"MICHAEL
A. LA PIERRE"
23 PRINT:PRINT"  COPYRIGHT (C) 1981 ALL RIGHTS RESERVED"
```

Printout 11-5

```
24 CLEAR175
25 IF INKEY$=""THEN25
26 CLS:PRINTTAB(23)"TOLERANCE CHART":PRINT:INPUT"DO YOU WISH TO REVIEW THE 'INTR
ODUCTION/INSTRUCTION' (Y/N)";A$:IFA$<>"Y"ANDA$<>"N"THEN26ELSEIFA$="Y"THENGOSUB15
00
27 CLS:PRINT"SEVERAL INPUTS ARE REQUIRED TO START.....":PRINT:INPUT"ENTER THE NU
MBER OF MACHINE CUTS TO MAKE THIS PART";Z8:PRINT:INPUT"ENTER THE TOTAL NUMBER OF
 BLUEPRINT DIMENSIONS";Z9
28 IFZ9<Z8THENZ9=Z8
30 DIMT(Z8+5,7),P(Z9+5,7),B(75,7),L(25,2),A$(80):G$=".####":IFA$="Y"THENGOSUB160
0:GOSUB1210:ELSEGOSUB1210
40 REM SUB TO PRINT PLANE LINES
41 CLS:PRINT"YOU WILL NOW BE ASKED TO INPUT THE LOCATING SURFACE AND THE SUR-FAC
E TO BE CUT, FOR EACH MACHINE CUT, ALONG WITH THE TYPE OF CUT(FROM THE TABLE JUS
T PRINTED OUT).":PRINT:PRINT"SIMPLY HIT 'ENTER' WHEN ALL CUTS HAVE BEEN ENTERED.
":GOSUB2000
50 PRINT:INPUT"HOW MANY SURFACES ARE GOING TO BE MACHINED ON THIS PART";A1:IFA1<
31ANDA1>2THEN70ELSECLS:IFA1>30THENG$="MAXIMUM OF 30"ELSEG$="MINIMUM OF 3"
60 PRINT:PRINTTAB(5)"*** ENTRY ERROR ***":PRINT:PRINT"THIS HAS A ";G$;" PLANES":
PRINT:PRINT"PLEASE TRY AGAIN":GOSUB2000:GOTO50
70 DIMR(A1):AA=INT(64/(A1+1)):CLS:A3=1:A2=A1:GOTO120
80 CLS:A3=1:A2=A1:FORC1=1TOA1:FORC=1TOB-1:IFT(C,3)=C1THENNEXTC1:IFLP<>0THEN100EL
SE265ELSENEXTC
90 PRINT"PLANE NUMBER";C1;"HAS NOT BEEN CUT":LP=LP+1:NEXTC1
100 PRINT:PRINT"PLEASE REDO AND CUT THESE":GOSUB2000:B=0:CN=0:Y=0:N=0
110 REM SUB FOR MACHINE CUTS
120 LP=0:CLS:GOSUB390
130 B=B+1:PRINT@953,"* ":PRINT@916,"*    ";:PRINT@960,"NUMBER OF CUTS MADE:";B-1;
:PRINT@932,"*   ";:PRINT@896,"LOCATING SURFACE NO.";:INPUTT(B,2):IFT(B,2)=0THEN8
0ELSEIFT(B,2)>A1ORT(B,2)<0THENB=B-1:GOTO130ELSECN=CN+1
140 PRINT@920,"MACHINE TO";:INPUTT(B,3):IFT(B,3)>A1ORT(B,3)=T(B,2)ORT(B,3)<1THEN
140ELSET(B,1)=CN
150 PRINT@940,"TYPE OF CUT";:INPUTRE:IFRE>5THEN150ELSEIFA(RE)=0THEN150ELSET(B,6)
=A(RE):Y=Y+1:N=N+64:IFT(B,3)>T(B,2)THENA$=">"ELSEA$=" <"
160 IFT(B,2)>T(B,3)THEN170ELSEPRINT@(((AA*T(B,2)))+N+1),"-";:A2=T(B,3):A3=T(B,2)
:GOTO180
170 A2=T(B,2):A3=T(B,3):PRINT@(((AA*T(B,3)))+N+1),"-";
180 FORA=1TO((AA*ABS(T(B,2)-T(B,3)))-2):PRINT"-";:NEXT:IFA$=">"THENPRINT@(((AA*T
(B,2)))+N)," *";:PRINT@(((AA*T(B,3)))+N-1),A$;:ELSEPRINT@(((AA*T(B,2)))+N-1),"*";
:PRINT@(((AA*T(B,3)))+N),A$;
190 IFY=13THENPRINT@896,STRING$(60," ");:FOR C=1 TO 12:PRINT:NEXT:PRINT@0,STRING
$(60," ");:PRINT@64,"CUT";:PRINTB;:N=128:Y=2:A3=1:A2=A1
200 GOSUB390:GOTO130
210 CLS:PRINT:FORI=1 TO A1:FOR J=1 TO D-1:IF P(J,2)=IORP(J,3)=ITHENNEXTIELSENEXT
J:GOTO240
220 GOTO340
240 CLS:PRINT:PRINT"PLANE NO. ";I;"HAS NOT BEEN GIVEN ANY DIMENSION TO REFERENCE
 IT   FROM.":PRINT"THERE WILL BE NO BASIS WITH WHICH TO CALCULATE A MACHINE CUT
TO CREATE THIS SURFACE.":PRINT"PLEASE REDO THE DIMENSION TABLE AND CORRECT THIS.
"
250 GOSUB2000
260 REM BLUEPRINT DIMENSIONS
265 CLS:PRINT:PRINTTAB(20)"BLUEPRINT DIMENSIONS":PRINT:PRINT"YOU WILL NOW BE ASK
ED TO INPUT THE SURFACES THAT EACH BLUEPRINT DIMENSION GOES FROM-TO, ALONG WITH
THE DIMENSION AND TOLERANCE":PRINT
266 PRINT"NOTE: EVERY SURFACE THAT IS BEING MACHINED MUST HAVE A DIMENSIONASSOCI
ATED WITH IT.":GOSUB2000
270 Y=2:CLS:GOSUB390:Y=0:CN=B-1:M=0:D=0
280 PRINT@768," ":D=D+1:PRINT@960,"NUMBER OF PRINT DIMENSIONS ENTERED:";:PRINTD
-1;:PRINT@832," ":PRINT@832,"FROM SURFACE NUMBER";:INPUTP(D,2):IFP(D,2)=0THEN21
0ELSEIFP(D,2)>A1THEND=D-1:GOTO280
290 PRINT@864,"TO SURFACE NUMBER";:INPUTP(D,3):IFP(D,3)>A1ORP(D,3)<1THEN290ELSEC
N=CN+1:Y=Y+1:PRINT@896,"B.P. DIMENSION";:INPUTP(D,4):PRINT@928,"TOLERANCE, + OR
-";:INPUTP(D,5):P(D,1)=CN:M=M+64:IFP(D,3)<P(D,2)THEND1=P(D,2):P(D,2)=P(D,3):P(D,
3)=D1
```

Printout 11-5 continued

```
300 IF P(D,5)>=1 THEN P(D,5)=P(D,5)/1000
310 M1=(P(D,3)-P(D,2))*AA:PRINT@(P(D,2)*AA+M),STRING$(M1,"-");:PRINT@(P(D,2)*AA+
M),"*";:PRINT@((P(D,3)*AA-1)+M),"*";:PRINTP(D,4);:IFY=12THENM=128:PRINT@640,STRI
NG$(63," ");:PRINT@832,STRING$(63," ");:FORC=1TO12:PRINT:NEXT:A3=1:A2=A1:Y=2:GOS
UB390
320 GOTO280
340 D1=1:GOSUB410:PRINT@512,"DUE TO THE LENGTH OF THIS PROGRAM, WE ARE NOW STORI
NG YOUR DATA ON DISC AND LOADING THE SECOND HALF OF THE PROGRAM";:OPEN"O",1,"DAT
A":PRINT#1,A1,B,D,Z
350 FOR X=1 TO B-1:FOR Y=1 TO 7:PRINT#1,T(X,Y):NEXTY,X
360 FOR X=1 TO D-1:FOR Y=1 TO 7:PRINT#1,P(X,Y):NEXTY,X
370 FOR X=1 TO Z  :FOR Y=1 TO 7:PRINT#1,B(X,Y):NEXTY,X
380 CLOSE:RUN"TCHART2"
390 FORA=A3TOA2:FORC=(15424+(AA*A))TO16255STEP64:POKEC,149:NEXTC:NEXTA:IF(N=0)OR
(Y=2)THENIFA1>20THENFORA=2TOA1STEP2:PRINT@((AA*A)-2),A;:NEXTELSEFORA=1TOA1:PRINT
@((AA*A)-2),A;:NEXT
400 RETURN
410 REM TRACKING TO FIND CUTS
420 IFD1=1THENBB=B:FORD1=1TOD-1ELSEFORD1=B-1TO1STEP-1:H=0:I=0:BB=D1
425 IFD1=1THENPRINT".....AND WE'RE OFF !!!!!!!!":PRINT@128,"THE COMPUTER IS NOW C
REATING BALANCE LINES TO REACH PRINT      DIMENSIONS.";
430 Z9=Z:FORB1=BB-1TO1STEP-1:IFT(B1,3)=P(D1,2)THENH=B1ELSENEXTB1
440 FORB1=BB-1TO1STEP-1:IFT(B1,3)=P(D1,3)THENI=B1ELSENEXTB1
450 X=H:XX=I:IFX<ITHENX=I:XX=H
460 IFT(X,3)>T(X,2)THENIFT(X,2)=P(D1,2)THENP(D1,6)=X:GOTO750
470 IFT(X,3)<T(X,2)THENIFT(X,2)=P(D1,3)THENP(D1,6)=X:GOTO750
480 IFI=0THENIFP(D1,3)=T(D1,3)THENFORJ=1TOD1-1:IFT(J,2)=P(D1,3)THEN510ELSENEXT:P
(D1,6)=.999:GOTO750
490 IFH=0THENIFP(D1,2)=T(D1,3)THENFORJ=1TOD1-1:IFT(J,2)=P(D1,2)THEN510ELSENEXT:P
(D1,6)=.999:GOTO750
500 REM TO FIND ALL LINES INVOLVED
510 S3=1:S4=1:L(1,1)=XX:L(1,2)=X:S5=XX:S6=X
520 FORS1=S6-1TO0STEP-1:IFS1=0THENS4=S4+1:S6=0:L(S4,2)=999:GOTO530ELSEIFT(S1,3)=
T(S6,2)THENS4=S4+1:L(S4,2)=T(S1,1):S6=T(S1,1)ELSENEXTS1
530 IFS6>S5THENNEXTS1ELSEIFS6=S5THEN570ELSE540
540 IFS5=1THENS3=S3+1:L(S3,1)=999:GOTO570
550 FORS2=S5-1TO0STEP-1:IFS2=0THENS3=S3+1:L(S3,1)=999:S5=0:GOTO560ELSEIFT(S2,3)=
T(S5,2)THENS3=S3+1:L(S3,1)=T(S2,1):S5=T(S2,1)ELSENEXTS2
560 IFS5>S6THEN550ELSEIFS5=S6THEN570ELSEIFS2=0ANDS1=0THEN570ELSE520
570 IFS3<S4THENCC=S4ELSECC=S3
580 IFS3-1=0THENFA=L(S4-2,2):FB=L(S4-2,2):GOTO610ELSEIFS4-1=0THENFA=L(S3-1,1):FB
=L(S3-2,1):GOTO610ELSEIFL(S3-1,1)<L(S4-1,2)THENFA=L(S3-1,1):GOTO600ELSEFA=L(S4-1
,2):IFS4-2=0THENFB=L(S3-1,2)ELSEIFL(S4-2,2)<L(S3-1,1)THENFB=L(S4-2,2)ELSEFB=L(S3
-1,1)
590 GOTO610
600 IFS3-2=0THENFB=L(S4-1,2)ELSEIFL(S3-2,1)<L(S4-1,2)THENFB=L(S3-2,1)ELSEFB=L(S4
-1,2)
610 IFT(FA,2)=T(FB,2)THENB6=FA:B7=FB:B2=T(FB,3):B3=T(FA,3):GOTO650
620 IFT(FA,2)=T(FB,3)THENIF(T(FA,2)>T(FA,3)ANDT(FB,2)>T(FB,3))OR(T(FA,2)<T(FA,3)
ANDT(FB,2)<T(FB,3))THENB6=FA:B7=FB:B2=T(FA,3):B3=T(FB,2):GOTO650
630 IFT(FB,2)=T(FA,3)THENIF(T(FA,2)>T(FA,3)ANDT(FB,2)>T(FB,3))OR(T(FA,2)<T(FA,3)
ANDT(FB,2)<T(FB,3))THENB6=FA:B7=FB:B2=T(FB,3):B3=T(FA,2):GOTO650
640 IFT(FB,2)=T(FA,3)THENB6=FA:B7=FB:B2=T(FB,3):B3=T(FA,2):GOTO650ELSEIFT(FB,3)=
T(FA,2)THENB6=FA:B7=FB:B2=T(FA,3):B3=T(FB,2)
650 GOSUB1160:FF=FB:CA=1
660 FORC=1TOCC:IFL(C,1)=FF+CATHENFB=L(C,1):GOTO680ELSEIFL(C,2)=FF+CATHENFB=L(C,2
):GOTO680ELSENEXTC
670 CA=CA+1:IFCA>B-1THEN740ELSE660
680 IFB(Z9,2)<>T(FB,2)ANDB(Z9,3)<>T(FB,2)THENCLS:PRINT"ERRATIC MACHINING IS TAKI
NG PLACE. tHE PART CANNOT BE MACHINED LIKE THIS.":GOSUB200:RUN
690 IFT(FB,3)>B(Z9,3)ANDT(FB,2)=B(Z9,3)THENB6=Z9+B+D-2:B7=FB:B2=B(Z9,2):B3=T(FB,
3):GOSUB1160:GOTO670
700 IFT(FB,3)<B(Z9,2)ANDT(FB,2)=B(Z9,2)THENB6=Z9+D+B-2:B7=FB:B2=T(FB,3):B3=B(Z9,
3):GOSUB1160:GOTO670
710 IFT(FB,3)>B(Z9,2)ANDT(FB,3)<B(Z9,3)THENIFT(FB,2)=B(Z9,3)THENB6=Z9+D+B-2:B7=F
```

Printout 11-5 continued

268

```
B:B2=B(Z9,2):B3=T(FB,3):GOSUB1160:GOTO670ELSEIFT(FB,2)=B(Z9,2)THENB6=Z9+D+B-2:B7
=FB:B2=T(FB,3):B3=B(Z9,3):GOSUB1160:GOTO670
720 IFT(FB,3)>B(Z9,3)THENB6=Z9+D+B-2:B7=FB:B2=B(Z9,3):B3=T(FB,3):GOSUB1160:GOTO6
70ELSEIFT(FB,3)<B(Z9,2)THENB6=Z9+D+B-2:B7=FB:B2=T(FB,3):B3=B(Z9,2):GOSUB1160:GOT
0670
730 CLS:PRINT"ERRATIC MACHINING IS TAKING PLACE.  THIS PART CANNOT BE MACHINED L
IKE THIS!!!!":GOSUB200:RUN
740 IFB(Z9,2)=P(D1,2)ANDB(Z9,3)=P(D1,3)THENP(D1,6)=B(Z9,1)ELSESTOP
750 NEXTD1:IF F2<>0 THEN RETURN
760 REM TO ASSIGN TOL PO BAL DIM & MACH CUTS
770 TP=B+D-2:FORTB=1TOD-1:TL=P(TB,5):TF=0:IFP(TB,6)<TPTHENIFT(P(TB,6),5)>TLORT(P
(TB,6),5)=0THENT(P(TB,6),5)=TL:GOTO850ELSE850
780 TC=P(TB,6)-TP
790 T6=B(TC,6):T7=B(TC,7):IFT6<TPANDT7<TPTHEN800ELSETF=T(T7,6)+TF:TC=B(TC,6)-TP:
GOTO790
800 TF=TF+T(T6,6)+T(T7,6):TC=(P(TB,6)-TP)
810 T6=B(TC,6):T7=B(TC,7):IFT6<TPANDT7<TPTHEN830ELSET9=(T(T7,6)/TF)*TL:IFT(T7,5)
>T9ORT(T7,5)=0THENT(T7,5)=T9
820 TL=TL-T(T7,5):TF=TF-T(T7,6):TC=B(TC,6)-TP:GOTO810
830 T8=(T(T7,6)/TF)*TL:T9=(T(T7,6)/TF)*TL:IFT(T7,5)>T8ORT(T7,5)=0THENT(T7,5)=T8E
LSET9=T8-T(T6,5)+T9
840 IFT(T7,5)>T9ORT(T7,5)=0THENT(T7,5)=T9
850 PRINT@256,"TOLERANCES ARE NOW BEING DISTRIBUTED TO THE MACHINE CUTS.";:NEXTT
B
1080 REM SHIFT PRINT DIM TABLE (P) TO TABLE P1 - SET TAB P TO 0 THEN GOSUB FOR S
TOCK REM BAL DIM
1090 DIMP1(D-1,7):FORF2=1TOD-1:FORF3=1TO7:P1(F2,F3)=P(F2,F3):P(F2,F3)=0:NEXTF3,F
2:GOSUB1160:FORF2=1TOB-1:FORF3=1TO3:P(F2,F3)=T(F2,F3):NEXTF3:XX=P(F2,2):IFXX>P(F
2,3)THENP(F2,2)=P(F2,3):P(F2,3)=XX
1100 NEXTF2:PRINT@384,"JOW WE'RE CREATING BALANCE DIMENSIONS FOR STOCK REMOVAL."
;:GOSUB420:FORF2=1TOB-1:T(F2,7)=P(F2,6):NEXTF2:FORF2=1TOD-1:FORF3=1TO7:P(F2,F3)=
P1(F2,F3):NEXTF3,F2
1110 FORTB=1TOB-1:TL=0:IFT(TB,7)=.999THENT(TB,6)=.999:GOTO1140ELSEIFT(TB,7)<BTHE
NT(TB,6)=T(TB,5)+T(T(TB,7),5):GOTO1140ELSETC=T(TB,7)-TP
1120 T6=B(TC,6):T7=B(TC,7):IFT6<BANDT7<BTHENTL=T(T6,5)+T(T7,5)+TL:GOTO1130ELSETL
=TL+T(T7,5):TC=B(TC,6)-TP:GOTO1120
1130 T(TB,6)=TL+T(TB,5)
1140 NEXTTB:RETURN
1150 REM CREATE BAL DIM AND ORGANIZE THE TABLE
1160 Z=Z+1:CN=CN+1:B(Z,2)=B2:B(Z,3)=B3:B(Z,1)=CN:B(Z,7)=B7:B(Z,6)=B6:C=Z:IFB(C,2
)>B(C,3)THENMM=B(C,3):B(C,3)=B(C,2):B(C,2)=MM
1170 IFB(C,6)>B(C,7)THENIFB(C,6)<BTHENMM=B(C,6):B(C,6)=B(C,7):B(C,7)=MM
1180 REM SUB TO FIND ANY OF THA SAME BALANCE DIM
1190 IFZ<2THENZ9=1:RETURNELSEFORC=1TOZ-1:IFB(C,2)=B(Z,2)ANDB(C,3)=B(Z,3)ANDB(C,6
)=B(Z,6)ANDB(C,7)=B(Z,7)THENZ=Z-1:CN=CN-1ELSENEXT
1200 Z9=C:RETURN
1210 CLS:PRINT@15,"MINIMUM OPERATIONAL TOLERANCES":PRINT:PRINT:S$(1)="1) ROUGH C
UTS":S$(2)="2) SEMI FINSH CUTS":S$(3)="3) FINISH CUTS":S$(4)="4) ROUGH GRINDS":S
$(5)="5) FINISH GRINDS":PRINT:FORW=1TO5:PRINTS$(W):NEXT:PRINT
1220 PRINT"ENTER THE MINIMUN OPERATION TOLERANCES THAT CAN BE HANDLED KN    THE P
ROCESS EQUIPMENT. THESE TOLERANCES WILL BE A BASIS FOR       ASSIGNING TOLERANCES
TO THE MACHINE CUTS."
1240 K=213:FORW=1TO5:K=K+64:PRINT@K," ";:INPUTA(W):PRINTS$(W+1);:NEXT
1245 LPRINTTAB(10)"OPERATION TYPES":LPRINT" ":LPRINT"TYPE"TAB(9)"NAME"TAB(20)"MI
N. TOL.":FORQ=1TO5:IFA(Q)=0THENNEXT:GOTO1246ELSELPRINTTAB(1)S$(Q):TAB(22)USINGG$
;A(Q):NEXT
1246 LPRINT" ":LPRINT" ":LPRINT"REFER TO THIS TABLE WHEN ASKED FOR THE TYPE OF C
UT.":FORQ=1TO5:LPRINT" ":NEXT
1250 RETURN
1500 CLS:PRINT"WELCOME TO PHE WORLD OF TOLERANCE CHARTING !!!!":PRINT:PRINT"PRES
S ANY KEY ON YOUR KEYBOARD WHEN YOU WISH TO CONTINUE.":GOSUB2000
1510 PRINT:PRINT"THIS PROGRAM IS DESIGNED TO ALLOW THE USER TO INPUT THE
 MACHINING SEQUENCE THAT IS TO TAKE PLACE ON A PART AND          THE BLUEPRINT D
IMENSIONS THAT ARE TO BE CREATED AS A RESULT.":GOSUB2000
```

Printout 11-5 continued

```
1520 PRINT:PRINT"BALANCE DIMENSIONS ARE THEN COMPUTED AS NEEDED TO REACH EACH OF
     THE BLUEPRINT DIMENSIONS.":GOSUB2000
1530 PRINT:PRINT"A BALANCE DIMENSION IS A DIMENSION THAT IS  CREATED  AS A RESUL
T OF ADDING OR SUBTRACTING TWO MACHINE CUTS, OR A MACHINE CUT AND ANOTHER BALANC
E DIMENSION.":GOSUB2000
1540 CLS:PRINT:PRINT"THIS PROGRAM IS DESIGNED TO COACH YOU ALL THE WAY THROUGH."
     :GOSUB2000
1550 PRINT:PRINT"ON THE FINAL PRINT-OUT THAT YOU WILL RECEIVE, A BALANCE DIMEN-
     SION WILL BE DESIGNATED AS o--------------------o ,WITH THE CUTS INVOLVED IN ARR
IVING AT THIS DIMEJSION EXPLAINED TO THE RIGHT.":GOSUB2000
1560 PRINT:PRINT"A MACHINE CUT WILL ALWAYS BE DESIGNATED WITH A DOT AND ARROW,
     *---------------> , WITH THE DOT BEING ON THE LOCATING SURFACE  AND THE ARROW O
N THE CUT SURFACE.":GOSUB2000
1561 CLS:PRINT@0,"CENTER ";STRING$(20,"-");"  --  ";STRING$(20,"-");:FORI=1537
0TO15500STEP64:POKEI,149::POKEI+40,170:NEXT:PRINT@64," LINE";:PRINT@84,"SAMPLE P
ART (4 SURFACES)";:PRINT@320," "
1562 FORI=15562TO15573:POKEI,131:POKEI+29,131:NEXT:FORI=15574TO15700STEP64:POKEI
,149:POKEI+17,170:NEXT:FORI=15702 TO15719:POKEI,131:NEXT
1563 PRINT@201,"1";:PRINT@341,"2";:PRINT@360,"3";:PRINT@243,"4";
1570 PRINT@384,"THE FIRST STEP IS TO LABEL ALL SURFACES ON THE PRINT LIKE THE
     EXAMPLE ABOVE"
1580 PRINTTAB(5)"(2) NUMBER EACH OPERATION CUT IN THE ORDER THAT THE PART
     WILL BE MACHINED: 1,2,3,4,5...ETC.":GOSUB2000
1590 PRINTTAB(5)"(3) NUMBER EACH BLUEPRINT DIIENSION, IN ANY ORDER, 1,2,3,4,
     5...ETC.":GOSUB2000:RETURN
1600 CLS:PRINT:PRINT:PRINT"  YOU WILL NOW BE ASKED TO ENTER THIS INFORMATION INT
O THE  COMPUTER.":PRINT:PRINT"THE FIRST INPUTS WILL BE OPERATION TOLERANCES.":GO
SUB 2000
1610 PRINT:PRINT"YOU WILL BE ASKED TO INPUT THE MINIMUM TOLERANCE THAT CAN BE
     HELD FOR THIS TYPE OF OPERATION.":PRINT:PRINT"IF ANY OF THE OPERATIONS DO NOT A
PPLY TO THE MACHINING$OF PHIS  PART, SIMPLY HIT 'ENTER'.":GOSUB2000:RETURN
2000 IFINKEY$=""THEN2000ELSERETURN
```

————————— **Printout 11-5 continued** —————————

```
10 CLS:PRINT@459," ";:PRINTCHR$(23)"TOLERANCE CHART":PRINTTAB(10)"PART 2":PRINT:
PRINTTAB(9)"WRITTEN BY":PRINTTAB(7)"MARK E. ALDER":PRINTTAB(4)"MICHAEL A. LA PIE
RRE":PRINT
12 PRINTTAB(5)"COPYRIGHT (C) 1981"
20 CLEAR175:G$="  ,####"
30 OPEN"I",1,"DATA":INPUT#1,A1,B,D,Z:DIMT(B,7),P(D,7),D$(A1),B(Z,7),A$(80):FORX=
1TOB-1:FORY=1TO7:INPUT#1,T(X,Y):NEXTY,X
40 FORX=1TOD-1:FORY=1TO7:INPUT#1,P(X,Y):NEXTY,X
50 FORX=1TOZ:FORY=1TO7:INPUT#1,B(X,Y):NEXTY,X:CLOSE
60 GOSUB1010:GOSUB540  :FORC=1TO80:LPRINTCHR$(61);:NEXT:LPRINTTAB(16)"MACHINE CU
TS & BALANCE DIMENSIONS":LPRINT" ":LPRINT"LINE":LPRINT" NO.":LPRINT" "
70 REM TO PRINT CHART
80 BA=60/(A1+1):FORBB=0TOB:FORNA=1TO80:A$(NA)=" ":NEXT:IFBB<>0THEN100  ELSEIFA1>
16THENFORNA=7+BATO71-BASTEPBA*2ELSEFORNA=7+BATO71-BASTEPBA:AN=NA:IM=IM+1:B$=RIGH
T$(STR$(IM),1):IFIM>A1THEN175  ELSEIFIM>9THENA7=A7+1:AN=AN-A7:B$=RIGHT$(STR$(IM)
,2)
90 A$(AN)=B$:NEXT:GOTO175
100 FORNA=7+BATO71-BASTEPBA:A$(NA)=CHR$(124):NEXT:NX=NX+1:IFNX=1THEN175  ELSEB2=
BA*ABS(T(BB,3)-T(BB,2))-2:IFB2<0THEN175  ELSEIFT(BB,2)>T(BB,3)THENNB=T(BB,3)*BA+
7:A$(NB+1)="<"ELSE140
110 FORNC=NB+1TONB+B2+1:IFA$(NC)=" "THENA$(NC)="-"
120 IFA$(NC)=CHR$(124)THENA$(NC)="+"
130 NEXT:A$(NC)="*":GOTO170
140 NB=T(BB,2)*BA+7:A$(NB+1)="*":FORNC=NB+1TONB+B2+1:IFA$(NC)=" "THENA$(NC)="-"
150 IFA$(NC)=CHR$(124)THENA$(NC)="+"
160 NEXT:IFA$(NC)=CHR$(124)ORA$(NC)="+"THENA$(NC-1)=">"ELSEA$(NC)=">"
170 LPRINTBB;
175 FORNC=7+BATO71-BA:LPRINTTAB(7);A$(NC);:NEXT:JK=((BA*(A1-1)+12))
```

Printout 11-6

```
180 IFBB=BTHEN190  ELSEIFBB=0THENLPRINTTAB(JK)" +/-    LINE":NEXTBBELSEIFBB=NXTHE
NLPRINTTAB(JK)" TOL   INV.":GOTO100:ELSEIFNX=1THENLPRINT" ":GOTO100  ELSELPRINTT
AB(JK)USINGG$;T(BB,5);:LPRINT" ";:IFT(BB,7)=.999THENLPRINT"SOLID"ELSELPRINTT(BB,
7)
190 FORZ1=1TOZ:IFB(Z1,7)>B+D-2THENBZ=B(Z1,7)-B-D+2:IFB(BZ,7)<BORB(BZ,6)>BBTHEN28
0  ELSE220
200 IFB(Z1,7)<(D+B-2)THEN210  ELSEIFB(Z1,6)<>BBTHEN280  ELSE220
210 IFB(Z1,7)<>BBTHEN280
220 B3=BA*ABS(B(Z1,3)-B(Z1,2))-2
230 REM CHART FOR BAL DIM
240 GOSUB440  :FORNA=0TO80:A$(NA)=" ":NEXT:FORNB=7+BATO71-BASTEPBA:A$(NB)=CHR$(1
24):NEXT:NF=B(Z1,2)*BA+7:A$(NF)="o":FORNG=NF+1TONF+B3+2:IFA$(NG)=" "THENA$(NG)="
-"
250 IFA$(NG)=CHR$(124)THENA$(NG)="+"
260 NEXTNG:A$(NF+2+B3)="o":IFJ2<10THENF$="##!#"ELSEF$="##!##"
270 LPRINTB(Z1,1);:FORNG=7+BATO71-BA:LPRINTTAB(7)A$(NG);:NEXT:LPRINTTAB((BA*(A1-
1)+12))USINGG$;B(Z1,5);:LPRINT" ";USINGF$;J1;D$;J2
280 NEXTZ1:NEXTBB:LPRINT" ":FORC=1TO80:LPRINTCHR$(61);:NEXT:LPRINTTAB(16)"BLUEPR
INT DIMENSIONS":LPRINTTAB(JK-2)"LINE.INV."
290 REM TO PRINT B.P. DIM
300 A7=0:AN=0:IM=0:NX=0:FORD2=0TOD:FORNA=1TO80:A$(NA)=" ":NEXT:IFD2<>0THEN320  E
LSEFORNA=7+BATO71-BASTEPBA:AN=NA:IM=IM+1:B$=RIGHT$(STR$(IM),1):IFIM>A1THEN350  E
LSEIFIM>9THENA7=A7+1:AN=AN-A7
310 A$(AN)=B$:NEXT:GOTO350
320 FORNA=7+BATO71-BASTEPBA:A$(NA)=CHR$(124):NEXTNA:NX=NX+1:IFNX=1THEN350  ELSED
D=BA*(P(D2,3)-P(D2,2))-2:IFD2=DTHEN350  ELSENB=P(D2,2)*BA+7:A$(NB)="*":FORNC=NB+
1TONB+DD+1:IFA$(NC)=" "THENA$(NC)="-"
330 IFA$(NC)=CHR$(124)THENA$(NC)="+"
340 NEXT:A$(NC)="*":LPRINTP(D2,1);
350 FORNC=7+BATO71-BA:LPRINTTAB(7);A$(NC);:NEXT:IFD2>0ANDD2<DANDNX>1THENLPRINTP(
D2,6):NEXTD2ELSELPRINT" ":IFNX=1THEN320  ELSENEXTD2:LPRINT" ":FORI=1TO80:LPRINT"
=";:NEXT
360 LPRINT"PROCESS DIMENSIONS AND TOLERANCES":LPRINT" ":LPRINT" CUT":LPRINT"NUMB
ER"TAB(16)"DIMENSION +/- TOLERANCE"
370 R$=" +/- ":FOR I=1 TO B-1:LPRINT" ";T(I,1);:LPRINTTAB(18)USING"##.####";T(I,
4);:LPRINTR$;:LPRINTUSINGG$;T(I,5):NEXT
380 FOR I=1 TO 5:LPRINT" ":NEXT
390 CLS:PRINT"HERE IS THE FINAL COPY OF YOUR TOLERANCE CHART."
400 PRINT:PRINT"AT THE BOTTOM OF THE CHART IS A LIST OF THE MACHINE CUT DIMENSIO
NS TO BE USED ON YOUR PROCESS DIMENSIONS."
410 PRINT:PRINT"WOULD YOU LIKE TO:":PRINT:PRINT"(1) RUN THE PROGRAM AGAIN":PRINT
"(2) END THE PROGRAM":PRINT:INPUT"ENTER THE NUMBER";CC:IFCC=1THENRUN"TCHART1"ELS
ECLS:END
440 REM SUB TO ASSIGN LININV FOR PRINTOUT
450 IFB(Z1,6)<BTHEN470  ELSEJA=B(Z1,6)-D-B+2:JB=B(Z1,7):IFB(JA,2)=T(JB,2)THENIFT
(JB,3)<T(JB,2)THEND$="+":J1=B(Z1,6):J2=B(Z1,7):RETURNELSEIFT(JB,3)<B(JA,3)THEND$
="-":J1=B(Z1,6):J2=B(Z1,7):RETURNELSED$="-":J1=B(Z1,7):J2=B(Z1,6):RETURN
460 IFT(JB,3)>T(JB,2)THEND$="+":J1=B(Z1,6):J2=B(Z1,7):RETURNELSEIFT(JB,3)>B(JA,2
)THEND$="-":J1=B(Z1,6):J2=B(Z1,7):RETURNELSED$="-":J1=B(Z1,7):J2=B(Z1,6):RETURN
470 G1=B(Z1,6):G2=B(Z1,7):IFT(G1,2)=T(G2,2)THEN480  ELSEIF(T(G1,2)>T(G1,3)ANDT(G
2,3)>T(G2,2))OR(T(G1,2)<T(G1,3)ANDT(G2,3)<T(G2,2))THEND$="-":J1=G1:J2=G2:RETURNE
LSED$="+":J1=G1:J2=G2:RETURN
480 IF(T(G1,2)>T(G1,3)ANDT(G2,3)>T(G2,2))OR(T(G1,2)<T(G1,3)ANDT(G2,3)<T(G2,2))TH
END$="+":J1=G1:J2=G2:RETURNELSED$="-":IFABS(T(G1,2)-T(G1,3))>ABS(T(G2,2)-T(G2,3)
)THENJ1=G1:J2=G2:RETURNELSEJ1=G2:J2=G2:RETURN
490 LPRINTSTRING$(75,"-"):NEXT:FORXX=1TO5:LPRINT" ":NEXT:CLS
500 FORTB=1TOB-1:TL=0:IFT(TB,7)=.999THENT(TB,6)=.999:GOTO530  ELSEIFT(TB,7)<BTHE
NT(TB,6)=T(TB,5)+T(T(TB,7),5):GOTO530  ELSETC=P(TB,6)-TP
510 T6=B(TC,6):T7=B(TC,7):IFT6<BANDT7<BTHENTL=T(T6,5)+T(T7,5)+TL:GOTO520  ELSETL
=TL+T(T7,5):TC=B(TC,6)-TP:GOTO510
520 T(TB,6)=TL+T(TB,5)
530 NEXTTB
540 CLS:PRINT@0,"CENTER ";STRING$(20,"-");"  --  ";STRING$(20,"-");:FOR I=1537
0 TO 15500STEP64:POKE I,149:POKEI+40,170:NEXT:PRINT@64," LINE";:PRINT@84,"SAMPLE
 PART (4 SURFACES)";:PRINT@320," "
```

Printout 11-6 continued

```
550 FOR I=15562 TO 15573:POKEI,131:POKEI+29,131:NEXT
560 FOR I=15574 TO 15700STEP64:POKEI,149:POKEI+17,170:NEXT
570 FOR I=15702 TO 15719:POKEI,131:NEXT:EE=268:TT=0:R$="LEFT--->"
580 REM SUB FOR CUT DIRECTION & FINDING DIMENSIONS
590 PRINT"YOU ARE ASKED HERE TO INPUT WHICH DIRECTION THE SURFACE FACES - LEFT O
R RIGHT ('L' OR 'R') - THE SURFACE THAT THE STOCK WILL BE ADDED BACK ON.   ";
600 PRINT"(IN THIS SAMPLE: SURFACES 1&2 ARE 'L' WHILE    SURFACES 3&4 ARE 'R')":
PRINT@201,"1";:PRINT@341,"2";:PRINT@360,"3";:PRINT@243,"4";
610 FOR I=1 TO 3:PRINT@EE,"        ";:FORJ=1 TO 100:NEXT
620 PRINT@EE,R$;:FOR J=1 TO 300:NEXTJ,I
630 IF TT<>1 THEN R$="<---RIGHT":TT=1:EE=297:GOTO610  ELSEPRINT@705,"* * YOUR PA
RT HAS";A1;"SURFACES * *"
640 FORXX=1TOA1:PRINT"WHICH DIRECTION IS SURFACE";XX;:INPUT"FACING ";D$(XX):D$(X
X)=LEFT$(D$(XX),1):IF D$(XX)<>"L"ANDD$(XX)<>"R"THENPRINT"USE 'L' OR 'R' ONLY!!!"
:XX=XX-1
650 NEXTXX
655 FORTB=1TOB-1:TL=0:IFT(TB,7)=.999THENT(TB,6)=.999:GOTO658ELSEIFT(TB,7)<BTHENT
(TB,6)=T(TB,5)+T(T(TB,7),5):GOTO658ELSETC=T(TB,7)-TP
656 T6=B(TC,6):T7=B(TC,7):IFT6<BANDT7<BTHENTL=T(T6,5)+T(T7,5)+TL:GOTO657ELSETL=T
L+T(T7,5):TC=B(TC,6)-TP:GOTO656
657 T(TB,6)=TL+T(TB,5)
658 NEXTTB
660 CLS:PRINT"YOU ARE NOW ASKED TO INPUT THE AMOUNT OF STOCK TO BE REMOVED.":PRI
NT"* NOTE: THIS MUST EXCEED THE MINIMUM STOCK REMOVAL (M.S.R.).":PRINT"INPUT C
AN BE EITHER IN THOUSANDS OR DECIMAL NUMBERS (10 OR .010)"
670 PRINT:PRINT"MACHINE CUT","M.S.R.","DESIRED S.R.":PRINT
680 FORXX=1TOB-1:SR=T(XX,6):IFSR=.999THENNEXTXX:GOTO730  ELSEPRINTTAB(4)XX;:PRIN
TTAB(16)USINGG$;SR;:PRINTTAB(35)"?";:INPUTT(XX,6)
690 IF T(XX,6)>=1 THEN T(XX,6)=T(XX,6)/1000
700 IFT(XX,6)<SR THEN PRINT"DESIRED S.R. MUST EXCEED M.S.R.";:PRINTTAB(35)"?";:I
NPUTT(XX,6):GOTO690
710 NEXTXX
720 IFZ=0THEN750
730 FORXX=1TOZ:IFB(XX,6)<BTHENB(XX,5)=T(B(XX,6),5)+T(B(XX,7),5):NEXTELSENEXT
740 FORXX=1TOZ:IFB(XX,5)=0THENIFB(XX,6)=0THENNEXTELSEB(XX,5)=T(B(XX,7),5)+B(B(XX
,6)-B-D+2,5):NEXTELSENEXT
750 FORXX=B-1TO1STEP-1:PL=T(XX,3):SR=T(XX,6):IFSR=.999THENNEXTXX:GOTO820  ELSEFO
RYY=XX-1TO1STEP-1:IFT(YY,3)=PLTHEN760  ELSEIFT(YY,2)=PLTHEN780  ELSENEXTYY:GOTO8
00
760 IFT(YY,2)>T(YY,3)THENIFD$(PL)="L"THENT(YY,4)=T(XX,6)+T(YY,4)ELSET(YY,4)=T(YY
,4)-T(XX,6)ELSEIFD$(PL)="L"THENT(YY,4)=T(YY,4)-T(XX,6)ELSET(YY,4)=T(YY,4)+T(XX,6
)
770 GOTO790
780 IFT(YY,2)>T(YY,3)THENIFD$(PL)="L"THENT(YY,4)=T(YY,4)-T(XX,6)ELSET(YY,4)=T(YY
,4)+T(XX,6)ELSEIFD$(PL)="L"THENT(YY,4)=T(YY,4)+T(XX,6)ELSET(YY,4)=T(YY,4)-T(XX,6
)
790 NEXTYY
800 NEXTXX
810 REM SUB FOR ADDING UP B.P. DIMENSIONS FOR MACHINE CUTS
820 CLS:PRINT:PRINT"AT THIS POINT, I HAVE CALCULATED THE TOLERANCES AND STOCK":P
RINT"REMOVALS FOR EACH OF THE MACHINE CUTS.  NOW I NEED THE BASE    DIMENSIONS
OF THE MACHINE CUTS, YOU MUST NOW DETERMINE THEM FROMTHE BLUEPRINT DIMENSIONS AN
D ENTER THEM."
830 FORI=15680 TO 15743:POKEI,140:NEXT:PRINT:PRINT"NOTE-- ENTER ONLY THE BASE DI
MENSION OF THE MACHINE CUT, I WILL DETERMINE THE PROCESS DIMENSIONS":PRINT
840 FOR C=1 TO B-1
850 FOR CC=1 TO D-1
860 IF(T(C,2)=P(CC,2)AND T(C,3)=P(CC,3))OR(T(C,3)=P(CC,2)AND T(C,2)=P(CC,3)) THE
N T(C,4)=P(CC,4)+T(C,4):GOTO880  ELSENEXT
870 PRINT"ENTER THE BASE DIMENSION FOR CUT NUMBER";C;:INPUTDI:T(C,4)=T(C,4)+DI
880 NEXTC:RETURN
1000 REM TO ADD UP MACH CUT TOL
1010 TP=B+D-2:FORTB=1TOD-1:TL=0:IFP(TB,6)<BTHENP(TB,7)=T(P(TB,6),5):GOTO1040 ELS
ETC=P(TB,6)-TP
1020 T6=B(TC,6):T7=B(TC,7):IFT6<BANDT7<BTHENTL=T(T6,5)+T(T7,5)+TL:GOTO1030 ELSET
```

Printout 11-6 continued

```
L=TL+T(T7,5):TC=B(TC,6)-TP:GOTO1020
1030 P(TB,7)=TL
1040 NEXTTB
1050 REM SUB TO PRINT WORK-SHEET
1060 PRINT:IFX$<>"N"ANDX$<>"Y"THENINPUT"DO YOU NEED INSTRUCTIONS FOR THE WORKSHE
ET (Y/N)";X$:IFLEFT$(X$,1)="Y"THENGOSUB1250
1070 LPRINT" ":LPRINTCHR$(27);CHR$(14);"WORKSHEET FOR TOLERANCE DISTRIBUTION":GO
SUB1180 :L2=0
1080 LPRINT" ":LPRINT"BLUEPRINT";TAB(30)"MACHINE CUTS":LPRINT"DIMEN.+/-TOLER.":L
PRINT" ":FORL9=L5TOL6:LPRINTTAB((L9-L2)*3+19)L9;:NEXTL9:LPRINT" ":FORXX=1TOD-1:Y
=XX:LL=0:IFP(XX,6)<BTHENLL=LL+1:A(LL)=P(XX,6):GOTO1100 ELSEY=P(Y,6)+2-B-D
1090 LL=LL+1:A(LL)=B(Y,7):IFB(Y,6)<BTHENLL=LL+1:A(LL)=B(Y,6):GOTO1100 ELSEY=B(Y,
6)+2-B-D:GOTO1090
1100 FORL9=L5TOL6:FORL8=1TOLL:IFA(L8)=L9THENA$(L9)="*"
1110 NEXTL8:IFA$(L9)<>"*"THENA$(L9)=" "
1120 NEXTL9:LPRINTP(XX,4);"+/-";:LPRINTUSINGG$;P(XX,5);:LPRINTTAB(21)CHR$(124);:
LO=20:FORL9=L5TOL6:IFL9>9THENLO=LO+1
1130 LPRINTTAB(3*(L9-L2)+LO)A$(L9)CHR$(124);:A$(L9)=" ":NEXTL9:LO=18:LPRINT" ":L
PRINT"(NEW) +/-";:LPRINTUSINGG$;P(XX,7);:FORL9=L5TOL6+1:LPRINTTAB(3*(L9-L2)+LO)C
HR$(124);:IFL9>9THENLO=LO+1
1140 NEXTL9:LPRINT" ":LPRINTSTRING$(62,"-"):NEXTXX:IFL6=B-1THEN1150 ELSEGOSUB122
0 :GOTO1080
1150 LPRINT" ":LPRINT" ":LPRINT"MACHINE CUT","+/- TOLERANCE","CHANGES","= NEW TO
LERANCE":LPRINT" ":FORXX=1TOB-1:LPRINTTAB(4)XX;:IFT(XX,5)=0THENLPRINTTAB(18)"NON
E"ELSELPRINTTAB(19)USINGG$;T(XX,5)
1160 LPRINTSTRING$(75,"-"):NEXT:FORXX=1TO5:LPRINT" ":NEXT:CLS
1162 FOR I=1 TO D-1:IF P(I,7)<=P(I,5)THENNEXT:GOTO1170
1164 PRINT:PRINT"PLEASE TAKE NOTICE:":PRINT:FOR I=1 TO D-1:IF P(I,7)>P(I,5)THENP
RINT"FOR BLUEPRINT NO.";I;"  YOU ENTERED A TOLERANCE OF";:PRINTUSINGG$;P(I,5):PR
INT"THE NEW TOLERANCE OF";:PRINTUSINGG$;P(I,7);:PRINT" EXCEEDS THE BLUEPRINT TOL
ERANCE":PRINT
1166 NEXT:PRINT:PRINT"I WOULD ADVISE THAT YOU CHANGE THE MACHINE CUT TOLERANCES"
:PRINT
1170 INPUT"DO YOU WISH TO CHANGE ANY OF THE MACHINE CUT TOLERANCES (Y/N)";C$:IFC
$="Y"THENGOTO1410 ELSE RETURN
1180 L5=1:IFB-1<11THENL6=B-1ELSEL6=10
1190 RETURN
1220 REM FOR INCREMENTS
1230 L2=L2+10:L5=L5+10:IFB-1>L6+10THENL6=L6+10ELSEL6=B-1
1240 RETURN
1250 REM SUB FOR INSTRUCTIONS FOR TOL. DISTRIB.
1260 LPRINT" ":LPRINTCHR$(27);CHR$(14);"WORKSHEET INSTRUCTIONS":LPRINT" ":LPRINT
"INTRODUCTION :":LPRINT" "
1270 LPRINT"    THE CHART ON THE WORKSHEET SHOWS THE BLUEPRINT DIMENSION AND TOL
ERANCE AS   ORIGINALLY INPUTED, ALONG WITH THE NEW TOLERANCE THAT YOU MAY EXPECT
 AS A RESULTOF THE 'MACHINE CUT' TOLERANCES THAT ARE LISTED BELOW THE CHART."
1280 LPRINT" ":LPRINT"    THE 'MACHINE CUT' TOLERANCES WERE DERIVED PROPORTIONAL
LY, USING (1) THE ORI-GINAL BLUEPRINT TOLERANCE, (2) THE MACHINE CUTS INVOLVED I
N CREATING THIS DIMEN-SION, AND (3) THE TYPE OF MACHINING TAKING PLACE AT EACH C
UT."
1290 LPRINT" ":LPRINT"    AN '*' HAS BEEN PLACED UNDER EACH MACHINE CUT THAT THE
 COMPUTER HAS DETER- MINED IS INVOLVED IN CREATING THIS DIMENSION.":LPRINT" "
1300 LPRINT"    AT THIS POINT, THE COMPUTER HAS DONE AS MUCH AS POSSIBLE, AS FAR
 AS DISTRIB-UTING TOLERANCES MATHEMATICALLY.  IT IS UP TO YOU TO MAKE ANY NECESS
ARY CHANGES.":LPRINT" ":LPRINT" ":LPRINT"INSTRUCTIONS :":LPRINT" "
1310 LPRINT"LET US SAY, FOR EXAMPLE, THAT WE HAVE A BLUEPRINT TOLERANCE OF .005
AND A NEW   TOLERANCE OF .004.  WE WISH TO MAKE A CHANGE TO INCREASE THE NEW TOL
ERANCE TO   USE THE FULL .005.":LPRINT" "
1320 LPRINT"(1) LOOK AT ALL THE MACHINE CUTS INVOLVED WITH THIS DIMENSION (AS MA
RKED '*')        AND DETERMINE WHICH OF THESE CUT TOLERANCES YOU WISH TO INCREASE
 BY .001."
1330 LPRINT"  NOTE: THE .001 MAY BE DISTRIBUTED OVER MORE THAN ONE MACHINE CUT I
F YOU SO         DESIRE.":LPRINT" ":LPRINT"(2) NEXT TO THE '*', FOR THE MACHI
NE CUT THAT YOU HAVE CHOSEN, WRITE IN '+.001'.":LPRINT" "
```

Printout 11-6 continued

```
1340 LPRINT"(3) NOW FOLLOW THIS MACHINE CUT COLUMN UP AND DOWN, PUTTING A '+.001
' WHEREVER      THERE IS A '*' IN THAT COLUMN.":LPRINT" "
1350 LPRINT"(4) TAKE NOTE THAT WHEREVER YOU HAVE ENTERED A '+.001', THE TOLERANC
E OF THAT       BLUEPRINT DIMENSION IS ALSO INCREASED BY .001.":LPRINT" ":LPRINT
"(5) ADD THE .001 TO THAT MACHINE CUT IN THE BOTTOM TABLE.":LPRINT" "
1360 LPRINT"(6) CONTINUE ON WITH ANY OTHER NEW TOLERANCES THAT YU WISH TO INCREA
SE OR DE-       CREASE.":LPRINT" ":LPRINT"(7) ADD OR SUBTRACT ANY CHANGES IN THE
 BOTTOM CHART TO GET THE NEW TOLERANCE FOR     EACH MACHINE CUT.":LPRINT" "
1370 LPRINT"(8) ASSIGN WHATEVER TOLERANCE YOU DESIRE FOR MACHINE TOLERANCES MARK
ED 'NONE',      AS THESE CUTS ARE NOT DIRECTLY INVOLVED IN BLUEPRINT TOLERANCES.
"
1380 LPRINT"  NOTE: KEEP IN MIND-(A) THE HIGHER THE TOLERANCE, THE HIGHER THE ST
OCK REMOVAL,    AND (B) THE MINIMUM TOLERANCE OF THIS OPERATION SHOULD BE OBEYED
.":LPRINT" "
1390 LPRINT"(9) INPUT THE NEW TOLERANCES TO RECEIVE AND UPDATED CHART INCORPORAT
ING THE         CHANGE.  (YOU WILL BE ABLE TO MAKE FURTHER CHANGES IF NECESSARY.
":RETURN
1400 FOR X=1 TO 5:LPRINT" ":NEXT
1410 CLS:PRINTTAB(13)"NEW MACHINE CUT TOLERANCES":PRINT:PRINT"ENTER A NEW TOLERA
NCE (OR ELSE <ENTER>)":PRINT"CUT NO.","CALC. TOL.","NEW TOL.":FORXX=1TOB-1:PRINT
:L9=T(XX,5):PRINTTAB(2)XX;:IFL9=0THENPRINTTAB(19)"NONE";ELSEPRINTTAB(19)"+/-";:P
RINTUSINGG$;L9;
1420 PRINTTAB(40)"+/-";:INPUTT(XX,5):IFT(XX,5)>.999 THEN T(XX,5)=T(XX,5)/1000:NE
XT XX:GOTO1000ELSENEXT:GOTO1000
```

Printout 11-6 continued

Summary

This chapter began by defining the importance of tolerance control and how tolerance control can be achieved by charting. This computer program is an important contribution to computer assisted Manufacturing Engineering because, again, manual engineering efforts have been automated.

Reflect for a moment on the power of BASIC as a programming language and how a microcomputer has performed most of the mundane tasks of tolerance charting.

Bibliography

Wilson, Frank W., Editor-in-Chief. *Manufacturing Planning and Estimating Handbook*. Dearborn, MI: Society of Manufacturing Engineers, 1963.
Wade, Oliver R., *Tolerance Control in Design and Manufacturing*. New York: Industrial Press, Inc., 1967.

Optional Lab Assignments

Lab Assignment 11-1 (least difficult)

Write a computer program that calculates the statistical method of relating tolerances to interacting dimensions for assemblies. The formula is

$$\sqrt{Ta^2 + Tb^2 + \ldots \ldots Tn^2} = \text{tolerance of the results}$$

Where:

$Ta=$ tolerance (nominal) first part

$Tb=$ tolerance (nominal) second part

$Tn=$ tolerance (nominal) last part

Lab Assignment 11-2 (moderate)

Write a computer program designed for castings or forgings that assists the engineer in establishing the lengths and diameters by adding casting allowances and tolerances.

CHAPTER 12

Getting Started

In the first 11 chapters of this book, many facets of Manufacturing Engineering have been explored in a new light. Just as the hand-held calculators made the sliderule obsolete some years ago, today the microcomputer will obsolete the hand-held calculator. Since the introduction of the microcomputer in 1975, major strides have been made in equipment dependability and versatility. Equipment manufacturers, through competition, have provided improved dependability, while hobbyists have provided new ideas for increased versatility. The engineer's next logical question should be: How do I get started? This chapter addresses itself to two major subjects: getting started and the future.

Getting Started

Training

The first step in getting started is training. There are five ways that computer programming training can be accomplished and advantages and disadvantages of each are expressed.

Self-training is the first option. BASIC is a language that is very easy to learn, and self-tutoring is necessary even if other options are exercised. However, self-training in a business atmosphere seems a rather haphazard way of trying to organize the problem. A tremendous amount of dedication is necessary to accomplish training objectives using this option. Another aspect of self-training is that the process is too slow. The training problem should be approached on several fronts simultaneously.

College training. Next, consider college training. Most colleges and universities have course work in computer programming. Course offerings generally follow two separate and different paths. Many institutions provide course work in a Data Processing program or curriculum. This training, at present, is devoted to the education of people who plan to make a career in data processing. The programming languages studied are usually mainframe-oriented, and the nature of this study is systems programming. In addition, it is not in concert with business objectives to send an engineer back to college for a second degree in data processing.

Other course work is available in the form of related courses. Most colleges and universities do offer individual courses in BASIC. These courses are devoted to general training in the language or business programming, and while they do provide a foundation in the language, they are rarely designed to offer very much for the engineer. At this writing, there are very few institutions which offer programming course work specifically designed for the Manufacturing Engineer. As the need develops, perhaps the future will correct this situation. If, however, this is the only type of training available to you, it will provide a start. Another possibility exists in out-of-plant seminars. A number of national organizations, such as the American Management Association, are providing seminars devoted to computer training. For the most part, these seminars are designed for the managers and do not provide any hands-on programming experience. The reasons are quite evident considering the equipment requirements in conducting a seminar that provides hands-on training. Yet a second element is qualified engineering instructors. While this type seminar does fulfill a need, it falls short of the Manufacturing Engineer's requirement.

In-plant seminars. Another option is the in-plant seminar. There are some real advantages to this idea. First, the equipment problem is minimized. If a company interested in improving their Manufacturing Engineering Department's computer skills were to purchase two microcomputer systems, an in-plant seminar could be conducted. A morning session could be devoted to classroom training for four engineers and afternoons devoted to hands-on programming. Because the nature of computer programming requires both desk time and terminal time, afternoon sessions could be split into a pair of two-hour sessions for each team of engineers. This idea also has other merits. The instructor chosen to provide the training can formulate the course work to suit the individual problems of that specific facility. The major drawback is finding a qualified instructor. Note the term "qualified instructor." "Qualified" means a person who is a Manufacturing Engineer and who understands computer programming. There are two options available: a consultant or a college instructor. The consultant's role will be discussed later in this chapter. The second option, that of college instructor, is probably the best option available and probably the least expensive. Side benefits can develop from this type arrangement as an alliance between industry and institutions of higher learning is a necessary ingredient for longer-range improvement of engineering curricula.

Before we leave the subject of training, one last idea should be explored—the college workshop. If your facility is located near a college or university that has both a Manufacturing Engineering curriculum and has microcomputer course work, then elements of a computer workshop are practical. Some institutions are currently performing this service, while others are developing plans.

Equipment

The equipment part of the problem of getting started is a complicated element because it requires both knowledge and good judgment. First, thought must be given to what size system to purchase. Size here is defined as minicomputer versus microcomputer. With terminology changing every day, it may be difficult to define exactly the differences between the two. But at this writing, a minicomputer is defined as a system that costs from $15,000 to $250,000, while a microcomputer system costs less than $15,000. For the engineer, this may seem a loose definition but it represents the industry's definition. Each approach has its advantages and disadvantages so trying to provide guidelines is difficult. While all computers essentially perform the same tasks, approaches to hardware selection will vary depending on objectives. The minicomputer with several terminal stations scattered throughout the engineering department is an approach popular with some companies. This approach is one which can support a variety of objectives but has implications regarding other elements of the organization. On the other hand, some company's first computer exploration would have found that purchasing two or three microcomputer systems for engineering satisfies their requirements. Because this book is written to encourage the engineer's first effort, no attempt will be made to debate the merits of one system over the other.

Next, a microcomputer system will be defined. As a minimum, a stand-alone microcomputer system for industrial use should include the following hardware:

1. Base computer with a minimum of 48K bytes of RAM.
2. Twin 5 1/4" disk drives.
3. A printer that will accept 8 1/2" standard fan-fold paper.
4. A CRT.
5. RS232 compatability.

Reliability and service. There are several manufacturers producing microcomputer systems as described above, and it is not the purpose of this text to promote one over the other. The purchaser should be extremely sensitive to reliability and service. The explosion now occurring in the microcomputer electronics industry has created a proliferation of companies all busily involved in computer production. An analogy might be made with the early days of automobile manufacturing. Back in the early 1900's, scores of companies tried to produce automobiles. Today, American automobile manufacturers can be counted on one hand. The microcomputer industry is undergoing many of the same growing pains. In five years, many of these small, underfinanced companies will fall by the wayside. System reliability is defined here as the ability to withstand industrial usage, day after day. Equipment service is very important. Once a computer is programmed and used every day, a certain dependency on it develops. Computers are subject to downtime just as another piece of equipment, and thought must be given to service. Once a microcomputer malfunctions, it must be shipped to a service center for repairs. Repairing a micro by having a serviceman come to your establishment is very expensive. For this reason, start with at least two complete systems and investigate the service aspects thoroughly. Many Manufacturing Engineers in industry are very hesitant to purchase serial number one of a new machine tool on the market. Without pursuing the logic of this fact, their rationale can be defended, for the most part. The point is, the same care and caution should be exercised by the engineer who intends to purchase a computer system for industrial use.

Standardization. Item five of microcomputer hardware states "RS232 compatibility." "RS232" is terminology used by the electronics industry to define standard interfacing connections.

While this young computer industry is developing, standardization still remains a problem. From the user's standpoint, the lack of standardization at this point in the industry's development provides yet another caution. Interfacing pieces of hardware manufactured by different companies can be a source of problems and frustration. RS232 compatibility means two things to the user:

1. Electronically different pieces of equipment should be compatible.
2. Other new peripherals which may be purchased in the future should be compatible.

As the industry continues to develop, new peripherals come to the market-place. A partial listing of peripherals, both old and new, are briefly discussed.

The Teletype ASR-33 is a standard piece of equipment that can be interfaced to a minicomputer or microcomputer. The ASR-33 can be a very useful peripheral because it offers almost every function required for a computer system—printing, keyboard input, paper-tape punching and reading. Interfacing the unit, however, may require purchasing a modification kit from the computer manufacturer.

A high-speed paper-tape peripheral device may be a requirement. There are such devices on the market and most are RS232 compatible.

A modem is another device that can be interfaced to a microcomputer. A modem is a data communications device that permits sending and/or receiving computer data over telephone lines. The popularity of these units is growing as new services develop.

Computers also can be interfaced to the outside world. The possibilities that this activity offers are fascinating. Often the external device or devices are non-standard and require special interfacing techniques. To achieve this, a knowledge of solid-state and digital electronics is required.

Two other peripherals mentioned here and discussed later in this chapter are a plotter and/or a digitizer.

Documentation and Obsolescence. The next subject under consideration should be computer documentation. Documentation is defined as the software support supplied by the computer manufacturer telling how to operate the equipment. Lack of proper documentation is an industry-wide problem. As computer manufacturers rush to be first in the market-place with their new hardware, the last element is to document their system. If this element is not completed properly, or completed in haste, the aftereffects are felt by the user who is trying to operate a system that seems new and strange. In the long run, these computer manufacturers will fall by the wayside—but in the short term, it is the user who suffers.

The last topic to consider concerning equipment is obsolescence. As the computer industry continues to develop new technology the obsolescence time cycle remains short. The current cycle seems to be about three years. To some, the idea of purchasing a system that may be obsolete in three years is a worrisome problem. While no attempt will be made here to alleviate such fears, the nature of obsolescence should be explained. The purchase of a new microcomputer today only to discover a new generation computer is offered for sale tomorrow, would be—at best—disappointing. On the other hand, if an engineer or manager can see the advantages now of how a microcomputer can be successfully used to improve engineering efficiency and procrastinates the purchase, who is the loser? The nature of obsolescence is not that the computer stops working. Microcomputers of the future will be smaller, run faster, have more memory, use a 16-bit processor rather than an eight-bit processor and cost less. While pondering this dilemma, another question should be posed.

What is the competition doing?

Language

BASIC is an acronym for Beginner's All Purpose Symbolic Instruction Codes, and was developed by Dartmouth College in 1964.

The question of which language to use is often presented. There are many different opinions proposed to answer this question, some objective and some subjective. While it is beyond the scope of this text to present a treatise on computer languages, several observations should be made.

First, the most popular scientific languages in use today are BASIC and FORTRAN. PASCAL is a distant third. BASIC and FORTRAN are both powerful languages having high math processing abilities. Late in 1980, the author conducted a national survey of all colleges and universities in the United States that have four-year Manufacturing Engineering programs. The nature of this survey was to determine what types of computer applications courses are presently being offered and what programming languages are being used.

In regard to programming languages, the survey results showed a 50-50 split between BASIC and FORTRAN. Several other programming languages were represented, but in such low numbers they were discounted.

More recently, several microcomputer manufacturers have developed software for their equipment which can handle any of the three most popular languages.

A second point to consider is that there are many dialects of BASIC. Although BASIC is a widely used and accepted language, there are slight differences between Radio Shack^R BASIC and Apple^R BASIC[1]. One could not expect to write a program for a TRS-80[2] and expect it to run on an Apple computer. Aside from the slight language differences, there are major differences in the various disk operating systems from manufacturer to manufacturer. Therefore, interchangeability of programs written in the same language for different machines is nonexistent. The implication for the user just getting started is: Do not purchase one each of the most popular micros and expect to be able to write and use interchangeable programs. Advancements are taking place in some software houses to write compilers that perform this function. Once completed, however, it is doubtful much of this software will be made public.

Every computer can be programmed in assembler language or machine code. Assembler language is a low-level mnemonic code that communicates directly with the computer. The word "directly" means without the use of an interpreter. Programming in Assembler language or machine code is very tedious and requires much more time. Also, just as there are different dialects in BASIC, each central processing unit (CPU) or chip has its own code, and each chip is different. There is some justification for learning Assembler language and/or machine code. Once an engineer masters BASIC, this can be the next step. Machine code runs much faster than BASIC and there are some sub-routines that can require the computer to work calculating for several minutes. (An example of this is calculating discounted cash flow percents.) If a sub-routine were written in Assembler language or machine code, the calculation time could be shortened significantly. One other reason for learning these languages is for interfacing. The computer at its lowest level understands only ones and zeros. This is referred to as "logic one" or "logic zero," meaning the computer is a two-state device that understands either being on or off. Interfacing the computer to the outside world is accomplished at this level. In some systems, BASIC can be used for interfacing. Interfacing and programming in Assembler languages should not be considered as a necessary step in getting started.

Programming

This next section is written primarily for the departmental manager who must organize the programming effort. Before any serious programming effort begins, the departmental manager should give thought to how many people should be involved in writing computer programs. Throughout this book, a very positive attitude has been presented concerning the ease with which industrial computer programs can be written. There is, of course, another side to that coin. As seen or correlated to the classroom, not everyone can, or wishes to, work with a computer. In some respects, the computer can be rather intimidating to some people. Some people thrive on change and need change to stay revitalized, while others are content to stay

[1]*Apple is a trademark of the Apple Computer Corporation.*
[2]*TRS-80 is a trademark of the Radio Shack Division of Tandy Corporation.*

just as they are. These comments are not presented to explore the motivation of people, but should be present in the manager's mind when giving thought to organizing the work effort. The introduction of a computer system into an engineering department can, however, provide both an air of excitement and rejuvenation. So as to not dwell on the matter, we should conclude with several questions that should be carefully analyzed, before starting.

1. What types of programs should be written first?
2. How many people should be involved in the programming effort?
3. What should be the first programming effort undertaken?
4. Should a timetable be developed?
5. How should the program be reviewed?
6. At various stages in this process, how does one determine if the results are positive or negative?
7. Lastly, should the departmental supervisors and manager be able to write computer programs?

Once the programming effort is underway, other questions will arise. Computer file security is a subject that deserves thought. Many software companies are currently experiencing piracy of their work and are trying to develop ways of safeguarding against this practice. Some, in fact, have developed methods that prevent their software from being copied at all. While the clever programmer can usually find ways around this problem, the reader should be aware that the security problem requires study. Updating programs and duplicating diskettes are two other considerations that require thought. Perhaps some type of central system much like revision number control on drawings might be developed. As more computer programs are written and as older ones are updated or changed, the need for diskette masters and program documentation becomes apparent. Some additional thought also should be given to writing a simple systems and procedures document.

Consultants

A qualified consultant can be of enormous assistance in getting started. Notice the word "qualified" again. As the explosion continues in the computer industry, all matter of opportunities abound. In fact, many new industries have been created because of computer proliferation. The consultant is no exception. A qualified, experienced consultant can, nevertheless, assist the manager in the goal-setting process, training and even writing programs. The in-plant seminar idea presented earlier might be a good starting point. The seminar would provide ample opportunity for reviewing results before large expenditures are committed.

Contract programming by consultants is becoming more popular. The author is aware of several efforts in this respect. Most of them are positive and constructive but there are also one or two horror stories.

Another aspect of this subject is purchasing programs from software houses. There are literally hundreds of software houses that have sprung up over the last four or five years. This activity is already a million dollar activity. Most of the effort to date has been writing industrial computer programs for small business accounting systems, inventory control systems and general record keeping. Most of the larger computer manufacturers have developed and written programs mentioned above as well as word processing programs. Most of the programs written to date are written for the mass market and not for specific engineering problems. As this market becomes satisfied or saturated, perhaps the industry will look for other areas to provide revenue. These other areas could include writing programs for engineering applications.

The planning, organizing and execution of a successful effort to improve engineering efficiency through the use of the microcomputer requires keen thought. As in all Manufacturing Engineering efforts, program management is the key.

The Future

Today we are living in a world of rapid technological change and obsolescence. This industrial change is occurring on several fronts concurrently. It is also interesting to note that the computer is providing the basis for what might be referred to as the rebirth of the Industrial Revolution. The computer industry forecasts for the future read something like a novel. For example, one forecasts that by 1990, 33 million microcomputers will be in use. While this prediction may sound unrealistic to us, the computer industry believes it.

Earlier in this book, the concepts of Group Technology and MiCAPP were discussed with respect to Manufacturing Engineering. While these two concepts are not incompatible, they do represent somewhat different directions of engineering change. The next natural extension of MiCAPP for the future may be the addition of a digitizer and plotter to the engineer's work station. Envision if you will a typical Manufacturing Engineering work station which includes a computer terminal with disk drive and printer plus a digitizer and plotter. The digitizer could be used to digitize drawings and the plotter used to complete the last step of the process planning activity-drawing. If the prospect seems interesting, next think of merging the concept of MiCAPP with that of Group Technology. We are one step closer to the automated factory. The future also will bring about changes in the newly emerging industry of CAD/CAM. In 1980, the CAD/CAM business grew at an incredible 70% rate to an estimated $510 million. Although $510 million does not seem large in respect to the total computer market, this figure could be understated once peripherals (graphics displays, digitizers and plotters) are added. Forecasts for the 1990's are off the sales charts. Virtually every major change taking place today in American industry involves computers.

The Manufacturing Engineer of the future will require the same skills engineers have now with some new ones added. It was not many years ago that the best toolmaker was selected to become a Manufacturing Engineer. Technology has rendered this practice extinct. The Manufacturing Engineer is the key to improving our industrial society for tomorrow, a weighty responsibility. Predictions have been made for years about what the 21st century will be like with the advent of the totally automated factory. Once the reader understands all the ingredients are present now for the totally automated factory, the prospects suddenly become frightening.

No one can predict the future and no attempt to do so will be made here. Yet, some summerizing and concluding remarks are necessary.

For the engineer, the world of tomorrow will be one filled with change. Computers have already changed the way we live and think. While some may debate that this change has not been in the best interest of the individual or society, what we call technical progress continues to move unabated. Recently, many philosophical questions have been presented concerning where technology will take us in the future and the direction in which we should be moving. Also, other discussions are taking place suggesting that society may wish to choose other directions. Thinking about and discussing these questions is very healthy. But discussion usually stops once this question is posed: Who will choose? Meanwhile, technology marches on.

INDEX

Functional gages, 103
Future, 283
Future shock, 229
Future value of an investment, 116

G

Gages, 102, 103, 237
Gang drilling, 50
"GANTT", 193, 200-202
Gantt charting, 193
Go-Not go gages, 103
Graphics, 193-209
Grooving, 230
Group technology, 227-229, 283

H

Hand-held calculators, 277
Hole size, 143

I

Inflation, 115
Initial value of an investment, 116
In-plant seminars, 278
Inspection, 102, 171
Interest rates, 116, 127
Inventory, 211-213, 228
Investments, 115, 116

J

Jigs, 227

L

Language, 280-281
Lathe, 96-98
Launching costs, 81-97
"LEARN", 86-90
Learning curves, 81-99
Learning rates, 82
Least square fit, 144
Limits of accuracy, 39
Loading, 171
Locating points, 256
"Logic one", 281
"Logic zero", 282
Log-linear regression, 143

M

"MACH", 193, 198-200
Machine capability studies, 101-113
Machine load chart, 201
Maintenance, 211, 278
Maintenance program, 21-22
"MAN", 193, 202-208
Man-Machine charting, 202-206
Management, 41
Manpower analysis, 167-191
Material handling, 171
Material selection, 237, 238
Method improvement, 102

Methods-time measurement, 35-36
Milling, 37-38, 51-55, 81
Modems, 280
"MONEY", 115-119
Multiple regression, 143, 152-154

N

NC, See: Numerical Control
NC drill, 97
NC lathe, 132
Nominal interest rate, 117, 118
Non-linear regression models, 159-160
Numerical Control, 97, 132

O

Orthogonal polynomials, 162
Out-of-plant seminars, 278
Overtime, 199, 200

P

PASCAL, 280
P.E.R.T. charting, 193, 202
Preventative maintenance, 211, 212
Process planning, 283
Procedures documents, 282
Processing, 171
Product costs, 115
Productivity, 115
Programming, 78, 281, 282
Programs,
    "AC", 237-248
    "BAR", 193, 194-198
    "B.E.P.", 96-99
    "DEP", 126-128
    "DISCOUNT", 131-140
    "FORGE", 67-68
    "GANTT", 193, 200-202
    "LEARN", 86-90
    "MACH", 193, 198-200
    "MAN", 193, 203-208
    "MONEY", 115-119
    "RATIO", 168, 183-190
    "REG 1", 152
    "REG 2", 153
    "REG 3", 160
    "REG 4", 212-219
    "SFILE", 219-224
    "SFPM", 30, 41-67
    "STDEV", 107-112
    "TIME", 168, 169-171
    "T CHART 1", 261
    "T CHART 2", 262
Printer, 237
Project control chart, 203
Proposal evaluation, 128-130

Q

Quality assurance engineers, 101
Quality audit, 20
Quality control engineers, 101
Queveing, 228

R

S

T

U

V

W